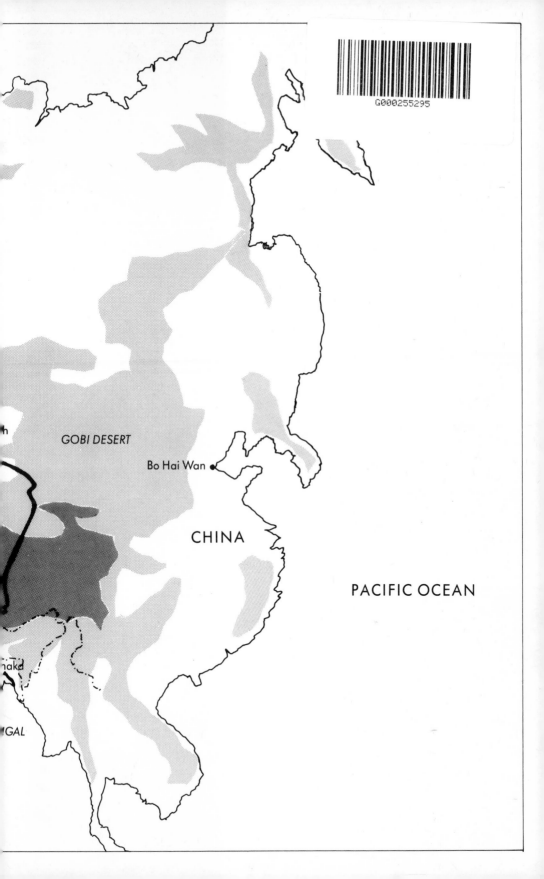

GOBI DESERT

Bo Hai Wan •

CHINA

PACIFIC OCEAN

GAL

Journey to the Centre of the Earth

Also by Richard and Nicholas Crane

International Cycling Guide, ed. Nicholas Crane

The CTC Route Guide to Cycling in Britain and Ireland,
Christa Gausden and Nicholas Crane

Cycling in Europe, Nicholas Crane

Running the Himalayas, Richard and Adrian Crane

Bicycles up Kilimanjaro, Nicholas and Richard Crane

JOURNEY
TO THE CENTRE OF
THE EARTH

RICHARD & NICHOLAS CRANE

BANTAM PRESS

LONDON · NEW YORK · TORONTO · SYDNEY · AUCKLAND

Transworld Publishers Ltd
61–63 Uxbridge Road, London w5 5sa

Transworld Publishers (Australia) Pty Ltd
15–23 Helles Avenue, Moorebank, NSW 2170

Transworld Publishers (NZ) Ltd
Cnr Moselle and Waipareira Aves, Henderson, Auckland

Published 1987 by Bantam Press
a division of Transworld Publishers Ltd

British Library Cataloguing in Publication Data
Crane, Richard, *1953*–
    Journey to the centre of the earth.
    1. Cycling – Himalaya Mountains
    2. Himalaya Mountains – Description and
    travel
    I. Title   II. Crane, Nicholas
    915.4'0452   DS485.116
    ISBN 0-593-01291-7

Photoset by Rowland Phototypesetting Ltd
Bury St Edmunds, Suffolk
Printed in Great Britain by
Mackays of Chatham, Chatham, Kent

To our grandfather, Albert Charles Crane, who first
took our fathers out to the hills

Contents

List of Maps ix

Acknowledgements xiii

1 Goodbye to the Open Sea 1

2 From the Madhouse to the Land of Morning Calm 22

3 Bogged Down in Nepal 39

4 Cycling the Himalayas 53

5 Xizang Zizhiqu, Qomolangma Feng and Rinbung Dzong 65
(Tibet, Everest, and a Little Town in the Middle
of Nowhere)

6 Lhasa and the Tourist Trade 86

7 Cycling Out to Desolation 99

8 The Big Descent 120

9 Sprint to the Gobi 129

10 Depression on the Silk Road 143

11 The Hottest Place in China 164

12 Urumqi and the Public Security Bureau 183

13 At the Centre of the Earth 203

Postscript 215

Appendix I. Equipment 217

Appendix II. Daily Log of Distances and Ascent 227

Bibliography 231

Index 233

Maps

1 Overall route map showing key towns and areas   x–xi

2 Bangladesh / India   xii

3 India / Nepal / Tibet   38

4 The Plateau   100

5 The Gobi, Taklamakan and Dsungarei Deserts   144

6 Altitude profile cross-section of ride   226

Endpapers   Map of all Asia showing principal place-names and the Centre of the Earth

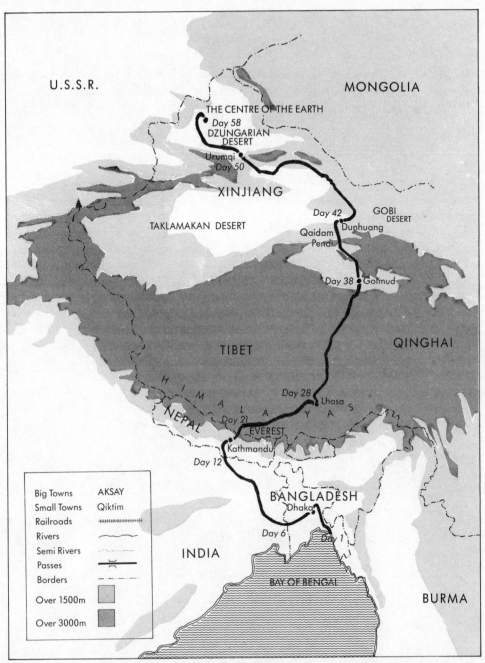

Overall route map showing key towns and areas

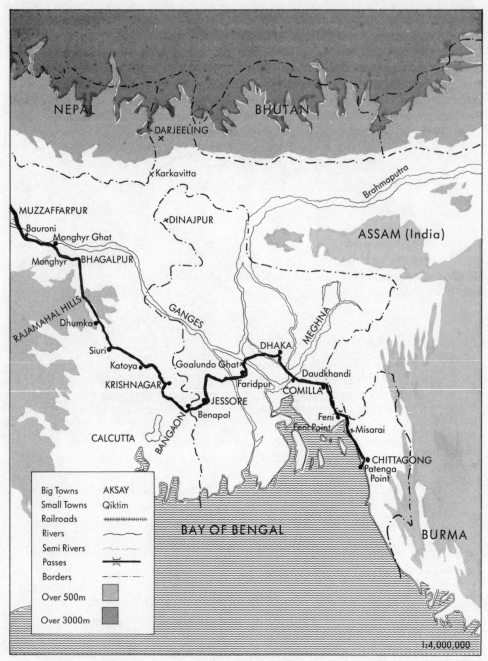

Bangladesh / India

Acknowledgements

Raleigh
Karrimor
Black's
Madison
Been Bag
Tiger Mountain
LansdownEuro
British Petroleum

We received direct assistance in cash or in kind from the above-mentioned sponsors, and from many others we benefited through experience, advice, assistance and encouragement. It is not possible to mention all of them though each deserves a special thank you. Steve Bonnist of Intermediate Technology did the backbreaking work of informing family and friends as well as the press about our progress. Hol Crane provided route analyses with breakdowns for mileage, roughness, altitude, tyre pressure and loss of weight of rider *en route*. Dr Mike Townend of Cockermouth provided the medical advice to counterbalance natural wastage due to climate, food, altitude, injury and Hol's theories.

Gerald O'Donovan of Raleigh built special 753 bikes one week before departure and Steve Bell did the link work to co-ordinate spares, and later the press. Mike Parsons gave us a free selection of Karrimor cycling gear, and Laurie Gray let us rampage through the Black's shops in Holborn and Tottenham Court Road for miscellaneous outdoor effects. Errol Drew kindly stood back as we ransacked his Beta Bikes shop for last-minute equipment. As soon as we got to Bangladesh, Shameen Ahmed gave us office time at Glaxo in Dhaka to finalize details. When we reached Kathmandu, just when the prospects of finding fresh equipment and getting into China looked bleak, Lisa van Gruisen (now Lisa Choegyal) came to our rescue and turned the Tiger Tops office over to Crane Enterprises in the same way as she had done three years previously for 'Running the Himalayas'.

We owe a great debt to Ados for initiating mega-adventures, and in our individual ways to Michèle and Penny. Our parents, brothers and sisters and their spouses have provided, and continue to provide, the love and warmth from which we can step out into adventure. They always welcome us back with open arms: Charles, Sandy, Hol, Naomi, Liz, Tony, Fiona, Phil, Bar, Rod, Ados, Karen, Chris, Fred, Jo, Sarah and Em. We thank many friends for the fun and help they have given us especially Pete Inglis and John Nixon, and for reading the manuscript: Don Young, Elizabeth Tyskiewicz, Sue Morris, Mark Eller, Andy Colley and Peter Murphy. Lastly we must mention the Foreign Affairs Department of the Government of the Xinkiang Ugyur Autonomous Region of north-west China and the Urumqi City Gong-An for nearly ruining the expedition and then mysteriously doing an about-turn and putting together the finishing touches.

ONE

Goodbye to the Open Sea

Several tramp steamers and a fishing canoe off the coast of Chittagong. A handful of ripples creeping in from the Bay of Bengal. Cousin Nick and I dipped our toes in the lukewarm water then turned our backs. That was the last we saw of the open sea.

Almost due north of us, several thousand miles away, lay our target: the Centre of the Earth. It's the most remote point on the earth's surface; the furthest from the open sea. No one has ever been there.

The Centre of the Earth lies somewhere in the heart of the Asian continental mass, isolated from the Far East by the empty expanses of the Gobi Desert, and guarded in the north by the frozen wastes of Siberia. To the south are the most formidable mountains in the world. The exact position of the Centre of the Earth – non-existent like the North and South Poles, yet as unique as the top of Everest and the bottom of the Mariana Trench – is fixed by triangulation. It is equidistant firstly from the Arctic Ocean, secondly from Bo Hai Wan in the Yellow Sea to the far east of China, and thirdly from here where we stood by the side of the Indian Ocean.

The time was noon on 1 May. A few minutes slipped by (as we put on our shoes and socks) before we waved goodbye to the local Bangladeshis who fished the sea and worked in fields nearby. They had crowded round in astonishment at two foreigners visiting their beach. By way of explanation, we tried to say that we were going to the place where there is no sea – but it didn't seem to make sense.

We carried our precious bicycles across the sand to the banana plantations and coconut groves which bordered the beach, then swung our legs over the saddles for the first of many adventures. We were excited and we were on our way to the Centre of the Earth.

Three hours later we collapsed in a tiny wooden chai house, strangled by the heat, drenched in sweat, dizzy from sunstroke and hemmed in by an oppressive crowd of children and young men. A radio blared out Bangladeshi music. Clouds of flies zipped by our ears and flitted across our eyelashes. Our heads were thumping, and the noise and irritations dissolved into a flickering blur. A thin man hammered metal very loudly beside us. It would have been bliss to have climbed into the engine room of a tramp steamer to lie down and sleep in a tool box. We gulped fizzy drinks and sipped at the thick, sweet tea, trying to calm our nerves and slake our thirst. Nick had wisely covered his arms and wrapped thermal long-johns around his head to protect against sun and heat, but I shortsightedly went for a tan and ended up with tender sunburn on top of heat exhaustion. Forehead, forearms and calves burnt red. After all this, we had only covered twelve kilometres. Already we had lost our way. The inside had fallen out of our wide-angle camera lens, and from under my luggage flap a piece of our waterproofs had disappeared.

Nick laughed, slightly apprehensively. 'Stunning start, eh?'

I munched on a corner of chapati and apologetically offered: 'It can only get better.'

I was optimistic that things would get better. In my experience they usually do – that little bit of luck always turns up just when needed. Nick summed it up when he said, as we flew out from London barely four days earlier: 'This is an opportunist's expedition.' We didn't know what would happen. That's not to say we didn't know what to expect. We had done some homework. Nick had already succeeded with many great bicycle adventures, I'd travelled the Andes, Himalayas, Korea and part of East Africa on foot. In the same way that our histories are different, so are our philosophies. Nick prefers to try to evaluate all options calmly and coolly, whereas I'm more likely to make a snap decision, frequently putting my foot in it. Underneath there has always been a niggling competitiveness – the sort on which siblings thrive. Silently, we acknowledged our differences. We felt that our attitudes and our abilities complemented each other, and thereby we had faith that together we had the potential to become a team fit to challenge the endless tide of problems ahead.

Our vision of the oncoming expedition was, in retrospect, rather naïve. We imagined a pleasant fast bike ride through some nice quiet little villages in Bangladesh and India, quickly reaching Nepal and the Himalayas where the proper adventure would start. Then we would be boldly attempting two things which had probably never been done before. Firstly we would set out to cycle across the Tibetan Plateau – that great purple lozenge on the world map – the most extensive and inhospitable high-altitude plateau in the world. Secondly, after tipping off the northern edge of the plateau back down almost to sea-level and swapping freezing cold thin air for roasting sand-desert, we'd try to pedal up the fabled Silk Road across the Gobi, following the footsteps of traders from thousands of years ago carrying silk and spices in exchange for gold and other precious items, including at one time glass, from the Roman Empire. Marco Polo brought his camel caravan this way. Genghis Khan rode his horse. We glibly set out alone on push-bikes. The total distance we guessed from the wiggles on the map would be somewhere around 5,000 kilometres. Knowing we could do 200 kilometres per day on flat smooth tarmac in Europe, we set ourselves a target speed of over 100 kilometres per day. Hence a total time for the journey of much less than fifty days, hopefully forty, maybe only thirty.

We cycled ultra-lightweight: no tent, no food, only one litre of water each. No support crew. Only one set of clothes. We snipped the labels out of our thermal underwear and cut the edges off our maps. Hopefully we were travelling light enough to battle over broken tracks in remote mountains and to buy food from families in the valleys as well as shelter from the intense sun, wind, dust and sub-zero temperatures. Altitude sickness, lung infections, dehydration, stomach upheavals and frostbite were all potential companions in the mountains. Thirst and hunger in the desert. Red tape could equally be a problem, particularly at the heavily guarded crossing from Nepal to Tibet, which is now under the austere Chinese umbrella. If we survived all this and successfully penetrated the heart of Asia, then we imagined it would be an easy day-trip to whizz out and metaphorically plant our flag (too heavy to carry – we planned to wave a well-used T-shirt instead) at the magical Centre of the Earth.

As it transpired, we discovered that we were, to say the least, over-optimistic and quite wrong in our predictions! Having covered only twelve kilometres in the first three hours, we were already way behind schedule.

Neither did the rest of the first day go according to plan. We had left Patenga Point soon after noon. We had stopped at the tiny wooden chai house for food at about 3 p.m. After two hours stabilizing our temperatures, heart rates and egos, we paid our few taka and set off again only to find that our intentions to start the expedition in good style by getting to sleep at dusk were transformed into a frantic dash through the failing light and rising wind to seek shelter before thick black monsoon clouds from the west burst over us. To our dismay someone up above was planning a sparkling send-off to our trip; our frantic dash failed, the daylight failed, the heavenly cisterns opened up and a torrential downpour hit us.

Nick's diary. Evening.
Not being used to the ferocity of monsoon rain, we pedalled blithely on as if, like an English shower, it would quickly pass and leave us damply refreshed. Asian rain, it seems, is different. We were soaked to the skin within minutes and, in the wake of spraying water, darkness arrived unnoticed. The experience which followed is one of those that you use as a benchmark for the rest of your life.

No lightning I'd ever seen compared with those fantastic, violent instants of bright white – almost blue – light which ripped the night to jagged shreds every few seconds. Ahead the road pulsed with water. Without the lightning we would have been unable to continue [for weight reasons, no lights were carried]. Part of me prayed for another flash so I could see my way ahead; part of me was wondering whether the next strike would target on a couple of Raleigh 753 racing bicycles! At first the rain was deliciously warm and cleansing, but the sheer volume of it quenched the heat from the land, the road and our bodies till we became cold. Even then the storm strengthened, with a tearing wind grabbing at roadside trees and pushing the bikes this way and that. Instead of a soothing stream of warm water running through our hair, we found ourselves being flayed by chilly nuggets. Unlit rickshaws suddenly appeared out of the darkness ahead of us and pedestrians passed by our elbows as black indistinct shadows flapping sheets of polythene over their heads. At one point I had a fleeting impression, like a poorly exposed photograph, of two rickshaws travelling south, locked together in urgent companionship, their riders' bodies arced and straining against the wind. Several times we were forced off the road by lorries splashing by with a lethal disregard for anything smaller than themselves.

So much was happening in the first day. In the mid-afternoon we'd been scorched by heatstroke – now it was replaced by hypothermia. We found a low dark chai house and hunched shivering over glasses of tea. We had only one set of clothes for the whole expedition and therefore nothing to change into then or at any other time. The relief from the storm was ecstasy and Nick wrote in his diary: 'Those cups of tea were, predictably, the best cups of tea that I'd ever had in my life.' The chai house had open walls, and rain beat loudly on the tin roof; around us were thirty or forty men clustered at the other tables talking quietly in the dim candlelight. Water streamed off the eaves, and the mud outside turned into a quagmire. We asked for a bed, but they indicated there was nothing there. When the storm abated, we had to set off once more into the darkness, heading north, hoping.

By the end of the day we'd had enough adventures to dissuade Alice from ever again stepping through the looking-glass. The expedition was already tougher and more arduous than we had expected. It had immediately gone right over the top. There were a whole range of problems we'd never anticipated. However, far from being depressed and dispirited, we were elated. It was quite hilarious that everything had gone so wrong so quickly. Mentally we were buoyant. It was exactly what we had been seeking in adventure: problems we couldn't predict yet which we could survive. It had been an exciting and entertaining day. In my diary I wrote: 'Day One – Phenomenal Fun! Real Adventure!' We could have been little boys playing outside in a pool of mud. Nick was feeling similar elation: 'This is satisfying, blissful, exhilarating. An escape from London's hectic bustle. It's the closest to Heaven that I've ever come.'

When we eventually got to bed at the end of the first day it was nearly midnight. We lay naked in the heat tossing and turning, swatting mosquitoes and wondering what more could happen to surprise us on this trip. We congratulated ourselves on surviving this far and tried settling our anxieties by grandly telling each other that our greatest strength was our depth of experience in travel adventure.

Nick has made a living for the past eight years out of writing and travelling. In his student days he took time off from studying for his geography degree to cycle across Europe with Doug Whyte. They slept in fields and on mountain terraces, lived off the land, and eventually reached Cape Matapan, the most southerly point of mainland Greece. With Doug again, Nick next cycled from Norwich to North Africa through high-summer heat, scorpions, and dysentery before graduating to island travel. A Corsican bandit once threatened to throw him over a cliff. Nick has always had a predilection for slightly reckless pursuits such as white-water rafting and ski-mountaineering. Always on the lookout for something a bit different, Nick led the first group-tour ride from Land's End to John o'Groats, and on bicycles with Pete Inglis – the gentle giant who later became photographer for the Bicycles up Kilimanjaro expedition – circumnavigated the biggest ice-cap in Europe: Jostedals Bre in Norway. Later, with Chris Crane, he went racing brakeless three-wheel buggies down the precipitous walls of the Rocky Mountains. Then with Ados Crane in 1984 he struck out to East Africa and rode the Kenyan Rift Valley. Others have had the pleasure of knowing Nick, befuddled by French wine, belayed in the dark to the Buchaille or beavering away under the lights of television cameras in the BBC's 'Now Get Out of That' – of course he did.

Nick's early days in Norwich were filled with weekends in the country, family trips in summer and the unusual ten-day mountaineering epics led by his father Hol, assisted by my father Charles, in Scotland every winter. A group of about ten friends and relatives joined in with these sessions of isolation and deprivation which successfully combined the two opposites of 'holiday' and 'ordeal'. On long days wading through deep snow or leaning into gale-force winds and rain on exposed icy ridges, we became acquainted with adversity and discomfort. There was also an element of competition: to be first up a peak, to be considered fit enough to carry the emergency pack, or to be recognized as sufficiently responsible to be in charge of the fuel or food stores. In adversity, we were bonded in spirit: on early-morning marches, talk and laughter held the weather at bay. As a group we found these challenges taught us teamwork, endurance and determination in difficult circumstances, all of which built up our own inner confidence and ability.

Hol's winter mountaineering weekends laid the basis for all future trips. While Nick cycled in Europe, I was led off to East Africa by younger brother Ados when he was only seventeen. After three months' hitch-hiking and a climb up Mount Kenya, I went bright-eyed to Durham University where I spent four years playing rugby, going scuba-diving and studying for a normal job. But the travel bug bit me and I broke away for a year as a guide/naturalist in the Galapagos Islands working on yachts with mostly American visitors. It was topped off with several months' gallivanting around on buses and trucks in Ecuador, Peru and Bolivia. That wore me down and I disappeared into academia at Reading University for another four years and a PhD before Ados came up with his inspiration for 'Running the Himalayas'. When we started on 18 March 1983 from Darjeeling in north-east India, we never believed we would get more than a couple of hundred miles into the journey. We thought some problem or other would stop us within the first twenty days. It was a search for our physical and mental limits. By finding them, we could satisfy our wanderlust and settle down to normal lives. We came close to our limits but were never broken.

In the final analysis, we did struggle on to complete a 2,000-mile, 101-day traverse from Darjeeling, through Nepal, the Garwhal/Kumaon Himalayas and Zanskar, to Rawalpindi in Pakistan. Our achievement on this adventure stunned us for a year; furthermore it has left an indelible mark on my ego so it will be mentioned once or twice more in this book. One of the significant aspects of that marathon is that Ados and I raised nearly £100,000 in sponsorship for the charity Intermediate Technology (IT). The money was raised partly by getting people to fill in sponsor forms, partly from doing lectures and guest appearances, and mainly by making a general plea through the media after our return for donations to be sent to IT. Ados and I paid for all the expedition costs ourselves from our own savings. All funds received on behalf of IT were used for their work on long-term development in the Third World, helping to show the rural poor how they can work themselves out of poverty using their own skills and local resources, thereby creating a viable future for themselves. IT has more than 200 projects in sixty countries; including water wells, bicycle trailers, fuel-efficient cooking stoves, spinning machines, fishing boats, veterinary services, rural workshops, irrigation systems and small-scale water power.

'Bicycles up Kilimanjaro' was the first combined expedition which Nick and I dreamt up. The bicycles and all the equipment were donated. We paid all the other costs from our own pockets, just over £2,000 each, as though it were a once-in-a-lifetime holiday. It was intended as a light-hearted jape but turned into a full-scale expedition, requiring concentration, determination and a good measure of initiative to succeed. Over Christmas 1984 and New Year 1985, we pedalled up to the summit of Kilimanjaro, the highest mountain in Africa, 19,354 feet above sea-level where there is permanent snow and ice, intensely bright sun, and we felt awful! The expedition was a great success both in terms of fun and achieving its goal of raising £30,000 for Intermediate Technology.

January 1986, we were having a drink at the Hand and Shears by the Church of St Bartholomew the Great, when Nick proposed: 'Fancy doing another expedition soon?'

'What sort of thing are you talking about? A repeat of the Three Peaks bike weekend, or another Bicycles up Kilimanjaro?'

'The latter, something big. I had been planning to go on the Trans-Siberian Railway with Granny. It's her ninetieth birthday soon. Overland to Tibet. The family dissuaded me.'

A new expedition sounded exciting to me. However, it would need an objective and what you might call a reason. Out of all the places in the world, Tibet would be nice but would not necessarily fit in. In more general terms I said: 'I'd like about a two-month trip, preferably really lightweight.'

'Small-scale.'

I thoroughly agreed with him. Too many helpers on Kilimanjaro had made it more complex, though also more fun in the evenings.

'No messing about with support crews, no hassles relying on other people.'

'Do you think anyone else should come?'

'Both Ados and Hol are tied up with other commitments at present.'

'So it's just us two.'

'Cosy!'

On 30 January, we met at my flat near Smithfield Market in central London for a serious brainstorming session. We were trying to create a super-adventure which would stretch us to the limits and double our fund-raising for IT. Key concepts were 'difficult without being agonizing', 'dangerous without being suicidal', 'exotic without being obscure' and 'awkward without being impossible'. The method we used was to sit down with a map of the world and a list of different sports, then let our minds wander randomly through all the various facets of odd information we knew about any place. Nothing was sacrosanct and nothing was called silly until we'd analysed its possibilities. We started at 3 p.m. and came up with projects such as Tricycles to the North Pole, Swimming the Atlantic, and Mules from Montana to Minnesota, which the readers of *Bicycles up Kilimanjaro* will know about. Within an hour we were getting our brains in motion but, however hard we thought, we kept coming back to 'China', the new exotic expedition location of the mid-1980s. The question was 'What can we do there that will be fresh and challenging?' At 5 p.m. Nick murmured, 'Remote . . . the remotest place,' and suddenly leapt in the air.

The Guinness Book of Records is a bible on these occasions and sure enough there in the chapter on The Natural World under 'CONTINENTS – LAND REMOTEST FROM THE SEA – WORLD' we read:

> There is an as yet unpinpointed spot in the Dzoosotoyn Elisen (desert), northern Xinjiang Uygur Zizhiqu (Sin Kiang), China's most northwesterly province, that is more than 1,500 miles, 2,400 kms, from the open sea in any direction.

We were elated. 'It's exactly what we want. Wonderful!'

We grabbed *The Times Atlas* and searched for those names. But no luck until we looked at the last bit of the *Guinness* entry and read: 'The nearest large city to this point is Urumqi to its south.' This was easy to find. Later in our research we learnt it is a newly expanded city and has 900,000 inhabitants reliant principally on irrigated farming in the desert below the snows of the mid-Asian mountain ranges. It's a crossroad of cultural currents from China, Russia and the Afghan/Middle Eastern civilizations. But it wasn't in the middle of our map. This created a problem. Where was this remotest place?

The discrepancy arises because, on flat maps of the world, land areas are distorted, usually by Mercator's projection. One needs to look at a globe to see a true perspective. To get an accurate computation we realized that it would be necessary to get involved in trigonometric calculations around a sphere, so we did some lateral thinking and decided to investigate navigation handbooks for yachtsmen in order to plot the true position. As it turned out over the next few weeks the mathematical manipulations were further complicated because we needed detailed survey maps of the coastlines at the three points of nearest open sea in order to determine their exact latitudes and longitudes. That problem also required defining the differences between open sea, estuary, river, beach and swamp.

The existence of this remotest place had been acknowledged for many years. Mildred Cable and Francesca French in their book *The Gobi Desert* describe their travels of the 1920s and 1930s, and note that the great deserts of Central Asia – Gobi, Taklamakan and Dsungarei – 'cover an enormous space of nearly six million square miles which never touches a sea coast and thereby presents a physical phenomenon without parallel on the face of the earth. The spot of the globe which is furthest removed from any sea or ocean is located within its northern portion, and this remoteness from any seaboard . . . induces extremes of heat and cold, and fierce winds which sweep across the desert with terrible force, whipping up dense sand-clouds which blot out the sun.'

Luckily we didn't read this on that very first evening. Indeed, far from looking at the problems, we speculated on the potential. It seemed that we might have stumbled on one of the very few 'pure' places in the world which are truly international and timeless. The Centre of the Earth belongs to everyone – it has no direct historical or political dependence. Since Urumqi is nearby and modern civil engineers can build roads over even the most hostile terrain, the Centre of the Earth could become one of the world's great tourist attractions.

We were very excited and turned our attention to outlining the journey. Time was ticking by. It was 9 p.m. and hunger rumbled in our bellies. It put a fresh urgency into our thinking. We cut away all the trivial and diverse thoughts which had mushroomed around the Centre of the Earth. Thinking simply, we said: 'If we're going to the most remote place in the world from the open sea, where do we start?' The answer was equally straightforward: 'At the open sea.' The purity and adventure would be heightened by going man-powered all the way – on bikes or on foot. No one in their right mind would want to try to walk that distance; we calculated it would take nearly a year. Therefore we would attempt to cycle.

One more problem before we left our brainstorming session in jubilation was to decide the title of the adventure. But it was obvious. Jules Verne had done a good job a hundred years ago dreaming up science fiction. Maybe in future years we will make use of his other titles: 20,000 Leagues Under the Sea on a unicycle, From the Earth to the Moon by elastic, or – Around the World in Eighty Somethings.

Next we wanted a code-name so we used the initials JCE and pretended it meant Joint Crane Expedition. We kept the expedition low-key and neither of us did very much for the next two months except tell a few friends that we were going on a bike ride to central Asia. 'Bike Ride to the Back of Beyond' we called it because we didn't want to set anyone else thinking about the Centre of the Earth in case they should try to beat us to it. We were paranoid about the possibility of competition. We budgeted JCE and decided that, assuming we got bikes and equipment free, it would ⟩cost £2,500 each of our own savings. We needed to know that we could recoup our costs by selling magazine articles, a radio programme, a book and lectures. If someone else got to the Centre of the Earth first, then our loss would be not only in our pride but also in our pockets.

Quite aside from the competition, one of our biggest worries was simply not being allowed into Chinese Tibet from Nepal. The first independent travellers for half a century had been allowed across the border barely two months before. We were told that it was virtually impossible to get hold of visas and permits. Merely to get to Lhasa by bike would be a major achievement. If we couldn't use this direct route over the Himalayas from the open sea in the Bay of Bengal, then we were prepared either for a 2,000 km bicycle detour west to Pakistan to use the newly opened (1 May 1986) Karakoram Highway leading over the Kunjirab pass to Kashgar and entering the extreme west of Tibet close to Afghanistan and Russia, or for a flight to Hong Kong and Beijing then starting cycling from the second point of closest open sea at Bo Hai Wan. If that failed, can you imagine the Russians letting us cycle across Siberia?

Having created the expedition and shaped the framework, we mulled it over for a few weeks allowing it to mature, thereby enabling dormant brains to churn out any problems. Then at the end of February we got together again and decided that the start-date should be 1 May. We hoped to be in front of the monsoon in Bangladesh and India, far enough behind winter for the Nepalese and Himalayan passes to be free of snow, and sufficiently ahead of summer that we wouldn't be fried to a crisp in the central Chinese deserts.

Early one morning in March we told Steve Bonnist, head of public relations at IT, about JCE and the secret target. He took it like a man, drank a strong cup of coffee and laughed nervously. It was he who had co-ordinated the fund-raising from previous exploits. He is a tireless worker totally dedicated to IT, and a very good friend. He recovered his breath and said calmly: 'What are you going to do – burrow down in a mechanical worm like Captain Nemo?' Three years ago he would have exploded in a fury of madness. These days he is so accustomed to loony trips and crazy japes that he no longer rises to the bait.

Six weeks before the start of this new IT fund-raising extravaganza, we set about getting equipment and finance – a difficult task as we couldn't reveal the destination. It seemed a good idea to try to get a single commercial sponsor to pay for everything in exchange for having all the promotional opportunities. We engaged Sarah Pearson of SPA PR company to do a lot of telephoning and talking, but to no avail. She summed up our lack of success: 'Who in their right mind will back a secret expedition?'

As March disappeared and the first few days of April slipped by, our official start date of 1 May loomed large. We had to get our skates on. The departure date from Britain was set for 23 April so in the space of three weeks we had to get visas, money, flights, maps, clothes and jabs against tetanus, typhoid, cholera, hepatitis and, last but not least, the bikes – bicycle fever is a serious ailment causing weak legs and sore backsides in addition to rather long story-telling sessions. It is not cured by any known jab nor by large amounts of cash which might enable the subject to buy a motorcar. The only suspected antidote is indulgence.

Two weeks before departure, we had no bikes, no special clothes, no air tickets, no India or China visas, no Chinese vocabulary, and had barely read any texts on China. Contingency plans abounded: we could have taken our own racing bikes from four years ago (if these broke down we could buy local Chinese bikes), we had an assortment of cycling and climbing clothes which had the advantage that we knew how they performed, and with a few hundred quid cash we could have bought an air ticket at a few hours' notice. We weren't going to need to know the language; smiles and gesticulations usually suffice, and we thought we'd quickly pick up basic words. Also, we didn't need to leave Britain exactly when we had said and our route in Asia was speculative. Only the target was fixed, and only our determination concrete.

Raleigh came up trumps ten days before departure and offered made-to-measure bikes in state-of-the-art 753 tubing built by Gerald O'Donovan who masterminded the bikes for Raleigh's Tour de France victories. Mere mortals worship pictures of this man (look at his initials). We stepped into his office for tea and gazed at the decades of cycling mementoes on his walls. We spent a couple of happy hours discussing frame angles, wheels and tyres (see Appendix I). We settled for a 14/17/20/24/28 block. I gaily chose a 52/40 chain-ring while Nick selected a more prudent 49/39. This gave me a top gear of 100.3 inches and bottom of 38.6 inches. Nick's were slightly lower. The conversion to inches is done by calculating the distance the bicycle travels for one revolution of the pedals, then computing the diameter of wheel on a penny-farthing which would travel the same distance for one revolution. Of course a penny-farthing, or 'ordinary' as they used to be called, has a fixed wheel: no gears. If anyone tried riding a 100.3-inch wheel – one and a half times as high as a man – they'd get a few burns between their legs! Steve Bell co-ordinated the help from Raleigh and agreed, at our request, to set up equipment drops in Dhaka, Kathmandu, Lhasa and Urumqi. The day before we were due to fly we proudly collected our bikes.

Mike Parsons of Karrimor was super-enthusiastic. He always is. He's provided rucksacks and panniers for both our previous expeditions. With four days left we were rushing madly around collecting all other essentials. Black's Camping and Leisure and Madison Cycles came quickly to our assistance for most of the needs, Molly Lowe of Been Bag at short notice willingly made up special salopets, and Laurie Olsen of LansdownEuro whom I'd met at a conference in the plush surroundings of the Waldorf offered to meet subsistence costs on the Tibetan Plateau – if we ever got there.

On the day before our supposed departure we went to get some last-minute flights, but to our surprise found that no one flies to Bangladesh on Wednesdays. So instead we got three days' welcome breathing-space until the next flight. This break enabled us to get Indian visas on Thursday, pannier racks and plane tickets on Friday. We were nearly ready to go.

Nick had tried in several places for Chinese visas. We knew all along that these would be difficult to get whereas visas for Bangladesh, India and Nepal were no problem. China has only started opening up to tourism over the last ten years: foreigners were first permitted in small numbers to Tibet merely three years ago. The Nepal–China border linking Kathmandu and Lhasa opened to tourists in 1985 and visitors had to travel in controlled package groups. The first individual travel-permits to cross the border had only been issued on 1 March 1986. Furthermore, we not only wanted to travel independently, which usually means by bus or truck, but we also wanted to cycle.

There are several different channels in London through which one might get a Chinese visa. Initially we told them what we intended to do, but we changed that when we got one heart-stopping letter back saying 'You will not be allowed to do your expedition. The border Kathmandu to Lhasa is not open.' Our contingency plan was to buy visas somewhere in Asia, possibly Hong Kong, as we had heard of people who had done that. However, it was worth checking again the other outlets in London without telling them where we intended to go, or why or how. On the Thursday after we should have left, Nick called at the new China UK Travel Bureau in Cambridge Circus and to our total astonishment they said 'Yes. One day turnaround.' We collected our passports at 4 p.m. on Friday: less than twenty-four hours before we got on the plane we had our China visas.

That night we brought all our gear together in Nick's flat in the Barbican and got rid of half the stuff we didn't need. (We kept the other half of the stuff we didn't need, flew it to Bangladesh, then discovering that we still didn't need it, we flew it straight back to Britain!) By the time Sue Winchcombe knocked on the door at 8 a.m. we'd had eighteen minutes' sleep and were ready to pile the gear into her van to be chauffeured to Heathrow.

On the plane we each had slightly different methods of coping with tiredness during the ten-hour flight; I had four two-hour sleeps, Nick had beer and a double gin and tonic followed by two glasses of wine with Drambuie and Cognac chasers.

As we prepared for the descent to Dhaka we had time for a quick word with, on the one side, a journalist reporting on charity work in the Third World and, on the other, two blokes from the oil rigs going for a week's relaxation in Bangkok. . . .

Arrival in Dhaka was D-Day minus four. As we stepped out of the plane the hot humid air thudded into us. We weren't ready for this. All our clothes were geared to high altitude, dryness and cold. In Bangladesh it was hot and wet – the wettest place in the world. We were at sea-level in the tropics wearing snow-goggles. Not many tourists before us have gone to the Indian subcontinent carrying guide-books only about China.

Dhaka was colourful and noisy. Rickshaws, many with intricately painted designs on their hoods, dominated the roads, their bicycle bells tingling all the time. It only cost a couple of pennies for a ride across town. Most roads were dirty tarmac, some were rubbly dirt. Old colonial buildings still stood in a few places, while the city centre was faceless office blocks barely taller than the scruffy lean-tos below where we bought chai or roasted corn. The pavements were crowded with people; some bare-foot, some in suits. The rich were rich and the poor were poor. Very few fitted into the middle.

Nick. Letter home.
Dhaka has drawn many refugees in from the country, and we passed an encampment in the city, where hundreds were living in small huts of tin, wood, cardboard – any scrap of fabric pressed into use. Hardly anyone seems to have a 'possession' and even that first symbol of wealth – personal transport/the bicycle – was rare. Children naked or in rags. Nobody we saw actually appeared to be starving, but the majority of the country is right on the subsistence level of existence. It's difficult to come to terms with the poverty of the Bangladeshis versus the obvious wealth and health of ourselves. Some of the sights are pitiful: the man with twisted stumps for legs dragging himself along the dirt gutter, and the tiny girl with matted hair and huge brown eyes, carrying a baby no more than a few months old,

and asking for 'one taka' (about two pence and enough to buy two chapatis). The value of one of our bicycles alone would set up a Bangladeshi family for life.

In Dhaka there were shop windows with transistors and shiny ornaments, and sweatshops with lines of thin men hunched over sewing machines. It is hard to adjust to this situation and often easier to accept and use it than fight it and fit it to our Western philosophies. In a more savoury sweat-shop, Lord Ling's in Green Road, we had our salopets minutely adjusted to fit like a birthday suit – an important job because these salopets would be worn all day every day, and some nights, for the duration of the ex-pedition. Molly had made them out of synthetic wind-proof stretchy material which was easy to wash and drip-dry. We would only have to dunk them in water before we went to bed and hang them out overnight to stay more or less clean. We planned to do that every few days when they got unbearably high. They had the added advantage of being fleece-lined and comfy as well as brightly coloured and fun.

We had a lot of other things to cram into our last three days. We had to make final adjustments to the bikes and to the rest of the equipment. We had to trace a contact, Richard Fielder, in the British High Commission, and also find an acquaintance of my father by the name of Shameen Ahmed. We found him behind a smart desk and an array of telephones. He was extremely friendly and set up local media coverage in addition to giving us dinner and much background chat about his country. It turned out that he is about the same age as us, is PR Manager for Glaxo in Bangladesh and his hobby has for ten years been reading the news on national television. Understandably the motto on his desk reads: 'Most of us get what we deserve, but only the successful will admit it.'

Shameen's help left us free to dive into our internal wranglings; for instance, 'Exactly what bits of gear should we take and how should we load the bikes?' I was in favour of leaving virtually everything behind. Nick argued for an extra bit of equipment here and there plus a couple of spares for the bikes. He was right because we'd have had no adventure if we failed for want of a simple spoke or an emergency pair of specs (we both wear contact lenses) or fractionally too few clothes (we had a pair of leg-warmers in addition to long-johns, salopets and over-trousers). We also had to ask the question, 'What route in detail will we take from Dhaka to Kathmandu?'

At this stage, one day before the start, we didn't even know exactly where we would start, so we were up late at night poring over detailed maps of the Bangladesh coastline to find a starting-point which was accessible and beside the open sea. After much debate we decided this should be Patenga Point. Late on the last afternoon we boarded a train to nearby Chittagong and during the journey started to study the route back by bicycle to Dhaka, then on to Kathmandu. Thereafter we saw in our dreams no more than a hazy track through high mountains somehow reaching Lhasa, sometime stretching to the Gobi, somewhere finding the Centre of the Earth.

All we had in mind were the bare bones of the journey. The details would be hung on that framework as our adventure developed. Our ultimate objective would always remain the same, and the general pattern was predetermined, but the components would continually be moulded to fit the circumstances. We hadn't even finalized the computations for the Centre of the Earth because we thought we could do that when we got to Urumqi. There can't be many expeditions which set out from the start-line without knowing the destination!

Somehow it all came together and we started with a moderate level of sanity at noon on Day 1 from the attractively alliterative Patenga Point near Chittagong in southern Bangladesh. Heat exhaustion and a monsoon storm hit us before bed – mosquitoes hounded us through the night.

> *Nick. Day 2.*
> Day 2 started at 6 a.m. An early start to beat the heat. A fast ride north. Keen and enthusiastic at the crack of dawn. Riding *en echelon*; one behind the other, taking turns to break the wind and create a slipstream behind to suck the other rider along. Speed about 20 m.p.h. where the tarmac is smooth. Roads more or less free of traffic.
>
> The road hereabouts is running across the flood plains of the Ganges Delta – built high on an embankment above a sea of green paddy fields shaded with different greens according to the ripeness of the rice growing in them. Some are small square lakes, where rice is about to be planted; in others young shoots peep from the water in light, vivid green. Often we pass a man up to his knees in water ploughing behind a hunky black buffalo. Lean, brown cows wander about, as do lambs and innocent-looking dogs. Little children run up the walkways between fields to wave at us. In corners goats are tethered. Palms fringe the edges of the road.

Among clumps of trees we saw thatched roofs but nothing more of the lives of the people. Over this lovely rural scene, power-lines and telegraph wires laced the skies. Wails of singing from tinny transistor radios wafted across the breeze. From time to time a high-pitched drone sawed through our calm as a three-wheeled autorickshaw slowly caught up then passed irritatingly on ahead to its destination. When the trucks and buses came, they came with a vengeance, at breakneck speed, straight down the middle of the road. We shouted at each other 'Bus, bus. *Bus!* Fifty yards!' In panic, we would flip our bikes over to steer tight to the edge, shoulders slightly hunched in anticipation of being struck from behind. It was very scary when there was only one truck or bus – two from opposite directions were petrifying. Many times we gave up the unequal challenge and steered clear off the metalled surface on to the dirt and grass beside the bushes that lined the road. With careful balance and judgement we could get back on to the road without touching down, but on one occasion Nick squeezed a gap between the buses ahead and I was stranded, faced with a fast bus overladen with people in front and a large cement truck bearing down from behind. I turned ninety degrees left and found myself in a stone-breaker's yard.

Nick. Day 2.
Rickshaws scuttled by in clanging waves, parting before the relentless charging of buses and trucks. Knots of people in every field. Throngs in the villages. 'Doesn't it ever stop?' I said to Dick. The continual clamour of Bangladesh – from dawn to well after midnight – is still too much to comprehend. The sheer weight of human activity is on a scale beyond anything I could ever imagine. In villages the streets are crammed with people *doing* things – not sitting around with nothing to do, but actually zooming about with purpose: working in shops, making furniture, welding, mending buses and rickshaws, sewing clothes or selling medicine, Pepsis or cloth. Everyone seems to be busy, but with so little money to go around, the actual income from these businesses must be minute. This resourcefulness includes re-cycling what in the West would be called 'rubbish'. Consequently we don't see any material waste – the only pollution is organic: human and animal.

The essence of Bangladesh is the people. One of the most crowded countries in the world. There are 100 million people, more than 600 per square kilometre, nearly four times as dense as Britain. The average family size is seven – the same as my family, yet in Britain we are thought unusually large. Everywhere we stopped we drew huge crowds with a total of maybe seventy people packed solidly around us. We'd cruise from a quiet smooth cycle-ride through green paddies and gentle countryside into a hectic grey-black shanty village with the road crammed with people, rickshaws, battered buses and trucks. The moment we stopped the kids would rush towards us. Sometimes the crowd started forming even before we'd stopped.

In Feni, a village about eighty kilometres north of Chittagong, I leapt off my bike to run and check out a couple of chai houses to find some drink. Barely a minute had elapsed by the time I came back yet the crowd had grown to more than fifty. To get back to Nick and the bikes, pushing was no good. I had to shout 'Make way! Make way! Beep. Beep.' Everyone parted as though I were the prophet crossing the Red Sea.

I got back in the middle with Nick again and we gulped our drinks quickly. The crowd grew frighteningly. People were packed tight, leaning heavily on our bikes, getting excited. Little kids were pushing to the front, the elders pushed them back, elbowing and shoving and looking at us for approval. They laughed and pushed some more. Someone went off balance. He lost his cool. Suddenly they were all frantically excited. Pandemonium broke loose. We had to get out quick. We were scared. Pushing a bit, we took a few steps then leapt on our bikes hoping that not too many kids were hanging on to the pannier rack. A couple of tugs and we were free. Within a minute we'd picked up speed ahead of those running after us. A few minutes later we were safely out in the gentle countryside cruising smoothly in the bright sun past green paddies and women with packs of produce or urns of water on their heads.

In each place we stopped we learnt to drag our bikes as quickly as possible into the back of a chai house because that was the only way we could get any tranquillity. Even then people crowded in densely from the front, and our sanity was protected only by the rear wall. At times we feared that the little children would push that down from outside. The crowd blocked out all the light and cut off the cooling breeze. There would be a wall of faces in front of us and youngsters climbing on chairs, as well as a couple of little lads wriggling in through the gaps in the reed-matting walls. Each kid would sneak in as close as he possibly could, never quite touching us, but always extremely close – maybe with a smile he would even reach out to touch our glistening bikes. The villagers were always friendly and interested. Their fascination showed in their wide-eyed silence, almost turned to stone by astonishment. We met no aggression, no hostility, only curiosity. After a few minutes had slipped by, someone would come up with the familiar questions: 'What is your mother-country?' 'Where you come?' 'What is your name?'

We quickly learnt our first two words of Bangla – *doe cha*, 'two teas'. However, our linguistic capabilities limited themselves to pointing at someone else's food to get the same dish, and to simulating yawning and sleep to get a bed. To pay for our food and bed it was often simplest to hold out a couple of notes and let the cook take the appropriate money. The phrase 'Which way to X?' was a bit difficult but we usually managed to get through by simply saying the place-name in an enquiring confused tone. Often we had to repeat place-names several times before we hit on the correct pronunciation. My preference was to say quite a few words by way of introducing myself and my voice before I started asking questions. My words were of course in English but it seemed a lot better than nothing. Smiles proved the most effective intercourse.

We ate at any of the multitude of little tea-shacks by the road. Usually thatched, one room on a mud floor with rickety wooden tables and chairs. Always on the small side for us since Bangladeshis are smaller in stature. Open cooking in a smoky alcove at one end. Food might be a huge bowl of warm rice, or floppy chapatis like nan breads or thinner unleavened bread, maybe a small dish of bony chicken or gristly meat curry and typically a couple of types of vegetable curry and dahl. We ate with our fingers, right hand only, like all the locals. On all our travels we always bought our meals and never prepared our own.

In the chai houses, men do the cooking: in the villages, men mend the rickshaws and trucks. In the fields they are the ploughmen, trench-diggers, master builders and salesmen. They are the shopkeepers, businessmen, porters and drivers. They also hang around street corners and cafés. We hardly ever saw any women. They are full-time workers for the families, and because Bangladesh is Muslim they are meticulously hidden. Some of the few we did see wore a veil with their Indian, almost Hindu, brightly coloured sari which completely covers the rest of their body excepting hands and bare feet. In the fields they work, bent to the ground; clearing, planting, reaping. They are in the back of the villages, behind the homes, caring for children, cooking for men, tending the chickens and goats, carrying water with swaying elegance.

Dick. Day 2. Noon. Comilla.
A bit of friction this morning – Nick prefers riding fast and stopping regularly to refill water bottles. I find it easier to pedal at a more moderate pace but slog on for several hours between stops. Nick can cope with the abrupt stops and starts, but it throws me off my rhythm. I'd rather chance the water situation – though I have been getting a headache. We didn't really argue – just stated our points then rode silently for an hour.

However, it's small beer compared to the fact that we seem to have dropped like old hands into this trip. Merely twenty-four hours gone and yet it feels like weeks of adventure. The bikes and bags are part of us: we have such a small amount of gear that we already know exactly where everything is. The people, the towns, the bustle seem normal. We're not fazed by the food, the heat or the sea of paddy fields all around. It is as though we are seasoned travellers in this country and have already covered many hundreds of miles on these bikes with this equipment. It all feels 'right' and 'smooth'. So far so good. Each mini-adventure is fun by itself but none has sent us to the brink. It's uncanny. Almost too easy. Far simpler than we expected. No serious problems yet. The calm before the storm?

In the heat of the middle of the day we rested in Comilla, had some food, got some sleep. We woke sweating in the mid-afternoon hoping the place had calmed down but it was still crammed full of people and rickshaws. There was a model boat, ten feet across, hanging over the main street – symbol of the Boat party, who were strong in this area – whipping up support and enthusiasm for the National Elections scheduled for 7 May, in five days' time. These elections were the first free elections in Bangladesh for nearly twenty years, since the time when Bangladesh was East Pakistan. In fact since before that, when it was part of India, called East

Bengal – to this day the people are called Bengalis. The election could mean an end to the military rule. There was an awful lot at stake and election fever was running at a high pitch: propaganda on the radios, bunting in the streets, partying and speeches at night. Posters were plastered on the walls of chai houses and shops. On the previous night we had passed several election parties in the fields beating drums and drawing crowds once the day's work was done. Lorries went by packed with young men chanting. Autorickshaws had loudspeakers for electioneering. Three days later one went past us on the banks of the Ganges, and the canvasser was screaming so violently that he went hoarse and was reduced to a coughing heap with the loudspeaker still on!

The crowds were closing in as though for a soccer match. Two people were killed in Dhaka a couple of days after we were there. Where possible we tried to time our passage through an election crowd so that we could follow a vehicle as it blared its horn and cleared a path through the mass of people. People found us ultra-provocative in a friendly sort of way and clapped and cheered, but could easily have turned nasty and knocked us off. If we were lucky no one realized until we'd passed that there were two foreign cyclists hidden behind the vehicle.

Nick. Day 2. Evening.
A huge anvil-shaped cloud grew ahead of us until half the sky was filled with threatening grey. 'Wonder if it's a cyclone?' I said, fearing another aquatic thrashing. With dark rushing up (far quicker than nightfall in England), we paused on a bridge by the village of Elliotsganj. 'Shall we stop here,' said D, 'or go on?' 'I'm for going on' – thus we were committed. The big cloud evaporated into the orange of dusk. The night's drama came in the form of the biggest bug-attack I've ever experienced. The air was thick with flying objects which collided with us so densely that it was virtually impossible to open our eyes. My hair was stiff with trapped insects, my earholes plugged by gnats. With a coughing spit, D ejected some kind of bugette from his throat and yelled through the blackness that we had to stop to wrap clothes over our faces. A loud twang came from my front wheel as one of them met his end on a whirring fourteen-gauge stainless-steel spoke laced with meticulous artistry by F. W. Evans' very own Bob Arnold. Well into dark, we reached Daudkhandi Ferry and rode straight on. The boat slid from the bank with a roaring of its diesel engine. The river looked like thick vegetable soup. Across the water, we asked for bed and, as a crowd gathered, the peanut seller said: 'The other side.' In misery we traipsed back over on the ferry. Endured another crowd. Then retraced our tracks to the village of Daudkhandi proper.

The accommodation was hardly exotic. The luxury apartment was a tiny room barely big enough for two beds. Whitewash falling off the walls, shutters which didn't shut, and a door with a bicycle padlock to hold it closed. Rubbish under the beds and cockroaches in the corner. A tiny wooden chair, a tin washing-up bowl on the floor and that was it. Plenty of heat, humidity and insects. Nick flopped on the bed and poured with sweat. We'd cycled over 100 miles in the day. I asked for some water and got liquid which was thick and milky, almost opaque. Double dose of Puritabs. We put our bikes on the beds and went to find some food.

The evening started well at 9 p.m.: rice with the most succulent fish steaks in curry sauce. Then the electricity failed so we had a smoky oil lamp to write by. The lamp attracted lots of fascinating insects while our writing attracted lots of fascinated locals. At first a respectful interest then a few questions and offers to help us write. Things started hotting up. Someone looking haggard came in and leant right over into my eyes saying several times: 'There's been a killing in this town already today.' All rather distasteful. He went out then came back again with others, looking fiercer. He started hitting me on the chest and whirling his other arm around his head, chanting: 'One dead body.' Other people crowded around Nick and gabbled into our ears: 'Four people injured.' Not nice. Exit time. However, we didn't have time to get out because an officious-looking local bully came in and arrested us. At 11 p.m. he marshalled us down to the police station on suspicion of being political activists inciting riots.

Mr Nazrul Haq, the officer in command, sat behind a huge desk. A large cooling fan turned lazily on the ceiling. Two policemen stood guard on each door. The local clever-clogs had to wait outside. Mr Nazrul Haq wanted to know our political allegiances, and why were we spying, and how did we intend to start a riot? Why were we writing so much diary? Were we journalists? And, if not, why did we choose to study Bangladesh a few days before the very important national elections?

Sweat was pouring off our foreheads, and dripping down our necks. We were in a reasonably serious situation. Our clothes were filthy and sticky. The tidemarks of dirt around our socks were itchy. The sunburn had etched out swastikas where our gloves had been. Very dangerous. We hoped he wouldn't search our bags and find reams of diary notes, SLR camera gear, films, radio tapes and headphones and, worst of all, a Nagra tape-machine nicknamed the 'spy recorder' which the BBC lent us with the intention of making a Radio 4 documentary about JCE. Or indeed he might have looked in Nick's passport and found that he actually is a journalist!

Luckily Mr Haq calmed down when we put on our best smiles and fabricated a little story for him about being ordinary tourists who got a little lost and promised to go back to Dhaka and home as soon as possible. He showed his true colours and bought us Coca Colas at midnight. We settled down to discuss politics, 'Maggie' Thatcher and the Queen. 'What is wrong with Englishmen? They are all ruled by women.' He had especial admiration for the late Lord Mountbatten, 'the last colonial emperor'. It turned out that we were the first tourists to visit his area in his year of office. It's my advice to other tourists to ensure that we were also the last!

Day 2. Nick. Daudkhandi. 1 a.m.

We've had a police escort back to our doss-house and are relieved to find the bikes still safely on the beds. With the door locked a luxurious feeling of privacy has come over us, isolated from all of Bangladesh for the next few hours. In less than two days we've had sunstroke, cockroaches, constipation, monsoon deluges, thunder and lightning, swarms of insects, killer buses, riots and been arrested by the police. Our clothes, unwashed, are rotting gently in the perpetual high humidity since we got off the plane. Nothing normal seems to happen here – we haven't even had a puncture. With the door closed all that remains at 1 a.m. is the heat, the hammering of sewing-machines, transistor music from the rooms below, some fighting in the street, dogs howling and mosquitoes buzzing. We're drenched in sweat. Even the bloody cicadas are kicking up a continual frenzied cacophony punctuated every few minutes by geckos belching above our heads. This place is mad! The sooner we escape to India the better.

Day 3 necessitated crossing back over on the ferry then a fast smooth 50-kilometre ride to Dhaka punctuated by one more ferry. Nothing untoward happened. The main interest was the increasingly heavy traffic and narrower roads as we neared Dhaka. We either crept at walking speed along the verges over ditches and piles of dirt, or jumped into the stream of traffic and pedalled madly at 40 k.p.h. like ants joy-riding on the teeth of a chainsaw. It was quick – but one slip and we could have been dead.

Dhaka was a return to safety and sanity. We were out of reach of all the political frenzy, we could find our friends again and talk sensibly. We could relax in air-conditioned buildings, away from the insects and out of the heat, best of all we could find peace and quiet. We went for lunch at the Sheraton, bought a razor and had a shave. However, our hair remained all tussled, our clothes were filthy, and I had bicycle grease all up the back of my right leg. Shamelessly, we gorged ourselves. The staff treated us very civilly. Looking like this in Britain you wouldn't even be allowed to clean out the bins.

Suitably refreshed and refilled we felt much better and reviewed our progress: three days gone and 273 kilometres behind us. Therefore we were averaging barely ninety kilometres per day. That was far below our 100 kilometres per day target and simply not good enough. We resolved to get off to a good start on the next section to Kathmandu by cycling the first half-hour in the morning twilight before the proper dawn. To fill in the rest of the day, we tidied up a few jobs we had to do in Dhaka, such as writing home.

It turned out that we couldn't change money in the hotel so I started chatting up a couple of friendly ladies. They happily swapped my sterling notes for taka. We digressed to talking about our proposed bike ride out of the country, and the rotund homely lady, who I later found out was Mrs Berlin, a six-year resident of Dhaka who hails from New Jersey, laughed: 'You can't do that. Tomorrow is *Hartel*!'

'What's that?'

'It's the National Strike. Curfew from dawn to noon. Anyone out on the road gets stoned. They throw sticks and stones and bricks at you.'

'So how does anyone get about?'

'They don't. There's no buses, no cars, no trucks, no bicycles. Most wise people don't even dare walk.' For a woman as jovial as Old King Cole, she looked quite serious. 'Get yourself locked into your hotel room, and keep your head down.'

I mused: 'Seems like this place gets madder and madder.'

'That's right,' she says. 'If you want the acme of insanity, then that's here.'

It was all a bit depressing, our high-speed bike ride to the back of beyond seemed to be falling to pieces not because of lack of physical fitness or because of mechanical problems on the bikes, but because of socio-political problems, circumstances beyond our control.

Later, we went to the British High Commission hoping that they would have a different view, but Mike Greenstreet and Jack Woodcock, the bosses, virtually forbade us to leave Dhaka and advised us not to move at all until after the elections.

To finish off the story with Mrs Berlin, after she'd given us all the bad news I tried to lighten the conversation by digressing to tell her about the original overall expedition plan to get to the Gobi, preferably by cycling, in less than fifty days and then to find our secret destination. Her response summed up our adventures this far: 'If I was cycling to China, in fact if I was cycling anywhere, I wouldn't start in Bangladesh.'

TWO

From the Madhouse to the Land of Morning Calm

Bangladesh was playing merry hell with our plans; we were stranded in the capital Dhaka after covering a mere 269 kilometres. Our target ahead was supposedly to reach Kathmandu as soon as possible so that we could get stuck into the real meat of the adventure: the entry to Tibet and China. Unfortunately we both knew that our horizons had shrunk considerably and all we wanted to do was survive to the Bangladesh–India border and get out of this madhouse.

We took the advice of the British High Commission to stay in Dhaka, and Richard Fielder kindly booked us into the rather posh club of the British Aid Guest House Association. Here in colonial elegance we could in theory sip g and t's with the ex-pats and glean the inside story about this country. However, the reality was they were all into beer and pie and beans – which suited us fine, though we were less enamoured with the gossip. After months away from home, they were eager to question us about Britain and home politics as well as discovering the meaning behind our quaint enterprise. The general feeling was that we'd bitten off more than we could chew. 'You must be mad.' It helps. The periodicals on the table were the *Sunday Times*, *Woman's Own* and *Yachting World*, a curious contrast to the world of poverty and the slums beyond these walls. It was a good time for us to review our strategy so we slipped away to our bedrooms.

'Do you think, Nick, that we should hang around here like we've been told? Lose all tomorrow for the *Hartel*? Wait until after the elections? That would be four more wasted days.'

'It seems a shame. But how else can we do it? It'll take minimum three days, more likely four, to cycle out to India.' He paused and looked into the distance. 'One problem and we're delayed by a day. Plop right into the elections! Crowds, chanting, riots. We might be going home in a wooden box.'

North of Dhaka anything could happen, but I was keen to dash on. I saw the big town of Dinajpur on the map and said it must have a border-post and therefore reasonable roads. Nick said that's all very well in theory but you never know until you see it. I wanted to chase on despite the *Hartel*. I was prepared to ignore the expert's advice about election fever and live in hope that the people would be merciful. However, Nick was adamant.

'You're not catching me out on the roads tomorrow. Even at the best of times it's enough hassle having a white face and a gleaming racing-bike. It'd be suicide.'

'Oh, come on, Nick. There must be some way to make progress.'

I turned on the sort of whine that spoilt little boys have when they want something. We both knew that it would be best to find a way out quickly before friends back home laughed at us for setting out on a sprint ride to the Gobi and getting stopped in the Ganges Delta. As I was moping, Nick, who was studying the map, suddenly came alive. 'Look, Dick, I've got it! Change our route. Go out the safe way due west on the main road to Calcutta. It'll save a hundred kilometres. We can get there in two days.'

'Let's have a look.' I leant over the map. 'Yeah, you're right, it is shorter. That'd solve our problems here. Get out of Bangladesh before election fever explodes. And please the people we've talked to here by taking their advice.'

'That's a new line for you: "taking advice"!'

It went over my head because I was studying the map. The new route through India would take a couple of extra days because we'd do nearly 700 kilometres through India, instead of a short hop to Karkavitta in south-west Nepal from Dinajpur in north-west Bangladesh.

'It's a shame not to zip through the remoter bits of northern Bangladesh.'

'Forget your ethnic interests, Dick, there'll be plenty of excitement ahead. Let's measure up some of these distances and check out the new route.'

Everything looked good for our new plan. An hour later we went down to the bar to discuss it with some of the ex-pats. The Calcutta road was certainly the main land link for Bangladesh, though opinions differed as to its condition and how busy it was. However, they seemed to be unanimous that the only place for bed between Dhaka and the border was Jessore, and that it was also one of only three places where we'd be able to get food. Therefore, they said, we'd have to abandon our idea of never carrying any food whatsoever on this journey and put some on board. That was advice we didn't take.

Having decided on this new route and schedule, we adjourned to bed. On Day 4, we settled ourselves down for a day of leisure: taking stock, checking our gear, writing to as many people as possible at home (post-cards, a couple of letters, a report to Steve Bonnist at IT), getting ourselves psyched up for the dash to the border and having some fun. Various bits of equipment got ditched. The second spare inner tube was discarded along with one of two Campag cone-spanners. We decided to drill holes, following our usual obsession with weight-saving, into the other one, similarly with our small adjustable spanner.

'Say, how about doing the same to our shoes?'

'And drilling holes in the water-bottles?'

We kept the chain-rivet extractor in case the derailleur failed and we might have to shorten the chain, but Nick discovered how to remove its handle and so he chucked that away. The screwdriver was not needed for any structural parts of the bikes, and since we had adjusted everything to our satisfaction we left it behind. If necessary, we planned to borrow one off a truck driver *en route*. Similar logic governed our thoughts on oil and large spanners. We had six spare spokes and a spoke-key because, as Nick pointed out, a wheel going out of true was one thing which really could stop us. We kept a puncture outfit with ten patches but saw no need for spare brake blocks or brake cables. In the event of total loss of stopping power we each had half an inch of good rubber on the soles of our shoes. Failing that, nine layers of skin on the palms of our hands . . . and quite a lot of cartilage on our noses. . . .

After a careful half-hour scrutinizing our bikes, we decided that four different Allen keys were usually needed. However, two adjusted everything except the pannier racks and bottle-cages. So, at the risk of needing our heads examined, we left the other two behind. We finished cutting the labels off our clothes. Nick measured out two feet of cotton and selected one reasonable needle. He also had a serious dilemma: which pair of underpants? He had alternated between two pairs in the past few days to test them. Now one pair had to go. Our map had been cut down to size before starting, with the result that Bartholomew's 1:4,000,000 of the Indian subcontinent was reduced to a small dog-eared corner of the north-west. This must have saved about as much weight as cleaning the dirt off our shoes, but it made us feel as though we were trying. Nick trimmed down his picture of Penny, removing Newborough Beach and the Snowdon Horseshoe from the background. I'd taken the ultimate step by simply hoping to remember what Michèle looked like. Neither of our girl-friends seemed to mind us setting off under-equipped or ill-advised on our dangerous odyssey – though I don't think we'd asked their permission as such. Michèle was a long way away in the States and had already endured – dare I say enjoyed? – seven years of my idiosyncrasies. Penny was on the verge of a new breakthrough in her work leading to fresh responsibilities, so, provided Nick returned eventually, she enthusiastically supported his endeavours.

Nick. Day 5.

Absolutely hideous awakening, feeling grim and thick-headed.

We were past the armed security guards on the gate by 5.20 a.m. Hazy recollections only of the morning's ride. We both felt tired. We just time-trialled out of a for once quiet Dhaka, then sat in line astern pedalling for hour upon hour across the flat green landscape, a good breeze pushing us along in top gear. I can't remember many details. I saw an advert for BOSS FILTER

CIGARETTES, we passed an army camp with a soaring monument of skyward-reaching spikes. There was hardly any traffic compared to the Chittagong road, and after several hours D said we must have done about sixty miles (ninety kilometres). It was ages before we reached the banks of the Ganges and the crucial ferry crossing. A slight rise topped by a line of lorries in the trees told us we were there. It was an exciting moment to see the great river whose braided fringes create such a huge flood-plain. For three days we've been crossing the Ganges Delta. Now we are at the river itself.

Threading our way through a shanty-village built on the mudbanks, past tiny shops and masses of snack-stalls, we made our way down the muddy and rubbly roads to the jetties and ferries. There were all sorts of vessels going to many different places, mostly stubby wooden boats puffing black exhaust smoke and laden to the gunwales with locals and produce, some dignified freight barges under sail, and a few big steel ships like the one we were about to get on, capable of taking several buses and a dozen motor cars. A similar vessel had rolled over in mid-stream a month ago and drowned 200 passengers.

We were lucky not to have a long wait before we sailed. After the cool breeze of cycling, the high humidity made us sweat heavily and we were glad of the various refreshments offered on the quayside. Nick bought two 'daab' – green coconuts – the gent who sold them sliced off the top with his machete to expose the white flesh then made three quick slashes which left a neat triangular plug sitting cosily in the top. The fresh coconut milk was clear and refreshing, though it was slightly sour, tangy and a little musty. To glug down more than one or two would probably give an unaccustomed tummy a few problems.

We pushed off from Aricha at 10 a.m. and for the entire one-hour journey over to the other side at Goalundo Ghat we had a knot of people staring in amazement at the bikes and asking questions. For once we felt relaxed and were happy to entertain them as best we could through the language barrier. We spent most of the journey exploring all the English words they knew, teaching a few more and talking in sign language.

One little lad, who couldn't have been ten years old, had fizzy drinks for sale kept cool in a bucket of water. He was a real entrepreneur, selling drinks for eight taka which only cost six taka on the roadside stalls. Since he didn't have any change he persuaded us to buy extra bottles to use up the change he owed us, so we forked out more money. After four bottles each, we decided we couldn't drink any more. He wasn't to be foiled. In order to relieve us of our small change he dropped his price temptingly to seven taka.

Back on terra firma at Goalundo Ghat, our main road had reduced to a single track of herringbone-laid bricks; later it reverted to a tarmac surface but badly potholed in places. It seemed this main road to Calcutta wasn't as big as we thought. There were about thirty more kilometres' riding to get to Faridpur where we hoped we might be able to stop for the night. Although it was only early afternoon, we could clear our headaches and catch up on the lack of sleep the night before and also get another very early start which should see us to the border the following afternoon.

Leaving the ferry Nick punctured almost immediately, and we sat down in the midday sun to mend it. A crowd gathered to help and while they worked I relaxed by the banana palms, gazing out over the fields of green shoots to the solid grey waters of the Ganges and the white bulbous sails of the cargo boats. The other bank appeared as no more than a faint black line, and somewhere beyond it was that mass of human emotions at boiling point, ready, as we'd found in the past few days, to spring on any new interest. This side was quite different; here on the western banks people seemed much less excitable and much less aggressive. They weren't caught up in the frenzy of commercialism. They had more of the calm of the Indians a few hundred kilometres further west. Later we discovered that this side of the river is considered one of the remoter parts of Bangladesh, cut off by the river, and it appeared to be less crowded. Further on the land was undulating, not completely flat, much drier, the front yards of the houses being not grassy carpets but worn to dry dust.

Nick. Day 5. Afternoon.
We drank all our water at the puncture stop. It was 1 p.m. when we set off again and much too hot to be out. We both had splitting headaches. Crossing a little village, I spotted a water-pump and screeched to a halt to dive under. A smiling young man pumped gushes of cool delicious water over my head, down my neck, and filled our water-bottles. D at first declined to dip his head: 'I never on principle splash cold water over my head when it's as hot as this.' He eyed me enviously for a minute, eased into a smile, came and bent under the spout for his deluge. 'I'm thinking of changing a few principles.'

Thus quenched, and bonded a little closer by experience, we continued on our way and reached Faridpur, where by the end of Day 5 our route was heading due south: the opposite direction to the main thrust of the expedition. Our backs turned on the Chinese deserts.

Faridpur, a fairly conventional rural Bangladeshi market-town, was quite developed. It had several main roads and a couple of traffic police. Thousands of rickshaws like ants at a honey pot streamed through the streets. There was electricity, street lights and mains water in quite a few areas. We rented for 100 taka a room in the Luxury Hotel. It had a ceiling-fan, two camp-cots masquerading as four-poster double beds, and an *en suite* shower/toilet in fetching coarse concrete with dripping tap. We carried the bikes up to our room, which was at the top of a solid four-storey reinforced-cement hotel block. Out front we leant over the veranda and

looking down saw the throngs of people among the rickshaws below.
Electioneering was hotting up and we thanked our lucky stars that we'd
stopped early in the day. A truck-load of young men waving banners went
past, then three crowds of marching chanting supporters. Across the
roof-tops and palm trees we could hear the whining of loud-hailers on
autorickshaws in other parts of town. Later a bus-load with twenty or more
people standing precariously on the roof went slowly past while other
enthusiasts clambered on board. It was 3 p.m. We had a largish lunch
(simply two plates of rice each, three bowls of dahl and a dish of fish-curry
plus three Cokes, two glasses of tea and a litre of water) then planned to
have two hours' shuteye before having the same meal again and getting to
bed at about 7.30.

We had a nap, woke and had some food. Darkness came quickly and we
climbed up to go to bed. It was so hot and humid that we lay sweating as we
tried to write our diaries. Without warning, the electricity failed. We got a
candle. Suddenly it became very chilly. Then a few minutes later a huge
pre-monsoon storm broke out over Faridpur. Crashes and booms of
thunder were everywhere; many overhead, seemingly on the actual roof of
the building. Tongues of forked lightning snapped out continual illumina-
tion. Sheet lightning rocketed across the sky. There were phenomenally
high winds. Torrential rain was whipping horizontally through the
streets. All the trees were bending and flicking back and forth like a den of
snakes. It was the most amazing storm. Downstairs, dozens of pedestrians
and rickshaw-drivers were sheltering but the storm was blowing rain down
the corridors into the hotel. Outside it was jet black, then there would be a
thunderclap and everything would turn for a split second into a deep-blue
etching then flash out of sight again, before the next bolt of light ricocheted
across the heavens and everything reappeared bent and blown in another
direction. We were scared enough to be shut in our room. The wind was so
violent it wriggled through all the cracks around the door and windows.
Our candle kept blowing out. Very eerie, like Wuthering Heights. Nick
kept murmuring to me: 'This place is crazy.' We vowed to rise at dawn and
cycle 180 kilometres non-stop to reach the border and escape. We packed
our bags and tied our clothes together so we could find them in the dark of
the morning.

It was out-and-out riding from the crack of dawn, the sort when you
never remember where you've been, what you've seen: black tarmac and
my front wheel, or a Shimano 600 derailleur and Nick's backside.
Breakfast was a welcome break and we ate bananas wrapped in hot fresh
chapatis while we waited for a yellow pontoon-ferry to cross a small river.
We did 140 kilometres to Jessore fairly smoothly by midday, then in the
heat started to slow down and cycled in dribs and drabs to the border
another fifty kilometres further.

Over the last few kilometres the road deteriorated greatly and was
reduced to single track on concrete slabs. The country was drier than the
rest of Bangladesh we'd seen. Jhenighat, the last place before the border,

was like a cowboy town with dirt main street, saloons with verandas and uniformed army officers rocking along on rickety rickshaws. Clearly very little traffic uses this, or any other, land link to Bangladesh. Later we learnt that most of the international traffic goes out by boat from Chittagong. The border post was by contrast a couple of fairly smart bungalows and several large corrugated-iron Nissen huts. Quite a few people milled around; some were merchants and family travellers, but most seemed to be non-uniformed helpers and hangers-on.

We didn't envisage any problems but the first official gave us a shock by asking for our permits to exit by road from Bangladesh. We didn't have any. He persisted for a while then, when another official came to turn out every single little item in my pannier bag, he seemed to forget. The second official had a lot of fun discovering thermal long johns and a balaclava, and was intrigued by my tiny plastic teaspoon for eating. Strangely they left Nick all alone, which was lucky because he had £2,500 worth of tape recorder plus another £500 worth of cameras and films.

In the second hut the fat official informed us that only 100 taka may be taken out of the country. 'How much do you have?' Not wanting to be apprehended later, we turned out our pockets: 1,128 taka in total. He ummed and ah'd for a few moments then said seriously: 'All right.' He folded our money into our passports and kept his hands on them while he beckoned to one of the guards. We thought he was either going to fine us for trying to smuggle taka, or confiscate all our money. However, he said: 'Fine, but how about a little donation to my friend?' This line caught us unawares, but we weren't in a position to act 'holier than thou' as vanguards for the fight against corruption. Dutifully we each slipped the soldier 100 taka, he then turned his back on us and handed it to Fat Man, who slipped it deftly into an open-topped bag behind his desk where he presumably filed all his percentages – like the packet of ciggies from the man before us who was trying to lift two cases out of Bangladesh. Then our newly found friend bought us two Cokes and we had to have a chat while the other customers waited.

It was with unrestrained relief that we finally left the country. As a last gesture of lunacy, Bangladesh sent us off with a flourish in a twenty-minute hail-storm with ice lumps the size of conkers tearing leaves from the trees and pinging off the tin roof. Similar hailstones had killed thirty people near Chittagong the week before.

We broke over the border at 4.10 p.m. to the freedom and riches of India. Nick pointed out that 'by contrast to Bangladesh, India looks like a wealthy First World nation, but of course it's not'. The shops were tightly packed together and offered a wide choice of goods. They were spread over a maze of tiny bright streets crammed with people, bicycles and donkey carts. Along the alleys were fruit-sellers by the dozen selling piles of fruit undreamt of in Bangladesh. We feasted on apples, oranges, mangoes and lychees. Best of all, there was a profusion of pretty girls in fetching saris out in the streets. To a red-blooded man like me, it was all very exciting. A tall lady in vivid magenta and flowing shawl was floating past showing bare midriff and tantalizing ankles. Beside our café was a group of giggling girls in 1960s Western dresses. All with uncovered heads and questioning eyes. With carefully styled hair, manicured nails, necklaces and rings, they were dressed to be noticed. The fully covered, veiled Muslim women of east Bengal were far behind us, similarly the secluded hard-working women we passed in the afternoon on the other side of the border. The Indians were finer and richer and more reserved. Also they were less fanatically interested in foreigners. They weren't overwhelmed by us, whereas the Bengalis were either mesmerized or aggressively excited. In the first couple of hours in India, we pulled merely two calm groups of ten or less observers whereas in that time in Bangladesh we would have thrilled three or four big crowds of up to 100 men.

Nick. Day 7.
Election day in Bangladesh – and we're *not* there!! Slipped out by the skin of our teeth yesterday afternoon. We got up at dawn, at 5 a.m., this morning after a nightmare sleep. We'd enjoyed supper with mangoes, a tin of condensed milk and fresh lychees on a sprig of green leaves before crashing out at 11 p.m. on our shared double bed. We were dog-tired but tossed and turned with irritations. The mosquito net had holes, so we suffered in the dark, scratching and whimpering. I finally cracked at 3 a.m., turned on the lights and ceiling-fan, then we spent half an hour attacking the mossies with renewed savagery. Each 'kill' was accompanied by a cry of 'Got you. You little. . . .' Like caged gladiators inside our net we tracked, feinted and pounced, slapping the demons to death – some stuffed so full of blood they exploded with raspberry redness across our skin. Carnage over, we blocked all the holes in the net by tying knots and jamming them with long-johns. The two hours of sleep which followed – with the lights and fan full on – were almost perfect.

Ten miles along a quiet country road were quite sufficient for brave adventurers on Day 7 before stopping for breakfast. We were feeling lethargic, and there seemed no need to hurry because it was altogether a pleasanter country than yesterday's. We felt calm and relaxed; it was like watching a South Korean dawn as the sun rises out of the Pacific over sleepy fishing villages near Pusan. I would have loved to have Michèle beside me to enjoy it to its full. We dawdled and took more photographs than usual. Along the road were green leafy trees and little thatch huts, numerous but not overwhelming bicycles, lumbering ox-carts with creaking wooden wheels, people walking the road to work, schoolgirls in green and white three abreast under sun umbrellas, schoolboys with grey shorts grouped by the teacher's door.

We took breakfast in a lean-to with tiled roof supported on bamboo poles. Tea was on the brew and steam was pouring out of a cauldron smelling of lentils. They were both on charcoal stoves made from sheet metal and looking like large tin cans. This was different from Bangladesh where, except in the capital, they used wood-burning clay stoves. That country was more forested, whereas in India those who can afford it use charcoal. The poorer people dry cow-pats for fuel. Usually they're plastered on walls, but a mile back we had seen them drying on telegraph poles.

Sadly no chapatis were available for breakfast. The man in charge offered us biscuits, cake and factory-made bread, but we were steering clear of everything except hot food we could actually see cooking and fruit we could peel ourselves. For the first ten days in Asia we'd had no stomach problems, and that was quite a record as we ate in the most basic places.

Further up the road we came to a busy town called Krishnagar which had a network of streets among old colonial buildings left over from the days of the Raj. It was a hive of activity with small businesses set up in every little corner. Bicycle-menders and car-mechanics were the most common and there were those who pulled bikes and cars to pieces to recycle components and lots of people who turned scrap metal into farm-tools or bicycle trailers, or built truck-backs on to old chassis. Of course the streets were also packed with food stalls, fruit stalls, and trinket-sellers. Interestingly there were lots of magazine stalls, mostly recycling second-hand magazines.

In the midday heat, here stiflingly dry as opposed to the wet heat of Bangladesh which had rotted our clothes and stewed our armpits for the first week, we had to stop cycling. We doused our heads under a pump, and sat sipping fizzy orange through straws – matted hair, stubbly growth on our chins, sunburnt forearms with little bubbles of heat blisters. Our salopets were rolled down to our waists, showing weight-saving trimmed-down tummy-length T-shirts. They were very grimy from dust and perspiration. Sitting still in the shade we could control our temperature. However, if we started eating, our pores went into a frenzy: pumping out water like clams dug from the sands of the Solway Firth. To balance this output, we drank five litres of water, eight soft drinks and thirteen glasses of thick tea – each!

Nick took this opportunity to scrutinize the bikes. He did it every day but this day he did it with a vengeance, and just as I was settling down to snooze out the hottest hours of the day he dragged me off to a street-corner bike man and we set to with hack-saw and knife paring off extraneous metal from our beautiful bikes. Gerald O'Donovan would have approved of our zealous regard for efficiency. The simplest bits to cut off were the wheel guides on the brakes, the cable guide from the bottom bracket, and most of the plastic hooks from the pannier bags. Nick's *pièce-de-résistance* was to saw the gear lever in half. The bikes seemed to go a lot faster that afternoon.

We had a route decision to make here: either to go due north up the direct main road, parallel to the Bangladeshi border, and into the east end of Nepal, or to go on minor roads in a straight line to Kathmandu diagonally north-west, cross-country over the Rajamahal Hills, back down to the Ganges and onwards to enter the central part of Nepal at the border town of Raxaul. With only two people on the committee and no one to answer to, it was easy to have a friendly discussion, another cup of tea and make our choice. We went cross-country because it might be more fun. Our target for the day was Katoya, which seemed likely to be a local market-town, not on a direct trunk road to anywhere. Towards late afternoon as we closed in on the town we had a very pleasant ride through quiet lanes, free from motor traffic yet busy with pedestrians, cattle, ox carts and a few bicycles. A rickshaw appeared from time to time. The farms and villages were all mud-walled, in little groups often around a stagnant green pond with ducks under a canopy of palm trees. Women preparing food or carrying water in urns balanced on the head or hips, naked children running around, chickens, dogs, black pigs like warthogs and old men smoking in the shade. Young girls looking after younger children or helping the elder women at home or in the fields. Young boys helping Dad. Young men lounged in chai huts along the road showing off their Western dress or flashing their watches and bracelets. The general farm work went from dawn to dusk. All this part of India was like East Africa with oasis villages, tall palms and dusty roads.

Katoya was a long time arriving, but when it did it was one of the very special magical moments of the early part of the trip. We were bumbling along tiddly roads wondering where it had got to, when at long last a cluster of houses appeared. We thought this must be Katoya. Unfortunately the road petered out into a cul-de-sac. We stopped to ask the way and an old man pointed on through the trees. We got off, walked on, and there below us was a wide dark river with sandbanks. On the far side like a French Foreign Legion fortress were the town walls and rooftops of Katoya.

Nick. Day 7. Katoya. Evening.
We rode down on to the sandbanks – criss-crossed with the tracks of animals, people, carts and bicycles. In full spate the river must measure a half-mile wide. By the water's edge were some makeshift huts, with some men quietly sipping tea, and others loading jute on to a low, flat, bamboo pontoon. It was a biblical scene. As the sun dripped into the black line of trees on the far bank, we lifted our bikes aboard alongside several others. Not a ripple broke the surface of the river. Two boys poled us out from the bank into the stream, and as the current gripped the ferry they stowed the poles into the floorboards and leant into the urgent work of pulling us across the flow with paddles.

We slid in total calm across smooth black waters. Silent except
for the dip of paddles.

Under the arch at the top of the steps we were into the old, almost
medieval, town of Katoya. It wasn't quite as calm in town as outside, in
fact it was mayhem. Under tall black walls, tight tiny dark streets were
thronged by people split every few seconds, like silence split by the
tick-tock of a metronome, by flying bicycles with tingling bells. It was
dangerous; they had no lights. We started looking for a hotel but were
dragged off to see the police. The latter didn't seem to know why we'd
come to see them so they sent us off to find a hotel. That wasn't very easy
but after nearly an hour of being directed and redirected we stumbled on a
suitable establishment. Outside was a dead body on a funeral carriage.
Beside it a cow grazed on a huge pile of rubbish. There was so much dirt
and filth that even the cockroaches wouldn't eat in the cafés!

For the next two days we got going again, pedalling more seriously,
rejuvenated by the restful day from the border to Katoya. We went firstly
through more of the African-type plains villages, passed through the
oppressively hot town of Siuri at lunchtime where we were thrown out of
the café as soon as we'd eaten because they didn't approve of bikes by the
tables, and reached Dhumka for bed on Day 8. There we ate a monstrously
good meal recorded in my diary as 'Mountains of rice, bhindi bhaji, alu
gobi, chapatis and many dishes of vegetable curry, with bean stew and
bowls upon bowls of luscious runny dahl. The sort of pleasure you hope
never stops, so exciting you almost don't dare to eat it. Every time we stop
for food on this trip it turns out to be the best meal of our lives.'

Eight hours later, shortly before dawn, the strained chords of 'Happy
Birthday' seered into Nick's dreamland to haul him happily into Day 1 of
his next 365-day stretch. I had omitted to bring the champagne so we
cracked open a bottle of fizzy orange in the gloom. Nick gaily opened his
card – a picture of the bottom end of an elephant, like a huge round globe
with a tiny tail. On top sat a very bemused mouse. Inside Nim and Hol, his
mum and dad, had written: 'Hope you find your Centre.'

From Dhumka, we climbed higher to 1,000 metres and crossed the
Rajamahal Hills. It was sparsely populated. There were little hillocks,
rock-faces and lakes to look at. It was the first fully relaxed section: a
chance to rest our minds while our legs worked away eating up the miles of
rolling scrubland and grassland. It was gentle wilderness country, re-
freshingly free of people. Nick called it 'Beautiful riding – a lovely birthday
present'. It was a happy morning. We followed a good tarmac road, the
other traffic being mainly small trucks, large buses and pretty pony traps
going to market. It was difficult to believe the concerned young man in the
market who warned us not to be out on the roads alone because of 'rogues,
robbers and villains'.

By the middle of Day 9, we had coasted down the northern side of the
Rajamahal Hills towards the blisteringly hot plains of Bihar State. In the

heat of the midday sun, we saw no mad dogs, but we two Englishmen celebrated thirty-two eccentric years of Nick's unusual life by pedalling through the hottest hours of the hottest season in the hottest and driest part of India. The gates of hell were open – a metaphorical blast from the furnace trumpeted Nick's festivities. The temperature cruised up to 115°F in the shade. All the villages seemed ghost towns. Everyone slept in the heat of the day. The road was silent; the dogs slept; the birds roosted; even the flies didn't fly. The only sound was the squelch of our wheels along the squidgy tarmac. We decided that it was less severely hot to ride, and hence to feel a slight wafting of the thick suffocating air, than to pause for a moment and explode into a frenzy of sweating. To quell our raging thirsts that day, we downed thirty-six bottles of fizz. One hundred miles slipped behind us and we regained the banks of the mighty Ganges. Bed for the night was in the big and ancient town of Monghyr. We finished the day sitting on fold-up chairs on a raised concrete step in front of a well-lit barber's shop. We could buy drinks by leaning back and calling to the boy to pull more from the fridge. We were living in luxury. We had a sobering experience.

Dick. Day 9. Monghyr. Late evening.
This evening I felt a pang of sorrow for the poor of the Third World, stronger than I've felt for years. We sat on our pedestal sipping our drinks and facing the street where a typical small crowd gathered and we could watch the heart of India scrabble by: rickshaws, bicycles, a woman in a bright-blue sari with a water-pot on her head, a tramp or beggar, and then two local businessmen in white suits. Many other men in well-used suits and a playboy on a motor bike. A group of children came in sight. Two little girls, several boys, all about seven or eight, plus a toddler of three or four with a pink ribbon in her hair. One girl immediately catches the eye because she has a tatty ex-orange floral dress, bare feet like all her friends, and tussled jet black hair all over the place, unconsciously almost in modern Afro-style. Most captivating were her huge eyes dominating all her face. Dark, dark and deep inside. Not a smile, not a frown, not a puzzled look. She simply stood and stared. She came right forward directly in front of me and stared. And stared and stared. Hardly blinking. Total awe. She stared as though she never thought that I could see her. As though I was so high up, so far removed on my pedestal that I looked straight through her into the streets beyond. She simply stared. And I felt her eyes, those big dark eyes seeing deep inside my mind. Touching my heart, my soul and quietly reminding me that my world is so far removed from hers. Explaining that I am so condescending to think for one moment that I might be able to understand any of her life. I ask myself why am I so arrogant to believe I can see

her life yet she can't see mine. We are both so far removed that neither will ever understand. She stared on a few minutes more with big wondrous eyes then she was gone. Vanished with her friends back to their world of poverty to leave Nick and me with ours and the fizzy drinks, fans and mosquito nets.

Monghyr is on the south bank of the Ganges. There's no bridge. To get across, road traffic drives 100 kilometres west around a huge bend in the river. I didn't fancy that so I thought we should try to find a ferry. Nick thought we could be wasting our time searching for a ferry if there wasn't one. I said there had to be one for a place as big as this. He contested that the ferry over the Ganges would have been fifty kilometres back in Bhagalpur. Eventually we split it two ways and I was given an hour to find a ferry first thing in the morning; if not, then we pedalled round. We rose early on Day 10 at 4.30 a.m. to make the best use of the cool of the day and we headed off on a compass bearing north through town. When we found the Ganges we edged our way along the banks asking if anyone knew about ferries. A large man setting up his tea stall for the day directed us along to the railroad yard, then a thin young boy led us to a large red sandstone archway. I expected jetties and big front-loading ferries but found steps leading down into the waters where bathers took their morning cleansing. Across to the side, two hundred yards away, were a couple of boats and a few makeshift huts by the water. Not unlike Katoya, though maybe more like D-Day, busy with bustle at the crack of dawn and queues of people. The best part of 600 people got on to our flotation system which was a couple of large pontoons tied on to a central tug-boat with an inboard diesel engine.

On the other side of the ferry, at Monghyr Ghat (Ghat seems loosely to mean 'the other side'), the bamboo walkway where the boat tied up led only to empty sandbanks; everyone had to walk one mile to get to the proper river bank and fields. The odyssey was an incredible spectacle. We sat down in a bamboo three-walled chai shack to take in the scene. Two men showed us how they crush some sort of dry brown leaf like tobacco into the palm of their hand then rub in white calcium paste and once prepared pop it into the corner of their mouth. It's called 'dopey chai'! Is this stuff snuff or chewing tobacco, or is it something more like coca which I've seen Bolivian Indians preparing with calcium as a catalyst to fortify them against the harsh dry air and hard cold of the *altiplano*? They tried to persuade us to have a go and I tried to tell them that our resistance is so low that even the acrid smell of brake blocks burning on a steep descent makes us drunk.

We set off across the sands, saw barchan-dunes forming on one side, crossed a slight rise where murram-grass grows at the level of medium spate, crossed more deep sand, carrying the bikes to keep sand off the transmission, tried riding over some huge mud cracks where the plates were two-feet across and the bike wheel dropped down the cracks till it almost disappeared. Nick pulled me out and we climbed up on to the top of the bank to find the road. It was 10 a.m., and despite our fine intentions we'd lost the best part of the day and only cycled one kilometre. However, we had had a wonderful morning and maybe for that reason Nick forgave me my foolhardy stubbornness the night before to try the river crossing. We told ourselves it was head down from here to the border, a mere 300 kilometres away. We pulled out all the stops and got forty-seven kilometres to Barouni for bed. It wasn't an impressive total for the day but in addition to the late start we'd been delayed for an hour by a freak dust-storm which loomed up as a thick black pillar of dirt looking in Nick's words like 'a giant cyclone or some such death-dealing climatological device'. It was preceded by a ferocious wind and followed by instant calm and a deluge of rain which swamped the road in minutes. Half an hour later it was all gone. Clearly Bangladesh isn't the only place with weather problems in the pre-monsoon season.

The next day, Day 11, we succeeded with our most mega-day so far. We were up and on the road half an hour before the proper dawn so that our bodies and legs were warmed up ready to pedal hard as soon as there was enough light. We did fifty-two kilometres before the first stop at 6.30 a.m. for breakfast of chapati, curry and tea. Our official target for the day was Muzaffarpur, only fifty-five more kilometres, but we both knew we'd prefer to get to Motihari 100 kilometres further. Secretly, however, we had our hearts set on totalling nearly 250 for the day to reach the Nepalese border. We hammered on, taking turns to lead, five kilometres each, counting kilometre posts as they slipped by, oblivious to India, as though we were doing a Sunday-morning club ride back home in Britain.

Second stop was Muzaffarpur soon after 9 a.m. It's nice to put your feet on the ground and stand upright after two hours' hard pressure from the saddle. We had tea and pop and oiled the chains. Then in well under the hour we were off again and going strong. By noon we'd cracked 100 miles, in metric terms 160 kilometres. We'd only stopped twice in that distance, but the heat was starting to get to us and the rest of the day was punctuated by stops every half-hour to dunk our heads in water, gulp tea or order food. Mounds of rice and bowls of dahl vanished in seconds, slipping down our throats without touching the sides. Proclamations of 'The best ever', 'Just what we needed', 'If I'd been given a choice of all the meals in the world, I couldn't have chosen better', etc., etc., *ad nauseam*.

From our accurate records we calculated that the first two hours of the day were at 27 k.p.h., rising to 31 k.p.h. for the second section of fifty kilometres when we were fully warmed up but dropping to 28 k.p.h. as we started to tire on the portion up to noon, thereafter averaging 17 k.p.h. for the riding sections. This did, however, enable us to crawl through Motihari at 3.30 p.m. and struggle painfully yet happily to the border-post at Raxaul at 6.30 p.m., having completed 240 kilometres in a total riding time of ten and a half hours and an elapsed time of fourteen hours and ten minutes. We felt pleased. Nepal and Kathmandu were within our grasp at last. They were no longer names on a small-scale map of Asia but were almost tangible places of brick and people, of roads and mountains. We had nearly completed the run-up to the foot of the giant ahead: the unknown territory 4,000 metres above sea-level where maybe no cyclist had ever been before. We had nearly finished 'Cycling to the Himalayas'. Our first micro-success was virtually in our pocket.

We found a room in a reasonable hotel, then went for food in a run-of-the-mill chai house. Nobody made any fuss about us being there, presumably because foreigners are commonplace in this border town. The locals were in fact off-hand. We ordered the food, and I washed some of the grime off my hands in an equally grimy basin in the corner. As I smiled at my charming face in the mirror, the cockroaches ran for cover, leaving only their antennae poking out from the cracks.

'Pretty successful day. Ay not, Nick!'

'Not at all bad.'

'We're nearly into Nepal. Fancy that.'

'Isn't it great?'

A few weeks before I'd have hardly believed we could have done this ride. Nick agreed that merely reaching Nepal was quite a success in itself but, he pointed out, 'It's only the tip of the iceberg'.

I said, 'Yeah,' thinking of all the things which had gone before: Bikes up Kili which had been such fun, Running the Himalayas which had created so many new opportunities; indeed, there were other events before that such as the Three Peaks attempt by Nick and me in Easter 1982. That in a sense was our first JCE. Hol was the guru and whipmaster. It was forty-two hours on bikes over Nevis and Scafell Pike then my brother Chris led us up Snowdon in a freak snowstorm. Charles (my father) wrote a ditty about it, which began:

> From Scotland's snowy mountains,
> To Wales' icy plains,
> There's a long, long trail awinding,
> That was cycled by two Cranes.

Digging deeper into the past, one year before that, we did the Dudley Two-Man Marathon: cycling, canoeing, running and race-walking. We'd also both set out that year on 100-mile and twelve-hour time trials. In the latter, I forced myself up to 225 miles, but Nick did better and put three miles on top of that.

Nick halted me. 'Hang on, Dick. I don't mean an iceberg in that sense. I mean on this adventure. We've cycled a long way but really we've hardly started.'

'Oh, come on, Nick. We're nearly there. Kathmandu is only a couple of days away, maybe only two days.'

'I mean on a larger scale. So far we've seen Kathmandu as being our goal – mainly because the Centre of the Earth is too remote, too distant, to embrace into the concept of a bike ride. Every planning discussion we have refers to "when we get to Kathmandu". But now that we're just a couple of days away, the next stage to Lhasa is looming. It's scary.'

'I see what you mean. Trouble is we're not yet at Kathmandu. In fact we're not even in Nepal.'

'We haven't yet seen the Himalayas. Maybe tomorrow if we're lucky.'

'Then there's a couple of big passes, I think up to 8,000 feet. And a couple of deep gorges. We'll be like penguins stuck on your iceberg.'

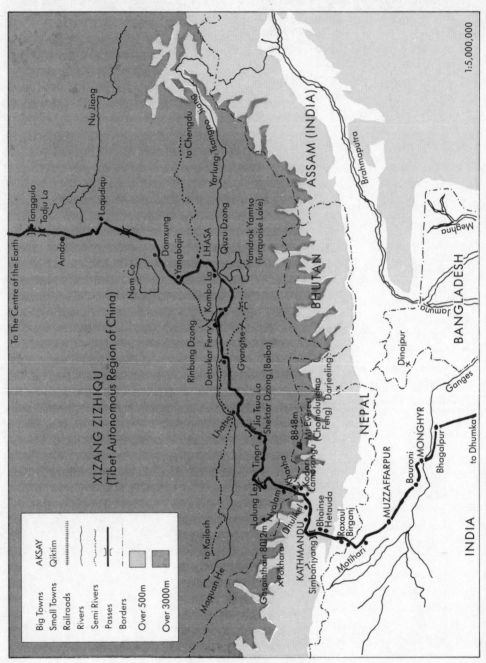

India / Nepal / Tibet

THREE

Bogged Down in Nepal

We crossed the border into Nepal with unexpected ease. The few officials were welcoming and friendly. The Indian immigration officer was rather scruffily dressed. He casually picked his nose and spat accurately into the corner of the musty room. His smart Nepalese counterpart, 200 yards up the road under a posh archway, was youthful and had glossy pictures of snowy mountains on the walls. We had angelic smiles on our faces and £1,000 cash stuffed down our underpants. The formalities were over quickly and we passed into the Nepalese border-town, Birganj; Nick to settle into breakfast, me to change some of our £1,500 traveller's cheques for Nepalese rupees. I did a quick survey at the bus station but there seemed to be no black market, so I asked a policeman to direct me to a money exchange.

'Down by the police station. Open for only two more hours. Today is Election Day.'

A cold sweat rushed over me as memories of Bangladesh came flooding back. Would there be rioting and crowd hysteria? Why was it always us that people were ganging up against? But we met no problems during the rest of the day. The Nepalese seem as calm and casual about elections as they are about most other things . . . including hygiene, which, if it's second-rate in India and poor in Bangladesh, is undreamt of in Nepal.

From Birganj we had to cycle 200 kilometres to get to Kathmandu. We hoped that two days would suffice. We'd been on the flat for the previous eleven days. Soon we would see the Himalayas and climb a couple of passes. We cycled out of town, on a flat straight tarmac road, heading due north across dead-flat fields, as level as the Indian plains and almost equally hot. The sun rose well up in the sky to our right. We were searching the horizon ahead for our first view of the fabulous mountains. In the heat haze it was difficult to see, then by and by, twenty kilometres from the border, the first row came into view rising abruptly out of the Gangetic Plains like a formidable black wall guarding treasures beyond.

Here we sat down under the shade of a big tree to rest. We were tired after the excesses of yesterday's sprint to the border, and relieved to get to Nepal. It was pleasant not to have any crowd around us, in fact no one paid the slightest bit of attention to us though several people passed by on foot or on vehicles. We would have liked to rest and sleep a few hours but we had no proper excuse for relaxation so we fiddled about pretending we were doing some jobs that had to be done and deliberately doing them slowly so we could stretch this peace a little longer.

Moving on, we cruised smoothly across more of the flat plains, dreaming of the hills ahead, then suddenly pedalled into a forest. Our world shrunk in around us: tall leafy trees, dry brown undergrowth and the buzz of insects. Bright little birds darted around. Despite the fact that after days on the flat we were now cycling slightly uphill, and sweating hard, it was all very pleasant. We had the road to ourselves, no bikes, no cars and only the occasional bus. The forest led into a gorge where there were some fields and houses. These were different from the low thatched homes we'd seen *en route* thus far: well built, timber-framed, two-storey, whitewashed, often with a little veranda. Typically there were banana and papaya trees near the house, also maize stored in racks up off the ground, sometimes under the eaves, away from the rats. A couple of children ran out shouting 'Bye, bye'. Then, as we passed on, 'Hello, hello'.

One of the most striking changes for me from the plains to the hills was seeing the first person carrying a load in a basket on his back, rather than balanced on his head. The Nepalese need a low-slung load to be able to manoeuvre it up and down the slopes. I was also struck by the footwear; most Nepalese seem to wear some sort of shoes or flip-flops whereas in India, particularly around Katoya, hardly anyone had shoes.

The road continued to climb a few more kilometres and we came on to a col with thick woodland still around us. There was a police checkpoint, which one could imagine marked the real entry to the Hidden Kingdom, and then we free-wheeled down eight exhilarating kilometres to Hetauda, our first proper Nepalese town: steep mountains rose up beside us. Hetauda was dusty and littered, particularly dirty and ramshackle compared to the India we had left behind us fifty kilometres ago. There were hundreds more dogs and millions more flies. We found a chai house on the main street, and lifted our bikes into the back, wedged behind our table. We had a view of the street. The women were as beautiful as the tall elegant Indians though slightly shorter and more podgy – like the Cumbrians I love. I found it difficult to understand how they walk around and work in elegant, clean, floor-length saris, while the men slop around in dirty old tatters and drab Western cast-offs.

Nick was studying a different subject: 'The proprietor looks a little like Buddha dressed in baggy white shirt and pantaloons. He has a crew-cut and tiny top-knot and an inscrutable smile. He's sitting on a chair, with his legs crossed under him in a lotus position, half-buried beneath his enormous belly.'

Nick. Day 12. 3.40 p.m. Hetauda.

Well – D went off to find someone with a hammer and punch so that he can flatten the rivets on his saddle, which are apparently boring holes into his backside. So, to fill the time, I asked the boy in here where I could get a shave. He took me a few doors down the road, to an open-fronted 'barbaric shop' – eight by six feet and four chairs. I was shaved; first by a cut-throat razor – the most hair-raising (hair-reducing) experience I've ever had. Ten days of growth came off in short swift scrapes sounding like a sickle through dry wheat. Each time the cold gleaming blade (I could see it in the mirror) came near my jugular I waited for that quick easy cut – or the little nick and threat, 'Give me money. Or your life!' I tried to leap out of the chair when he'd finished, but was thrust back into its hard wooden arms while the barber sharpened another blade on the leather strop. He advanced towards me with a gleam in his eye. Then re-lathered me and started all over again! I again tried to escape. Again got held down while he hosed me with clear liquid and sprayed something like DDT straight into my eyes. Half-blind, but feeling that nothing could be as bad as the shave, I then asked him to cut a 'little' off the front of my hair. Smiling, he snatched for a pair of scissors the size of garden shears and attacked the back of my head as if he was working on piece-rate. Handfuls of hair flew in all directions. I didn't dare make a sound or a move in case he sliced off my ear or misinterpreted a 'No more, please' for 'Gimme a crew-cut'. The final 'blow' (after I was nearly bald) came when he began the post-cutting therapy: violent facial massage, smacks to the back of my head and, most painfully, two violent twists which had my neck cracking like castanets. All the while the audience of little boys laughing fit to bust.

So now it's absolutely pouring with rain. We were half-inclined to ride on for a couple of hours until dark, but it's not clear whether we'd get to the next village. Maybe better tomorrow and go for a 4 a.m. start to get to Kathmandu in one day. The rain is probably afternoon only. This is certainly a dismal place.

While Nick was having his head exposed to the elements, I'd got my saddle smoothed and my bottom protected from further ravages. The bicycle-rickshaw mender who'd hammered the rivets in his little shed had also got interested in the missing pedal-cap on one side and had wired a plastic cap over the top to keep the dirt out. Thick black clouds had come overhead while I was there and some ferocious dusty winds raced down the main street blowing all the rubbish over the roof-tops and sending everyone diving indoors. The rain started before I got back to the chai house then came on very heavy. We studied the maps and saw that Kathmandu was only thirty-five kilometres north of us as the crow flies. However, crows don't ride bicycles. There were two alternative routes: firstly, along the main road which goes a long way west then back east to complete 231 road kilometres to reach Kathmandu; secondly, the old Raj Path, now suitable for motors, wiggling over a couple of big passes, rejoining the main road just before the Kathmandu Bowl and making 140 road kilometres to Kathmandu. We chose the shorter route, and since the deluge had reverted to a light drizzle we paid for our food and set off immediately.

The sun was trying to shine through and the vegetation was all fresh. Around the first few corners from town there were leaves and twigs strewn along the road. They must have been torn from the trees by the violence of the wind. Rippling water was running down the verges of the road. The open valley around Hetauda tightened into a steep valley. We realized it had been a major storm because the sun-baked gravels of the river-bed had flipped into a raging brown torrent. There were landslide scars high on the hillsides. Big branches had been snapped off trees and were lying upside down in the bushes. The dry gullies on the hillsides had turned into sparkling waterfalls, washing gravel and dirt down from above and across the road. The steep valley turned into a deep gorge. At one place a mud slurry cascaded frighteningly across the road, washing parts of it away and depositing large lumps of rock. The biggest shock was rounding a corner to find two stopped trucks. Ahead of them a massive diagonal of landslide debris had swooped down to block the road totally. It had swept hunks of tarmac down to the raging river 100 feet below. Boulders the size of the Tardis were caught up in the mélange. The truckies had barely climbed out of their cabs and no one else was around so it must have occurred merely a few minutes before. We thanked our lucky stars that we'd dithered about with beards and bottoms in Hetauda. Otherwise we might have been studying the avalanche from underneath!

We tried climbing over. It was extremely slippery, loose and dangerous. After about fifteen minutes the first men and boys from a nearby village got there to start tearing the debris away with their bare hands and a couple of shovels. We watched for a short while and took some photos, then continued on our journey just as a big yellow bulldozer appeared and with a few powerful scoops of its metal blade did the work of several hours for the men and boys, and cleared an acceptable swath for the trucks to drive over. Our excitement was nearly over for the day. We'd had quite enough and we pedalled carefully on to try to find a village where we might be able to sleep.

Further up, nestling under very high hillsides, at the junction of two rivers each coming from its own large valley, was the village of Bhainse. Other villages and farms were dotted around high above, ridge after ridge of them on seemingly inaccessible slopes. Thin lines of terraces were etched into virtually any sort of steep slope that wasn't a cliff. Bhainse was

only an odd-assorted row of houses and buildings along the outside of the
road which itself was tight up against the slope. We found a house which
doubled as café, asked for some tea, and sat down at a table surrounded by
the young ladies who ran the place, and their children. They all looked so
lovely: big round smiles, smooth fine dark skin and shiny white teeth.
There seems to be an age of changing from girl to young woman when they
put up their long thick black hair from a tussled mat to a tight bun like the
Indians on the plains. Some of them wear it in a long plait.

Nick. Day 12. 8 p.m. Bhainse.
Rice, dahl, vegetable and car-tyre casserole. The meat is
chewier than rubber. The dahl is a dentist's delight; mostly soft
and smooth but punctuated by pieces of gravel. I took a look in
the cook room; it's caked black with tar. Drinking water's
scooped from an oil-drum. A bare-bum kid crawled under the
table and one of the mothers was picking nits from the head of a
gurgling boy.
    It's nearly too gloomy in here to see. There's a single
strip-light over a game-board surrounded by twelve people. It's
like a cross between shove ha'penny, table football and billiards.
The two players shoot discs the size of coins across the table,
trying to knock other discs into pockets. One of the players – a
young man with a trendy moustache – is dressed in a red
wraparound skirt, broad-striped T-shirt and wide-brimmed
straw hat. Mr Cool of Bhainse. This place is like the local
nightspot. One of the youths is wearing a *Bhadgaon Topi* which
D tells me is the national headwear. It's a circular, rimless hat
like an upturned flower-pot, basically white and speckled
geometrically with a dazzle of bright colours.

It was quite a big room, maybe ten by five metres, though there was barely
enough light to describe it properly. Wooden pillars held up the floor
above. One side was all removable door-panels for when the weather was
good. There were seven small wooden tables and sets of benches and some
chairs. Along the back wall there were three ill-fitting doors and two
odd-shaped rooms curtained off by drapes. In there we could hear the
sounds of the girls putting the little ones to bed. Crates of soft-drink
bottles stood in one corner, though the billiards-players were drinking
neat vodka. A chicken was pecking rice off the floor under my feet – by the
time Nick and I finished eating, a lot more rice and spilt veg curry and dahl
littered the bare table-top. While we ate, a dumpy black puppy dog was
contentedly chewing a brush in the middle of the floor but then it ran into
our corner to chase a little porky squealer. 'Look out, Nick. It's going to
bite your ankle!' It got the piglet by the back leg. A girl of five or six came
running over to rescue it – she collapsed on top of the puppy and dragged it
off for cuddles. Little piggy porker snuffled off to the corner where there

was a pile of firewood, a three-wheeled kiddy bike and two tattered umbrellas. It was a menagerie there! A featherless duck with a coarse hacking cough set out across the floor, neck stretched out straight in front like it was on the chopping block. In a tick it was caught by the man in the white shirt who three hours ago was the Army officer at the police checkpoint down the road. It was amusingly bizarre – and wonderfully friendly.

All in all, we were both emotionally pooped after leaving India and entering the fabled Kingdom of Nepal. The chai shop owner let us sleep on the floor of his own room. He had a wooden bed and a thin straw mattress. For the first time on the trip we used our sleeping bags. They were laid out on top of our wind-proof jacket and trousers, directly on to the hard floor-boards. We were so desperately tired we slept solidly.

On Day 13 we set off before dawn, at 5 a.m., and were instantly enveloped in 'Cycling the Himalayas'. The plains of India barely twenty-four hours ago were another world. We pedalled in bottom gear up and up among a succession of high lofty ridges cloaked in thick green forest. The road wound in and out of almost every tributary gorge. We climbed up to each ridge merely to find another one towering above. We cycled past smart thatched mud-houses just above or below the road and could look into their patios where the children were playing with puppies and goats and chickens. The higher we got the more, not less, houses and farms there seemed to be. There were houses in groups of four or five forming little villages, but mostly they were solitary farms spaced a hundred yards from the next. Below us there were houses, above us there were houses, across the valley. All over. Spreading up and down the slopes everywhere. There were also terraces. In all directions we could look across to similar ridges with more clinging houses and terraces held on as if by Velcro.

Some measure of the steepness of the hills and the convolutions of the ravines can be gauged from the fact that when we stopped for breakfast we were still in sight of Bhainse after pedalling solidly uphill for three hours (except for two stops when Nick's stomach contractions got the better of him and he disappeared for a few minutes to study the foliage on the backsides of bushes). We had covered thirty road kilometres yet we were only five straight-line kilometres from Bhainse. In the morning when we had woken we had been only about 1,500 feet above sea-level, but suddenly we were 7,000 feet up in the air! The air got cooler, distinctly chilly, and we mounted to the pass of Simbanjyang at 8,116 feet, then swooped back down halfway to sea-level again at Palung where, switching into low gear, we commenced a grinding climb up to the pass at Tistung, nearly as high and cold as Simbanjyang. There we paused for a long while to look at the view, but though all around us ridges rose and fell in earnest – like our chests – there were no snowy Himalayas to be seen.

We peeled off from that high point and virtually plummeted like stones to lose nearly 5,000 feet in an hour. At Naubise we left rural Nepal behind because we rejoined the litter and diesel fumes of the grotty main road from Hetauda and pedalled past dry brown terraces up to the rim of the Kathmandu Basin. That point on the road is quite special because the overland traveller has come on a long long journey; at least twenty-four hours from Delhi, maybe thirteen days from Bangladesh, possibly two months or more from home. Always the target is Kathmandu and the basin in which it sits 4,000 feet above sea-level. On this approach you don't see it until the last moment, fifteen kilometres from the capital after the bus, truck or bicycle has crawled up several large switchbacks to what appears will be merely another pass with probably a swooping descent on the far side. But it turns out to be the lip of a gloriously green plateau dotted with villages and with a sweeping panorama of mountains as backdrop.

Nick. Day 13. Kathmandu Basin. Afternoon.
On the far horizon a band of spiky shining clouds – almost too white: our first glimpse of the Himalayan giants catching the last rays of the setting sun. All day long I've been waiting to see these mountains – that is the 20,000-footers – though with clouds around I'd given up hope. But now, at the end of our day of cycling more than 130 kilometres and climbing a cumulative total of 12,000 feet, I see them turn from brilliant white to gold, then fade away.

We stopped and celebrated with several glasses of tea from the roadside tea-stalls clustered under a big statue at the rim. They each had a score of wet glasses on a plank of wood and a kettle of steaming tea balanced on a fire in a bucket. We felt so generous we had one cup from each of three tea-sellers and went away smiling. There remained barely one hour's cycling to Kathmandu.

'There doesn't seem to be any sting in the tail to this superb day.'

'There's a black cloud and it's trying to rain.'

As we closed in on Kathmandu, we were half-prepared for a grand finale, a sort of punchline to spike our premature euphoria. A light shower was falling.

'Look, it's coming on heavier now.'

'If you showed it to a Bangladeshi and called it rain, he'd laugh at you.'

'You'd have thought the gods could have conjured up something more spectacular.'

That last comment got them riled and almost as we spoke a huge gust of cold wind blasted across the Basin and the heavens opened with a vengeance. It was heavier than anything either of us had ever seen before. The most immense raindrops were fired down at us. Riding carefully, we could almost dodge them as we cycled. Then they smacked on to the road, into the fields; punched through the trees like water-filled balloons, bursting on impact and bouncing back to be joined by thousands more pounding the countryside. They were so thick and heavy that the road was awash in seconds and we didn't have time to put on our waterproofs. All other people disappeared from the road and nearly all vehicles were forced to stop. Since we had no shelter we soldiered on with one hand closely guarding our eyes from the rain so that we could see out through a little gap in our fingers. It was worth pressing on; we were only ten kilometres from Kathmandu, the crossroads of our odyssey, the exotic yet easily accessible city which marked the end of the beginning of our journey.

Into the fabled city, drenched, elated, and lost among a mêlée of car horns, exhaust fumes, music, shouting, bicycle bells. It was dirtier and more squalid than I remembered it, yet also more Westernized. Perhaps the two go hand in hand. Our senses were swamped by a welter of scenes: bright shop fronts, speedy taxis, poor people sheltering under cardboard, street vendors selling cigarettes or hot snacks, mechanics squatting in lean-tos with car bits spread in front of them. Cows in the main streets, dogs in the gutters, piles of refuse. Street-lights, shanty houses, wooden huts, brick buildings, smart office blocks.

It took a while to find Thamel, alias Gringoland, the area where all the touroids hang out. There are many cheap, and not so cheap, hotels, plus tarty restaurants where homesick travellers can plug into quiche, lasagne and Black Forest gâteau. It's like an island of hippy culture and trash tourism plonked into the middle of one of the most crowded and least developed examples of an Asian city. There are many second-hand trekking/mountaineering stores. In the alleys, various Nepalese peddle hand-carved stringed instruments, kukris, bags and other junk. Nick saw this place as a cross between Covent Garden and Fort William: a strange world after so many days grovelling in the dirt, eating only rice, chapati and curry. It's a great opportunity to meet others: people who've trekked to Everest Base Camp or been white-water rafting at Tiger Tops Jungle Camp, or those who are about to go fresh and wide-eyed for their first trip into Nepal, or strange long-term itinerants. Nick found it a thrill and could have had a whale of a time if he hadn't had me as a millstone around his neck. Although I was super-excited to be back in Kathmandu, and I'm magnetically drawn to Thamel, I pretended to myself that I didn't like the one-upmanship of place: yet I swaggered around, out-pseuding the pseuds, silent and superior in the knowledge that we'd cycled all 1,481 kilometres from the Mouths of the Ganges to the capital of Nepal. We searched for half an hour and found the very same hotel, the Lumbini, where Ados and I had stopped while preparing for Running the Himalayas three years previously. The room we'd used was occupied so we got the first-floor one by the toilet. Then it was out for an evening on the town; we overdosed on soup, and steak and chips with salad followed by apple pie and custard and lots of hot chocolate.

Nick was drained: 'I could sleep for a week.' So he crawled off, with heavy belly, back to the Lumbini to crash out. I was so hyped up that I didn't want to go to bed. I sat up writing and planning for hours. Next morning I woke early with my head still buzzing with things to do. Last night's overload was having a similar effect at the other end of my torso. When Nick woke hours later he was involved in the same light relief. It was a problem which coloured all of our stay in Kathmandu, and indeed seems to grip the attention of every traveller to the city.

In Kathmandu the physical and spiritual aspects of our wilderness adventure were quickly submerged by the infinitely extensive minutiae of red tape and paperwork needed to prepare ourselves for the unknown territory ahead. There were many jobs to do: overhaul bikes, finalize equipment for the high altitude ahead, collect letters and packages, get diaries up to date, write to all the forty relatives, friends and supporters whose names and addresses we carried on a tightly scribed sheet of air mail paper, check out the need for China/Tibet visas and, most important of all, seek out any and all information about independent travel in Tibet.

We blew our first day in Kathmandu because by the time we'd had a luxury breakfast of porridge and eggs in the Paradise Restaurant it was early afternoon and the offices in town were closed. We did get some mail c/o the Malla Hotel: two communal letters from Steve Bonnist and the BBC about their tapes, and five personal letters for Nick. None for me. Who loves ya, Babe? I wasn't worried by not getting any letters; in fact in my perverse logic I dreamt that my friends didn't need to write to tell me they loved me. The advantage of this philosophy was that it kept me level-pegging with Nick. I felt that he depended on my previous Himalayan experience, I needed his cycling skills. It was for me a precarious situation of give-and-take because no events so far had stretched any of our abilities. He said later that the doubts he held about our partnership were suppressed by the drama of everyday travel in Asia and that to air them might risk casting an early strain on the expedition. This far into the adventure, we were in my view still no closer than colleagues. The true bond of friendship would evolve later when only teamwork could win.

Having lost the first day, the pressure increased because this was our last chance to prepare ourselves for the expedition proper. Everything up to Kathmandu had merely been a warm-up. Roger Chapman once said that an expedition has three components: fantasize, criticize, romanticize. He simplified it to: plan, do, recover. We had done our planning – that was in March and April in London, and the settling-in ride from the open sea. Now we had to start doing. Recovery was an unimaginable distance into the future. Some of the prospects ahead were frightening.

Nick. Diary.
Now that we're in Kathmandu, the next stage is looming. In fact we've just been looking at our map and letting the awesome distance from Kathmandu to Lhasa sink in with some sort of sobriety. And worse yet is that Kathmandu to Lhasa is nothing, absolutely nothing, compared to what follows! That's something we don't dare think about at the moment. What is looming is in a sense the very crux of the ride: the border-crossing from

Nepal to Tibet. It seems inconceivable that the Chinese will let us do this legitimately. Right now I'd be in favour of finding an illicit route over the Himalayas, and make a secret dash for Lhasa, hoping not to get picked up. Once in Lhasa we could pretend we'd just flown in from somewhere in China, and apply for the Tibet visa. The worst that could happen would be expulsion from Tibet/China and a few days in gaol. No, the worst that could happen would be a bullet in the bum from a trigger-happy border guard.

Assuming we survived the border-crossing, then we'd be stepping into the unknown. For 2,000 kilometres we'd be at 4,000 to 5,000 metres altitude, fearful of snow, hypothermia and biting winds. Optimistic authors describe habitation on the Tibetan Plateau as 'sparse and intermittent'; less flowery writers use the word 'non-existent'. Chris Bonington, also a Cumbrian, had written to me on 11 March 1986 and said: 'Settlements and "transport cafés" are few and far between.' We hoped to average well over 100 kilometres per day – but to survive we thought we might have to improve on that. The roads were expected to be all dirt. We hoped to find shelter in small farming villages in the lower valleys, some truck camps, and elsewhere in shepherds' huts or yak nomads' camps. We were prepared for the fact that some kids in the excitement of the moment might throw rocks at us. We didn't think we'd encounter any intentional malice; it was unlikely a yak herder would ping us with a shot from his or her sling. However, we worried if we might get eaten by wolves or trodden on by a yeti. Goodness only knows what happens in the Gobi Desert.

We'd done reasonably well on the expedition so far – we'd survived! The time-scale had gone a little haywire. I'd initially predicted to Steve Bonnist that the first leg to Kathmandu would take three days. Nick had reprimanded me and made me look at a map. Between his experience and my eagerness we'd settled for an estimate of six days. The dreadful reality was thirteen days! However, one good point was that our average was just over 100 kilometres per day, although while we languished in Kathmandu it was slipping away. We had hoped to build a big surfeit which would smooth out over the tough slow days on the Plateau. Our schedule had been to reach Lhasa on Day 15. That was clearly out of the question. It seemed a touch under 1,000 kilometres to Lhasa but useful information was needed for a sensible estimate.

Our initial feelers about independent travel in Tibet were very pessimistic. All the street-corner travel agents in Kathmandu said: 'Not possible', 'Only in organised bus tours', 'Four days, or ten days? $450 or $850?' 'No space available for three weeks', 'Bicycles? Not a hope in hell.' We showed the visas which we had so luckily bought in Britain sixteen hours before departure and they said: 'This doesn't cover Tibet', 'Hong Kong entry only', 'This must be registered and ratified before it's valid'.

The travellers and backpackers we talked to in Gringoland had all sorts of stories of people who'll get you a visa for fifty dollars, or smuggle you on to a bus for a lot of money. We met stacks of people planning to go to Tibet 'some time'. Nearly everyone knew someone who knew someone who'd been to Tibet. Mostly it was hearsay and rumour. We did find four people who'd been there on trucks or buses. We also heard a few tantalizing reports of people who'd seen mountain-bikes in Lhasa, but no one knew if they'd been flown in or had come in from mainland China in the east. Numerous people seemed to have heard stories of people who had been to remote villages or monasteries. Interestingly some of the best information on this had come in London from Bryan Hanson of the Globetrotters. One bizarre letter he showed me was from a girl who, while trekking out to a desolate Buddhist site, had met a friendly Tibetan and his daughter heading in the same direction. She travelled with them for several days. Out in the loneliness of the mountains, she'd rebuffed his amorous approaches during intervals when the little girl was asleep, then one night woke to find his nether appendage in her ear!

Less outlandish information gleaned in London came from Theresa Booth. She'd learnt Chinese and dressed up as a local in 1983, to try hitching across the Taklamakan via Urumqi and Turfan to Kashgar. She got arrested a few miles before her destination. She was threatened with all sorts of punishment. No amount of pleading or reason appeased the officials. As a last resort, she burst into tears. To her surprise, they relented and she was put on a commie truck and sent back five days across the desert through Golmud whence she came. Thus we began to get the feeling that independent travel was possible in Tibet and beyond, but it was by no means commonplace. We did wonder how on earth we would fare on bikes when so many people said it was 'impossible'.

Back in Britain, Steve Bonnist was wallowing in the problems of how to do some fund-raising from our trip when he didn't know where we were, how far we were going or when we'd get there. Hol, who thrives on problems like this, locked himself into his garage for a day and, though we didn't know it until we returned to Britain, came up with statistics which told Steve, and indeed the world, that it would be nine and a half days to Lhasa, two and a half days there and another twenty-one and a half to Urumqi. Indeed, it turned out that he'd calculated we'd be twelve days from the sea to Kathmandu – he hadn't allowed for one day lost to the Hartel!

Everyday life doesn't stop for grand planning. We had to eat and sleep. On the second day, Nick broke a tooth.

Nick. Day 14. Kathmandu American Embassy Dental Surgery.
Fixed the tooth. I've just had a Dental Experience: 'Lie back in the couch and relax' sounded a promising start. While he got his hardware together, Dr Elliot B. Higgins – dress: Levis, sneakers, open shirt – talked about the Norton he once owned and how it seized on the Interstate. Now he has a Honda 250 trail

bike with 'dual carbs' and 'would some day like to take it
to Tibet'. 'Just take it easy while I fix this rubber dam to keep
the crud out of your mouth, and that huge tongue out of my
way.' Drills and shrapnel. Panorama of the Himalayas on the
ceiling directly above. Hit the nerve turn up the music. 'Eddie
and the Cruisers – bought the album in Bangkok 'cos Eddie and
the Cruisers sounded my sort of band.' More drilling. 'Amazing
how this sounds like Bruce Springsteen – wash, please.' I'm
nearly asleep by now, it's so relaxing. Hit the nerve again,
'Baby, why do ya wanna hurt me?' goes Eddie and the Cruisers.
Elliot finesses his filling as if he's crafting an ivory carving.

Sings along to the music as he does so. 'OK, you're done,' and
I reluctantly get up from the most slumbrously relaxing thirty
minutes of the last few months. 'That's the best dental treat-
ment I've ever had,' I say fawning with gratitude in typically
British fashion. To which he replies: 'Just wait till we slap you!'
Forty-seven dollars.

While Nick lay back like Barbarella, I went to find Lisa van Gruisen, who
had been so helpful three years ago with Running the Himalayas. She was
just as 'fast, friendly, efficient and enthusiastic' as before with the additional bonus that this time she knew the route because she had organized
numerous trekking/exploration groups to Tibet through her office at
Tiger Tops/Mountain Travel. She bought Nick and me lunch in the posh
Yeti-something-Hotel then organized people to help us extricate our
parcels from Customs at the airport and check our visas.

Lisa brought us up to date with the travel situation in Tibet. The border
at Kodari had been opened last Easter to organized group travel, and as
recently as 1 March this year, two months before, to individual travel. It's
the only officially recognized route from the Indian subcontinent to China
excepting the newly opened Karakoram Highway through Pakistan and
over the Kunjirab Pass. She assured us that all the waffle about having to
go on a bus tour was perpetrated by the agents who sell the bus tours. She
gave us a letter of introduction to her Chinese contacts. Lisa's biggest
worry for us was the altitude, cold and sheer desolation of the Tibetan
Plateau. Twenty kilometres into China is a place called Nyalam, 4,000
metres above sea-level, thereafter she said it was sixty kilometres of
'nothing' to get to Dzongri Dzong, the next village. Could be pretty
interesting.

Lisa also put us in touch with Liz Hawley, one of the leading Himalayan
news correspondents. She noted a parallel between our expedition and
'Flying over the Hump' in the Second World War with supplies from
Calcutta to Burma and Chungking. She told us about the only people she
knew who had gone into China by bike from Nepal. One was a Hong
Kong-born Chinese, Victor Chang, who lived in Canada and had a valid
Tibetan travel visa, the other his Aussie friend who had none, so they

climbed over via a remote pass but were immediately arrested the other side and sent back. A mountain-bike expedition to Mount Kailash, the holy mountain at the source of the Indus, Ganges and Brahmaputra rivers, had departed Kathmandu heavily laden some weeks previously but no one had any idea how far they got.

Nick and I sat down to review all the information. Clearly some people were getting into China and Tibet through Kodari, all were travelling on trucks and buses, mostly direct to Lhasa, which by all accounts seemed to have quite a few tourists. Travel permits seemed obtainable for the roads south of Lhasa, but unavailable north of Lhasa. Food was reported as poor. The roads were dirt. They were very dusty and crossed large expanses of depressingly barren terrain between Kathmandu and Lhasa. The Tibetan Plateau seemed huge, distant and desolate. Nobody knew anything about travel north of Lhasa.

'So that's about the measure of it. Nowt to do but go and try.'

Having reached our decision we began to speed up proceedings in Kathmandu. Four days disappeared before we eventually left. We did send a package to Britain via an old friend, Colonel Mike Barratt. We did completely overhaul the bikes including waterproofing my saddle with butter. But we didn't find any of the packages of spares from Raleigh or our own equipment from Dhaka which should have been waiting. Neither did we see any of the tourist sights in the city. That'll have to come next time. For the present we were too busy thinking of Tibet and preparing things like final salopet and T-shirt modifications. Also we had stronger tougher hoods sewn on the Caldo cycling jackets and Velcro added to the overlap on the front zip. My bottom bracket had worked slightly loose, so I had to find a hammer and punch in a backyard workshop to tighten it slightly. We lost out badly on sleep because we had no mosquito nets.

Nick. Kathmandu.
The relief that we're setting off is increasing every minute. Kathmandu has been a frustrating and depressing hiccup in a journey that till four days ago was supercharged right from the day it was first dreamt up. Neither of us is any good at handling lack of progress, and (as D said this morning) we don't seem to have fully learnt the Kilimanjaro lesson: the only way to maintain momentum on these trips is to be totally self-sufficient. (I'd been whingeing in the same vein a couple of days ago – and all along I was slightly unhappy about setting up those equipment dumps.) Once you've built in contingencies in the form of equipment back-up, dumps or whatever, there's the risk that organizing the contingency arrangements takes over from the expedition itself. As I said to D last night: if we'd set off from Dhaka actually carrying all our spares, rather than relying on freighted advance dumps, we'd have saved a couple of days in return for carrying a few pounds of extra weight.

Well, the lesson has really rubbed in this time because I don't
think either of us will forget these repulsive days in Kathmandu.
The frustrating thing (and it's one of the reasons that we've
tried so hard to recover the kit) is that people like Raleigh's
Steve Bell, Steve Bonnist, Lisa van Gruisen have tried so hard
to trace the missing stuff.

Despite the delays and irritations of Kathmandu, it was comfortable and
civilized. For our last night in relative safety before the traumas ahead,
Nick persuaded me to change to the expensive luxuries of the Kathmandu
Guest House (ten dollars per night!) where we got room D-1 looking out
over the roof-tops of the city to the snow peaks. At first light I woke but
couldn't bring myself to stir from my warm cosy cocoon. The thought of
the difficulties, cold, hassles and exertion over the coming days held me
tightly in place: 'Dear Mother, I'd like to stay in this bed . . . the idea of
going out on to the Tibetan Plateau is enough to make me want to spend
the rest of my life here.'

FOUR

Cycling the Himalayas

The sun shone brightly. It was warm and calm as we cycled out from Kathmandu before the morning rush-hour. We headed north out of the city cycling through farmland and passing small copses of trees and quiet Nepalese villages. There was little other traffic to disturb us. We followed the good metalled road which leads off the Kathmandu Basin towards the valley of the Sun Kosi, then up towards the village of Lamosangu where the trekker's route to Everest branches off. Beyond there was beyond my experience. Three years ago with Ados I had come down this trail, supposedly 'Running the Himalayas' but at that stage reduced to walking, almost staggering, our bodies racked by food poisoning, sleeplessness and foolhardy over-exertion. I had said: 'We're beaten. We can't go any further.'

This section, Lamosangu to Kathmandu, was in a sense the crux of Running the Himalayas because by then we had mastered ultra-lightweight foot travel and survival in the high Himalayas. Ados and I knew by then that if we persevered through the physical hammering then we would probably, God willing, succeed. As it turned out, we did press onwards through a maze of adventure eventually to finish our 2,000-mile epic. We wrote a book about it, did magazine articles and lectures, were presented to the late Indira Gandhi, and Mrs Thatcher and Lord Hunt. It turned my world upside-down. I learnt that people are more important than mountains or competition, and also that perseverance and commitment take you far beyond imaginable bounds. Cousin Nick's Bicycles up Kilimanjaro had reinforced this conviction. JCE was, for me, on the verge of building on these blocks and reaching further. This Kathmandu –Lamosangu section appeared also to be the crux for Journey to the Centre of the Earth: we had settled into super-spartan cycle-touring – the big question was could we get across the border and, more important, could we do it in Tibet?

Our bikes rolled smooth as silk. No effort was needed to pedal them. The countryside slipped by as if in a dream. Riding a bicycle through Nepal, into the Himalayas, seemed to be the most natural thing in the world. It seemed absolutely normal, in fact a perfectly ordinary weekend leisure activity. The road led up the general hilliness on the front of the Himalayas and through the small town of Banepa, which I remembered from three years ago as having looked smartly clean and well stocked with shops, a distinct change from other poverty-stricken villages in east Nepal, but now on JCE it appeared squalid and dirty by comparison to equivalent towns on the truck routes we had come through south of here. At 9 a.m., with thirty kilometres behind us, we came on to the ridge at Dhulikel, five and a half thousand feet above sea-level. It was sparkling in the sun, surrounded by greenery with beautiful views of the snowy mountains ahead. It was time for breakfast. More important, here was Dhulikel Lodge where Ados and I had breakfasted on Day 18 of our expedition three years ago racing down from Everest base camp to Kathmandu to set a record. By almost pure coincidence, guided to a small extent by fate, today was also Day 18 of JCE. I reflected for a while and realized that it must also be the exact same time of day because Ados and I had risen early 'at the first cruel light of dawn' and run, walked and struggled about twenty kilometres to get here. We had staggered in exhausted and downhearted, but the peace, tranquillity and good food picked us up. Indeed, the Lodge was unchanged from those days; an oasis, cool and clean. There were several visitors sitting around the walls on cushions on the floor. We took our shoes off at the door, and left our bikes leaning outside by the flower-beds. No worry about locals or theft because the Lodge has its own gardens. The other travellers had books and were all busily reading in silence. We read the menu, which crossed interestingly between Western and Eastern dishes.

Nick and I took forty minutes' relaxation and noted that 'for JCE this marks the final run-up to the start-line'. For us the adventure into the unknown was to begin tomorrow. We would step out of the proven territory of Running the Himalayas. The Tibetan Plateau felt as though it would be like nothing we had ever known before. I felt quite small and humbled by the thought, and at the same time big because everything around shrank into insignificance. The people, mountains, houses, trees all vanished; I could only see the empty Plateau ahead. Maybe like a Wembley Cup Finalist footballer walking out on to the pitch; he forgets the stadium and the crowds around him.

For the time being all was sunny and easy, and we fairly zipped down the north-east side of the col from Dhulikel, on and on down and over two tiny bumps of intervening valleys to no more than 2,000 feet above sea-level where we met the Sun Kosi. The air was warm and moist, the foliage thick and green. Tucked under steep white cliffs, there was a solid concrete bridge over the strong smooth blue waters reminding me of adverts of bikini-clad nymphs by Caribbean coral reefs. A surveyor's sign read, 'Elevation (feet), 1,966' – remember England World Cup winners? So now we're at the bottom!

And then we started climbing.

It had the potential to be a fabulously long uphill. Possibly the longest continual road climb in all the world. Reaching to a height of over 17,000 feet (5,000 metres) at the pass called the Lalung Le. If all went well, something in excess of 15,000 feet of pedalling uphill over a distance of more than 150 kilometres following the Sun Kosi from the damp heat in this lush green valley of Nepal, through the Nepal–Chinese border halfway up the frontal forests of the Himalayas and then, as Lisa van Gruisen said, 'Out into the stark emptiness beyond: to thin air, a strong wind and sharp biting cold – to an experience you'll never regret'.

Nick. Day 18. Morning. Sun Kosi.
To our surprise a mountain-bike free-wheeled around the corner in front of us. Janet Niichel had pedalled about Pakistan before coming here. A few minutes later, her travelling companion, Ray, riding a heavily loaded Holdsworth, rolled round the corner. He had ridden for two years from Europe and needed some new tyres. Ray wowed and swooned over the quality of our bikes: 'Jeez, seven fifty-three – you need a special licence just to *buy* that!' We learnt about their ride up to Kodari to see the border-post. They'd only gone up the day before and wished they'd gone prepared to try to cross to China. Both were Californians. Pink balloons of bubble-gum extruded from Janet's mouth and popped definitively in the breeze.

The Sun Kosi was pleasant and warm. It was quite a narrow valley with the road squeezed tight beside the smoothly flowing river. Every revolution of the pedals took us a little bit higher up the side of the Tibetan Plateau. Each small slope represented elevation which, hopefully, we wouldn't lose until we came off the far side of the Plateau down to the Gobi. Each portion was for me one more step closer to breaking out from the stranglehold of Running the Himalayas. It had governed my life for three years and within a few hours I would emerge freely to a new adventure like a chrysalis breaking out of a cocoon. Every few miles I recognized sights I'd seen before, coming in the opposite direction, dragging my feet.

We cycled on and arrived at Lamosangu, seventy-eight kilometres from Kathmandu, in the early afternoon. There's a big metal bridge spanning the Sun Kosi leading off to Everest. Stumbling over this bridge three years ago, had come Ados and me. The ex-main road continues in degenerated fashion up the valley towards mystery, and that's where Nick and I would be going in a few minutes; but first a little nostalgia. Lamosangu was no more than a line of ramshackle huts and a cluster of unwashed kids totally dependent on the buses and trucks which stop or turn around there. It was a grotty little hole, yet it was my personal crossroads. Running the Himalayas lay behind, JCE lay ahead. It was where I would be able to venture out from the old into the new, and join Nick with full commitment.

'Let's have a cup of tea to celebrate,' I said cheerily. We selected the least disgusting of the disgusting little chai houses, brushed the worst of the food debris off the table, and sat down in a cloud of flies. The tea was poured lukewarm, the same colour as the faces of the kids outside, from a Thermos flask so grubby that it would have been less obnoxious to have poured it from our own socks. Nick observed: 'Probably stuffed with more bugs than all the Bangladeshi chai houses put together.' We left the tea and bought some bottled fizz.

As we mounted our bikes to start our new journey, I breathed a sigh of relief. The adventures of three years ago were most definitely behind me. Nick said nothing – let me live these hours alone. Later I learnt that he was nearly unaware of any barrier between us: 'I didn't realize that you (Dick) were reserving your commitment until you'd kicked Running the Himalayas.' For him the days building up to the Chinese border had been a bright exciting introduction to Asian cycling. Each of us was independently shaping and modifying our own styles and objectives until this point; both at the same time, we silently bowed to the immeasurable challenges ahead into which we were now heading together. I felt wondrously cleansed and ready for an epic. Suddenly my animosity, which had been holding us apart, vanished. From here on, we were both innocent novices thrown into the battle together. I had shrugged a great weight off my shoulders. We were a team. We were excited and we were on our way to the Centre of the Earth.

That there might be some big adventure ahead was suggested by certain aspects, or lack of certain aspects, of our equipment. We had no shelter, no food, only one litre maximum of water, and only the set of clothes we stood up in. Few people trek the mountains so sparsely equipped, let alone try cycling the Himalayas. The bikes were in themselves lightweight racers with no mudguards, no lights, no spare brake blocks. Many people ask us why we didn't have mountain-bikes similar to the heavy-duty cross-country machines we rode up Kilimanjaro. That's exactly the point; mountain-bikes are for climbing mountains. For this adventure we intended to stay as far as possible on roads, tracks and trails used by other vehicles and therefore more or less suitable for wheeled transport. If the worst came to the worst, we could always carry our bikes for short distances. They did have ten gears, but we'd decided that we'd travel sufficiently lightly laden that no specially low gears were needed so we simply had ordinary touring ratios. In Kathmandu we'd carefully scrutinized our needs and ditched such items as our cycling gloves. However, we did feel that we should be prudent and carry a spare tyre each. After all, there might be 4,000 kilometres of dirt road ahead! We put a new Specialized K4 touring tyre, 1¼ inches wide, on the rear wheel intending to swap it to the front at the border, left the wider 1½-inch Specialized Expedition on the front, and folded the other partly used Expedition which had ridden from Chittagong into our tiny saddle-bags. Guided by Nick's wide experience, we kept the tyres pumped up very hard. The all-up weight of our entire set of gear was 18 lb; that was including all our clothes down to shoes and socks plus the pannier bags themselves. The bikes weighed only 22 lb. It's certainly possible to travel ultra-lightweight, but you have to be prepared for certain discomforts and inconveniences *en route*. Having no toilet paper is clearly inconvenient. More so if all the water has frozen into snow.

Nick had, in a sense, taught me all I knew about cycling because he lured me back to exercise and the outdoor world when I was on the verge of middle-age spread at twenty-four. I then lived in Berkshire, so to cycle thirty miles to his Oxford home was fun. We did time-trials together, and I envied his repertoire of cycling anecdotes and his circle of fascinating, slightly eccentric, cycling friends. The Pedalling Club which I started, with John Rodd and Michèle, at Reading University was a direct copy of Nick's CATMOUS (Cambridgeshire College of Arts and Technology Mountaineering Society).

With Lamosangu and a number of other things behind us, we had only a small part of Nepal to get through and hoped to reach the border the next day. The road was partly surfaced, partly dirt, climbing gently all the way. Small hamlets beside the road, small fields crammed on to the banks of the river. Trees coated the hillsides above, and probably there were villages higher up where the slopes levelled off. We began to get worried about finding a suitable place for the night, and two hours before dusk, unusually early for us, we settled for a largish village where the road crosses the river from below the cliffs on one side of the valley to below the steep slopes on the other. This village, Bharbise, was a one-street transport town approximately ninety kilometres from Kathmandu. It had a row of higgledy-piggledy buildings along each side of the road. Many looked dilapidated and derelict but were lived in. All built much the same as the others; brick-walled base, wooden-framed upper, three- or four-storey, tiled roof, small windows, clay floors supported on huge beams, rickety bare tables and a couple of lightbulbs on strings. Bharbise was almost totally dependent on motor vehicles and passing trade. Like all such towns around the world it was squalid and unsavoury with obnoxious people and was the worst ambassador for its country.

Nick. Day 18. Bharbise.
Several 'hotels' can be found along the refuse- and animal-littered street – mostly twenty-five rupees per night. Dick researched the whole lot – even trying to buy the entire floor of one guesthouse for the night – 'Just right, we'll sleep in the back room and rent the two front ones as noise buffers!' In another place he nearly managed to rent a seven-bed dormitory and buy out all the other residents. While all this was going on, a band of grimy children with dirt and sores all over their faces, and

clothes which quite literally had never been washed, were driving me spare by massaging every moving part of the bikes. The place D finally chose (his other deals having fallen through) is quaint – like the loft in a Victorian flour mill. It's two metres square, on the top floor, above the street. The family moved out for us. There's just enough space for us to balance the bikes on the beds. One of us gets changed at a time. To get through the door, you climb on my bed. The whole building is filthy, not 'filthy' in a British sense, but in an Asian sense: our room is thick with strings of ancient spider's webs and the walls are stained and dirty with dust. Two of the walls are thin wood panelling with the sharp ends of nails sticking through – good for opening bottles of orange.

Down on the ground floor, literally mud-floored like everywhere except Kathmandu and Dhulikel Lodge, we sat down to some unimaginative food: hot rice, cold curry and dahl. The most disgusting muck swept from the floors was piled into a corner of the room. Beside it, a tin tub of grey water for washing hands. Dogs wandered freely in from the road, some lads playing hide-and-seek were darting in and out. The men in town were unsightly; dressed in tatty, dirty, black, brown or grey Western cast-offs. I'm afraid to say that men from non-Western cultures dressed in Western clothes always turn me off. It was a particularly dirty town with pigs in the street, vegetable matter rotting everywhere, little children squatting to relieve themselves on the front corners of buildings. Yet, despite all this casual dirtiness, Nepal is, in its own way, quainter and more endearing than the craziness of Bangladesh.

The lady of the house brought her little son, maybe two years old, to stare at our writing. The little kid was in a one-piece modern jump-suit, the lady in a patterned dark-red wrap-around wool skirt of maybe three or four layers. Her face was partly of round chubby Tibetan stock crossed with a touch of the taller finer women of the Plains. Particularly captivating was her traditional elegant jewellery. She wore long shiny earrings, and in the central septum of her nose she had a fine, silver, hooped nose-ring with tiny gold flowers. Pierced into the side of her nose, like most of the women hereabouts, she wore a chunky gold bauble made of seven to ten little spheres clustered together like the bright yellow stamen in a daisy. Probably she also had bangles and necklaces, but best of all was her thick black hair which was long and strong, down to her waist, plaited delicately and intertwined down its length with ribbons finished off with intricate gold twine which bound the ends in the small of her back and left loose the last few inches with flying red ribbons reaching down to her skirt.

That was our last night south of the Himalayas; in a few hours of the next day we would be cycling up the last twenty-seven kilometres to the Chinese border. As if enjoying the calm before the storm, we relaxed a little and took a walk up the hillside above. Each of us in turn stayed back to guard the bikes in the bedroom, the other climbed the stone steps up the back of town, passed some groups of older men – traditional white wool shirt, tight black waistcoat, and sculpted white calf-length leggings – and then a little higher up into the terraced sanctuary above the town with a splendid view over the valley.

Nick. Day 19. Bharbise. Early Morning.
We had the most appalling night – mosquitoes forced us to wrap ourselves in blanket and sleeping-bag, wear Goretex over-trousers on our legs and T-shirts pulled over our heads. For hours, I was *drenched* in sweat. We're at jungle height not far above sea-level; the air is close and clammy. Added to that the beds, we discovered, were built for the average Nepali, i.e. five feet long. We had to lie diagonally, feet hanging over the end. In the night dogs howled, barked and fought outside the window. To cap it all, I had to get up for a pee. I fumbled down the three flights of step-ladder, in the dark, unbarred the back door only to step straight into the slime and stench of the rubbish pit. Consolation as I stood relieving, was a beautiful clear night patterned with stars. It was so bad it was funny, and of course we had a good hysterical laugh when at 6 a.m. D cracked under the strain and let out one of his explosive belches – the sign to show he's decided to greet the new day. We ate six small biscuits we'd saved from last night, then wrestled the bikes all the way down to the ground – tight corners and shelves of dust – marvelling at how we got them up there in the first place. It was (no lies) great to get on to the bikes. The sense of freedom and release from grotesque night-halts sets me on a soaring high for the first few miles of every day.

The last vestiges of tarmac petered out soon after Bharbise. The valley stayed tight and in places was edged by waterfalls. Up above always we could see farms perched on the gentler sunny slopes. Terraced areas were edged by dark green forest. It turned out to be a long four-hour journey in which we ascended several thousand feet and hunger climbed right up beside us.

Kodari was another like Lamosangu. We were too wound up to stop for food, so cycled on with beating hearts towards the border post a little further on. A kid chucked a rock at my bike and I leapt off and chased him screaming up the hillside. The road led on, unmetalled but surfaced with well-conditioned smooth gravel, into a tight sunny gorge. It was clearly an impressive engineering feat. Possibly financed by the Chinese. Then we could make out the spectre which had commanded our thoughts ever since the day we dreamt up JCE. Ahead, maybe five kilometres away, blocking the valley, capped by a dark menacing cloud, cloaked in matted green and fronted by several large grey rock-faces, towered an ominous shoulder of the Tibetan Plateau. This guardian dominated the valley like the Giant Ogre at the top of Jack's Beanstalk: 'Fee, fi, fo, fum, I smell the blood of an Englishman; Be he alive or be he dead, I'll grind his bones to make my bread.' However, before we confronted that problem we had to deal with the trivia on this side. We had cycled just over 1,600 kilometres in nineteen days to get here. Our average daily mileage was worse than we had hoped, but it would all be irrelevant if we were stopped by the border formalities.

The Nepalese Exit Border was shoddy: a small dark hut with a wobbly table and a clay floor. The official was dressed in mufti; he was sitting on a wooden chair outside when we came. The only reason we knew he was the official is because we asked him: 'Are you the official?' As we pushed our bikes on towards China, at first with too many shivers in our legs to ride, we stared up at the prospects ahead. China officially enveloped Tibet, without opportunity for dissent, in 1950, the same frightening year of confrontations that South Korea was invaded by North Korean communist forces. On Friendship Bridge we stood a moment on the safe side of the red line painted across the middle, one hundred feet above the Sun Kosi, beside a sign proclaiming '1,770 metres above sea-level'. Ahead we could make out details of Khasha, the Chinese border-town, which in contrast to Kodari was stylish and quite out of keeping with this side of the Himalayas. It was foreign. We could see smart three- or four-storey office blocks, big glass windows, colourful new buildings. In one of those buildings our fate would soon be decided. However, they were one thousand feet or more above us, so we started pedalling. A light rain fell. There'd been much rain recently and the five-kilometre international road in this No Man's Land was extremely boggy and churned up. Our wheels kept slipping. We fought gallantly on upwards to the gods. Part way, a truck was stuck. To our surprise there were whites hanging around; they told us they'd come from Lhasa by truck in three days: 'Terrible journey. Absolutely barren empty monotonous countryside. Unbelievably hostile: dry, dusty, cold. This last two hours in the forest around Khasha and the front of the Himalayas has been the only good bit of the trip.' It was reassuring to know they'd got across the border, but knowing there was nothing ahead wasn't much use. A nice Brit changed some of our Nepalese rupees to Chinese money and explained something complicated about different sorts of money and similar sorts of notes and coins. I was confused.

Then suddenly we were there. Our entrance was marked by a green Chinese supply-truck with bulbous nose and high slatted back. A red flag flew over the handsome complex of offices which would have looked quite at home in Newcastle-upon-Tyne, but looked totally out of place in the Himalayas, 2,000 metres (6,500 feet) above sea-level. It had big glass windows, office chairs, clean linoleum floors – and guards with guns. We judiciously leant our bikes around the corner slightly out of sight, but not deliberately hidden so no one could accuse us of deception. At the health desk we had to fill in a form listing all the diseases we carried.

'Have you got anything, Nick?'

'No.'

'What about diarrhoea?'

'No, I haven't got that. I left it on the hillside two Ks back.'

At the immigration window we stretched up to give our passport to a pretty girl in smart green uniform with red epaulettes. She smiled nicely and studied them carefully for a minute then, leaning forward, she looked seriously at us from under her peaked officer's cap with its shiny Red Star of China and asked, in the same way as a traffic warden does when you try to drive off without a ticket: 'Where are you going?' We mumbled, 'Lhasa and Urumqi,' partly hoping she wouldn't hear and partly hoping she'd write 'Urumqi' in our passports. She repeated 'Lhasa' without batting an eyelid as though she hadn't heard the rest. The bicycles were not even commented on. Then at long last we breathed a sigh of relief as she reassuringly spent a long time lowering the stamp exactly on to our passports and pressing firmly, rocking slightly back and forth, giving us a little sideways grin to let us know we were into China.

> *Nick. Day 19. Khasha. 14.30 hours.*
> CHINA! We're in. WE'RE IN!!!
> Even now, an hour later, I can't believe we're into Tibet. So easily. This border crossing was meant to be the big stumbling block; the point from where we had to turn back and cross the Himalayas illegally, or ride 3,000 kilometres to the Karakoram Highway. But we're in. Our plan's working!

It was much more Chinese than we'd anticipated. We immediately saw oriental grins, the Red Star on walls, Chinese blue Mao suits and funny writing. Our stomachs were caving in with hunger by the time we'd done the formalities so we dived into the first chai house we came to. Huge bowls of noodles and meat with green-pepper Chinese stir-fry. To our delight, they gave us chopsticks to eat it with – we had to learn fast. From the outside this chai house looked just like its Nepalese counterparts, but inside it was astonishingly clean. The man and his wife were busy washing the floor – something unheard of in Nepal, and only briskly done with a fly-whisk in India. The walls were sheets of tin can hammered flat, carefully linked together and then painted pale green: the Nepalese would have simply cut out the tin panels and nailed them to the wood struts or maybe just stacked tin cans up to form an apology for a wind-break. The tables were nearly stable. There was good lighting, a smoke chimney on the stove, and something unheard of south of here: table-cloths – plastic and clean.

Nick reset our watch to Beijing time, which is used all over China. Four hours ahead of Nepal. This made it seem like mid-afternoon, though a stone's throw away in Nepal it was only noon. Beijing is so much closer to the rising sun that by the time dawn reaches the remote areas of western

China the best part of the morning has gone. However, the evenings are light until late. In theory it shouldn't have made any difference to our journey or to our eating because the local people tend to be principally subsistence farmers and nomads living by the sun.

We went to change some money. It was swift and easy. The bank staff were smart and friendly. The office was clean and tidy with a bare minimum of pieces of paper on the few desks in a large half-empty room the starkness of which highlighted the big wads of notes sitting on the tables within arm's length of us. Here we learnt a little about RMBs and FECs, the former being money that locals can use, the latter being Foreign Exchange Certificates. Both supposedly worth the same, although FECs are in fact more useful to richer Chinese because certain foreign luxury items can only be bought in FEC. Therefore we later found in some places a black market. However, the difference in value meant it was hardly worth swapping for the risk of police apprehension and gaol. The reason for having two different currencies was that we foreigners in theory could only buy in FEC, therefore bringing foreign exchange into the country. The reality was that the places Nick and I stopped which had heard of FEC were few and far between, though when they did appear they catered for lots of tourists, were expensive and had banks nearby. It was simpler all round for most of our route to swap quite a lot of FEC for RMB. Some of the money was in coinage but, luckily for us, there are both notes and coins of equal value down to almost worthless amounts, equivalent to less than the cost of a piece of chewing-gum. This was excellent for us because it meant we never had to carry coins.

By 5 p.m. we were ready to move; because of the change in time zones it would be light until nearly 11 p.m., so we thought that if there were no transport-guards stopping us from leaving Khasha, then we might complete thirty kilometres to the next village of Nyalam, which we were told really was on the edge of the Tibetan Plateau, beyond the thick green forests and out from under the rain cloud of Khasha. It was hard to believe we were truly in China because scenery like this with steep mountains and, behind us in the south, terraced slopes was by rights text-book Nepal. The road surface was stony dirt, quite difficult to ride but better than No Man's Land. As in Nepal there were regular kilometre-posts so in theory we could judge our distances. Unfortunately it was a bit disheartening because the distance on the post was 732 kilometres. Further than any signpost we'd ever seen before. More than a day's riding! The good thing was that Lhasa was now a tangible target, though admittedly a long way away, on not very good roads, at very high altitudes.

We set off optimistically, pedalled around a few hairpins and out of sight of Khasha, Nepal and all below. We slowed down a bit, marvelled at the snow-fields we could see close above us, thrilled to the steep rock faces and avalanche scars, and got tired. It started raining heavily, we got wet and cold, prayed for some sort of habitation to appear, felt miserable because the mist came down like a Scottish winter, pedalled a little more and got

worried. Five kilometres out of Khasha, we debated turning back to safety
for the night, then in the nick of time, ten kilometres further, came upon a
derelict shed and went inside. To our surprise it was already in use by four
Chinese road-workers who'd finished the day's work and were huddled
around the fire getting a brew on. They were more astonished than us:
dumbfounded. Nick and I did our mime for tired, cold, wet cyclists going
northwards: 'In that direction,' we'd say in English, doubling over
imaginary handlebars, alternately bending each knee as though we had an
uncomfortable itch between our buttocks, and heading straight through
the brick wall.

> *Nick. Day 19. China. Evening.*
> It's good to get in from the rain. They've let us sit by their
> electric ring. One of them has burrowed into his sleeping covers
> on a platform strewn with blankets. The bare walls are black-
> ened by smoke and the one tiny window-hole has been boarded
> up. Clothing hangs from a cat's cradle of lines strung above our
> heads. A row of dried birds, no bigger than sparrows, is hanging
> by the single electric bulb, and there is a general air of that cosy
> squalor you find in climbing-huts. The men are lounging about,
> wrapped in blankets, reading Chinese novels, talking now and
> then and joking. They seemed to find our mime enormously
> funny, but show no interest in going outside to see the bikes;
> perhaps it's too cold, or perhaps they simply didn't understand
> our gestures. One of the men played a mouth-organ for a while,
> then he and the youngest man began singing a duet from a
> hand-written book of songs. We hummed 'Wild Rover'. I've
> taken a closer look at the song-book. It's more than that. There
> are pages and pages of beautiful calligraphy mixed with detailed
> sketches and one remarkable water-colour of a red bird on a
> branch.

They settled us down for tea and food and gave us the most massive quart
enamel mug you've ever seen – complete with its own lid to keep it warm.
Each time we drank they topped it up. They tried to tell us excitedly in
Chinese and show us what work they did; we smiled cheerily and laughed
when we guessed it appropriate but mostly we didn't understand. One
thing they did show us was how they caught the little birds in a small pit
outside. They baited it with seed and the birds were trapped under a heavy
piece of wood. They gave us food: rice from a pressure cooker and
re-heated beans deliciously topped off by tiny red-hot chillies. Our heads
grew heavy with sleep so to indicate 'time for bed' I got out my sleeping-
bag and looked meaningfully around me. There wasn't much choice: the
bare concrete floor, or their cot. They invited us to share. So, despite the
laughter which erupted when our salopets were peeled off to reveal our
undies, we all climbed into bed and snuggled down. Sardines probably get

a better deal packed into a can than we did in that bed – they don't have to put up with octopuses pumping their calf muscles, or cuddling up to their torsos in the night. That's how we spent our first night in China; near the Nepalese rainforest, in sight of snowy mountains, almost on to the empty Plateau, snoring contentedly in a tiny hut and sandwiched in by four Chinese buddies.

FIVE

Xizang Zizhiqu, Qomolangma Feng and Rinbung Dzong

(Tibet, Everest, and a Little Town in the Middle of Nowhere)

Tibet lay ahead; just over the pass and around the corner. Today was going to be a momentous day. After years of dreaming, we would be able to see for ourselves, to feel and in a sense to touch this mysterious hidden kingdom. Tibet is by far the most extensive high-altitude plateau in the world, yet it is barely explored, sparsely inhabited and until recently very rarely travelled by foreigners. It is unique. For much of the past three decades since the Chinese seized jurisdiction in the early 1950s, it has been strictly closed. Before that it was always a reclusive society making no effort to encourage visitors and showing little interest during the past thousand years in venturing, for war or trade, beyond its borders. Most of the plateau is in excess of 10,000 feet above sea-level, some central areas are at 15,000 feet and passes between these basins reach to nearly 20,000 feet – nearly as high as the world bicycle altitude record, recently set by Ados Crane on the summit of Chimborazo in Ecuador. Curiously that mountain on the equatorial bulge is recorded in the *Guinness Book of Records* as 'The Mountain whose summit is furthest from the earth's centre'. Fierce storms sweep without warning across the northern plateau, and temperatures drop to minus forty in winter. There are no trees, so wood for building has to be carried up from distant lands and fires are made with dried yak dung.

Culturally Tibet has a long history, presumably beginning several thousand years ago with an unstructured, nomadic, semi-pastoral society having animist beliefs, then wholeheartedly taking on the mantle of Buddhism when it spread over the Himalayas from India in the seventh century AD. At this time Tibet was a reasonably powerful force in the tribal politics of central Asia, but since then it has been basically a peaceful country, happy to welcome the few travellers who braved the hardships of mountains and deserts and volatile tribes which guarded its strange lifestyle. Until this century, well over half the population was nomadic, there were no wheels except the prayer-wheel, one in six boys went to study in a monastery, celibate for life, and burial was in the sky – on an exposed mountain-ledge scavenged by vultures. Tibet's sheer inaccessibility kept foreign curiosity at a negligible level until the Tibetans, fearing the growing Russian and British empires, shut down its borders to everyone at the end of the nineteenth century – and thereby created a challenge. The race for Lhasa began in earnest. Several people tried, and failed, to slip quietly, unseen, into the Forbidden City disguised as pilgrims or beggars. Then in 1904 the British officer Younghusband, shooting locals right, left and centre, blasted his way from Sikkim on to the Tibetan Plateau and into Lhasa in the name of trade and holding the Russians at bay. However, there were no Russians. A trade mission was established, though it folded again after less than ten years.

Very few others visited Tibet during the first half of this century. The most remarkable, and best known by far, being Heinrich Harrer's seven-year sojourn following his escape from internment by the British in India in 1943. He made a hair-raising climb over numerous Himalayan passes to reach Lhasa. At every stage along his way he could have been deported or gaoled by the authorities. By guile he won through and went on to become mentor to the young Dalai Lama, who, as head of Tibetan Buddhism, was also in practice head of government. Everything came to an end when the Chinese unilaterally annexed Tibet in 1950 making it a semi-independent province of the second largest country in the world and changing its name to Xizang Zizhiqu, which literally means 'Autonomous Region Hidden in the West'. It remained strictly closed until the first foreigners were given travel permits to enter from eastern China in the early 1980s; two years ago the Nepal–China border was officially opened to a few organized tour groups and recently, on 1 March 1986, to independent travellers – like us.

After 1,608 kilometres of pedalling from Patenga Point we had got ourselves into Tibet. The hard part was not over – indeed, it had hardly begun. It was a long way to Lhasa, we had no idea what to expect, and even the first col and corner were a not inconsiderable challenge because they were another seventy barren and alien kilometres ahead, all on dirt road, all at high altitude (from now on all the distance to Lhasa would be high-altitude), climbing to the Lalung Le at 5,214 metres, more than 17,000 feet, elevation. My hope, based on my earlier experiences of the Tibetan Plateau around Zanskar, was that there would be villages, huts or nomads every ten or twenty kilometres even in the wildest places. Nick was sceptical.

We crept out from our Chinese friends at the crack of dawn on Day 20. Three of them were still cuddled snugly in their cot, the fourth was starting to get a brew on. Outside the sky was clear, the clouds of yesterday having blown away, but it was too early for the sun to shine into the depths of our valley. It was cold. For the first time we wore all our clothes except over-trousers. The road surface had dried out so the gravel was hard-packed and quite good to ride. We cycled the first few kilometres slowly and quietly, leaving the forests behind, then picked up enthusiasm when we passed between two huge shoulders of snow by the road and were laughing when the sun's rays caught us on the open zigzags among massive snowy mountains. We felt that we had entered real Tibet. Only thin pale grey-green grass covered the lower slopes, and bare scree was a short distance above us. The most significant marker of leaving behind Nepal and all it stood for was passing two herds of yaks coming down the road for the day's pasture. We stopped to admire the huge shaggy beasts lumbering by, about twenty-five of them interspersed with a few goats, all with little bells tinkling like waterfalls, herded by six women in long black skirts, three dogs and a little boy.

After two hours we reached Nyalam, the so-called first and last town on the Tibetan Plateau. It's an uninspiring collection of tin huts and brick buildings, tipped like a refuse heap behind the banks of a stream, in an area where there's absolutely no other sign of the human race except the dirt road – and virtually no sign of life at all, except the sparse grass and yak droppings. It's at 12,500 feet altitude with small green trucks parked in the street. All the several hundred people of the town seemed to be, not Tibetans, but Han Chinese from eastern China.

Nick. Day 20. Nyalam. 11 a.m.
Stopped for breakfast. First some great tea; clear, no milk, hot water with a few leaves for flavour, served in a glass, a sand-bank of sugar in the bottom. Then: momos (dumplings), stir-fry veg, meat stew and now egg noodles in soup. Three meals each. I'm eating as much as I can, and am a bit apprehensive lest there is no food for the rest of the day. We're out on our own, committed to reaching the next place of shelter – no chance of stopping mid-way. Ahead of us in the remaining ten hours of daylight is hopefully no more than sixty kilometres to the next village; that's what we gleaned from Lisa and others in Kathmandu. Incredibly, the locals here seem to think that there's nothing more for another 200 kilometres. Whoever's right, the biggest obstacle is the Lalung Le. A night in the open would really test our gear – or lack of it. Dick is happy! This is real adventure.

The road worked up the valley, staying reasonably close to the small river which ran down from here to become the impressive Sun Kosi in Nepal and then the giant Ganges leading right back down to where we'd started. The landscape was grand and open: everything was large scale. The further north we cycled, the browner and drier it became. We paused occasionally to look around us and marvelled at the new sensation of Tibet. By and by, to our delight (because it signalled safety), we came upon small fields tucked into the valley bottom and close to them, though on infertile ground too far from the river to be watered, were tight villages of square black flat-roofed Tibetan houses. The villagers in the fields wore dark

wool clothes wrapped thick around them against the wind. It whipped up
the dust from the arid land and pushed us on, up and up. Thirty, then
forty, kilometres dropped away behind us. There seemed no end to the
valley. Clearly the pass was further than we expected. We got some water
at 5 p.m. and, while stopped, noticed slight altitude headaches. Our legs
were beginning to feel weak. Then, setting out again, we were thankful for
the strong wind from behind. It was icy cold. Grass was very thin; all
trees, bushes and shrubs had disappeared for ever way back before
Nyalam. The river branched once or twice and the road climbed more
steeply. The altitude was probably 15,000 feet yet the scale of the scenery
decreased all the time and the road wiggled in among small rounded
hillocks like warts on the back of a toad. Snow patches lay around. There
were no high mountains above us; though, looking back or out to the side,
we glimpsed some from time to time. We were cycling out to the top of the
dome. Almost imperceptibly we reached the summit of the Lalung Le at
7 p.m. It was crowned by a superbly colourful tatter of prayer-flags
blossoming from the summit cairn in reds, blues, greens, whites and
yellows, all flapping madly in the wind, stretched out taut and horizontal
in a salute to the majesty of the mountains.

We stood on the edge, the very lip, of the Tibetan Plateau. To the south
the Himalayas filled our view. For so long they had been the barrier in
front of us; now we could look back at the world's most revered mountains.
Everest itself was out of sight off to the east; we hoped to see it later. To the
south-east was the hulking great lump of Gosainthain, also called Shisha
Pangma, which at 8,013 metres is one of the world's fourteen highest
peaks, all over 8,000 metres. They're all aligned along the southern side of
Tibet, stretching from Kangchenjunga in the east above Darjeeling to
Nanga Parbat in the west above Kashmir. It was difficult to believe that on
the other side of this wall were the crowded plains of India, the heat and
madness of Bangladesh, the fresh slopes of Nepal and the cool streets of
Kathmandu. We'd been there and somehow we'd forced our way past
these guards. Gosainthain was so big it was incomprehensible. A small
plume of cloud peeled off the top, other clouds were swirling up the
Himalayan valleys, yet we were in bright blue skies. It was bitterly cold.
We had no thermometer except our toes, and they suggested the temperature was sub-zero. We were puffing and panting from the climb and had
slight headaches, but the Diamox drugs we had taken to help us acclima-
tize during the past two days seemed to be working well. We had two more
days' worth of Diamox so we hoped in that time to be free from problems.
There was no sweat on our bodies because in the thin and dry air any
moisture evaporates instantly. We had a pee and set off immediately.
There was cause for concern because we'd had no food in our bellies for
over eight hours, only a couple more hours of daylight remained, and,
importantly, ahead of us, rolling away into the distance, coloured mostly
grey and brown but sometimes icy white, were the endless waves of the
world's largest, most alien plateau.

Nick. Day 20. Late Evening. Over the Lalung Le.
A flying-dirt descent pushed by the hand of the wind. It was freezing. No idea where we were going for bed. Hoping it wouldn't be a 16,000-foot bivvy. Next to a fast-sinking sun we hurtled down, losing as much height as possible. D was a bit upset when it turned out there was a second minor col. Then it really did look down all the way. The lower we got the warmer, or less cold, it became. Altitude headaches faded. At the first habitation, we stopped.

There were four single-room huts and an enclosing stone wall; all were well built, plastered smooth on the outside with mud and whitewashed. A youngish woman was outside shifting cans of water when we walked in. As we removed our hoods and started smiling, she disappeared inside and from another room some Tibetan cowboys appeared. We directed our pleas to them. They were shocked at first to see us, but like all Tibetans these guys were so confident and proud of their heritage that they wasted no time in strolling forward to look us over. They had yak-wool boots laced by leather behind their calves, with yak-skin soles beautifully sewn on to the vibrant red and green uppers. The bikes, for almost the first time in this journey, didn't seem to raise any interest, maybe because, being white and stopping in their remote home, we were so strange that our mode of transport was irrelevant. Two of them had their tussled black hair tied up in plaits bound over the top of their head with red cord. Though we didn't realize at the time, these two were Kampas, the notorious tribe of bandits who for centuries had hounded the Tibetans, and who recently put up the main resistance to the Chinese. They beckoned us into their room. We didn't know what to expect. Two other men came in with us.

Being out of the wind was luxury. We sat down on hessian sacks on the floor. It was quite small and dark, packed with junk like a cross between a rabbit-hutch and a second-hand men's shop in Brighton. Slowly our eyes adjusted to the stark white silhouette of the door and the yellow flicker of the fire in the middle of the floor. They all sat cross-legged. After too many years at office desks, our joints forced us to sit with our feet curled to one side – feet out in front, soles pointed at someone else, is considered very rude. It appeared that we were leaning back against horse harnesses, saddles, heaps of rugs and hides, sacks of flour and a couple of massive metal barrels. There were several green glass bottles filled with something and corked with rag. Each of the cowboys had his own fold of possessions tied up into a sheet: spoon, two brass cups, bits of string, some small pouches and rolls of something. Two of them had a few folded bits of paper. We slipped our panniers in behind us half-hidden under the pile of junk.

Salt tea was on the boil; we were offered small dirty lumps of yak's butter scooped out of an old tin like boot-polish to float on the tea. All Tibetans carry their own personal cups wherever they go; we drank out of the plastic containers we carried in bottle cages slung under our bottom brackets – when cycling these held bike tools, radio tapes and spare films. Out of his own possessions, one chap unrolled a bone and proceeded to carve off hunks of meat and eat them straight off his knife. These men were all strikingly handsome. They had round dark faces and enormous mischievous smiles. The two Kampas were young men, maybe the same age as us yet they seemed much more mature, as though they knew their trade and could stand alone and gallant, come hell or high water. The red braids were their mark of honour. Of the other two, the eldest was probably in his late forties with particularly rough weathered skin yet sparkling eyes. He had a wide felt hat. The fourth, scarcely more than a youth, had obviously not thought about his hair for a long time but simply left it dirty and wayward like a madman. They were a wild bunch. They had gold teeth among their yellow ones and leather thongs around their necks with red and blue beads. Their movements were very elegant and mostly directed to slipping their hands into our bags. A game ensued with Nick's snow-goggles, which we only retrieved by changing the subject to show them our map of western China – like a bored schoolboy the ring-leader put them in his pocket and didn't seem to mind, or notice, me lifting them out. The ruffian with tangled hair smiled brightly and untied a bag of tsampa: roasted barley flour, ready to eat, very powdery; you moisten a handful of it in salt tea, knead it into a ball, then pop it in your mouth. They all had heavy dark wool jackets, waist-length, fastening right over their chests, buttoned down and edged in gold or silver braid. Under the jackets were several ornaments and several shirts. One of them led me outside to show me his money-belt: thick leather with a mug-sized pouch riveted in brass and heavily embossed in silver. I didn't understand why he had led me outside to show it to me until he pushed it into my hands and folded my fingers around it. Since we had a policy of not buying souvenirs, I couldn't accept his bargain, though it was ridiculously cheap, approximately a bag of chips for a family heirloom. Then he tried to sell me a dagger. I declined. We turned to rejoin the others. Back inside, I was alarmed to see that Nick had a dagger held at his throat. Larger, more spectacular, the uses of this knife were being demonstrated in the hope of a sale. It seems that the word had got around this area of Tibet that the tourists whom these yak herders saw zooming past once a week in minibuses were frantically buying any sort of ethnic item in Lhasa. The Tibetans, new to trade, were prepared to sell anything to acquire cash. Any money is good money when you have none, but for tourists to capitalize on this innocence is rape.

As the pale glow from the door waned, a good hour passed sitting around drinking tea and eating tsampa. We were sufficiently exhausted just to stare into the fire having tried to write our diaries by the light of the paraffin lamp. They gazed proudly at us like new possessions, muttering sideways to each other, and every so often making a play for our panniers. They got their hands on our lighter and that created a lot of fun. Instant fire. Every time we leant over to hold out our hand for the return of the lighter the Kampa grinned cheesily at us. When I dipped my hand in his pocket, he whipped it out and held it crushed in his fierce grip. Finally the lighter was slipped down the inside of his under-garments. We never got it back. Luckily it turned out we never needed it on the rest of the journey – probably because what you don't have you don't miss.

By the time darkness was solid outside we were desperate for sleep. They didn't seem to think this was a good idea and pointed out to the road. However, at that time of night we had no choice so we brought out our sleeping-bags, which started again all the games of Finders Keepers. We fumbled for some small notes to show we would pay for food and bed. They happily accepted, and the leader, who had pocketed it all, held out his hand for more. We gave him a little more, and interestingly he gave us some back, so it seems they had no intention of blatantly ripping us off. Lying down was difficult in this room which was only about twelve by fifteen feet and already stacked with stores. However, we fell asleep easily, happy to slip into oblivion for several hours and, if they stole our bags or knifed us, then we'd worry about it tomorrow. In our half-slumber we noticed an hour later they'd crept away, so we woke each other, stepped outside for a minute's business under the moon, then rearranged our bags to get better beds and fell asleep again. To our dismay another hour later the rogues returned to shuffle us around while they unrolled rugs and skins for sleeping. No one could lie straight out, we were head to head or leg to shoulder, hotch-potch, curled up like kittens. Even when they seemed asleep, the bloke near me kept kicking into my knees as though to remind me not to take up too much room. Needless to say we didn't sleep too well for the next few hours. Another problem – breathlessness – became apparent. We were sleeping very high at probably 14,000 feet and we had to, as it were, remind ourselves to breathe deeply lest we forget and fail sufficiently to oxygenate our blood. Eventually we passed into dream-land but all too soon it was dawn. The man in the felt hat was setting about lighting the fire and we clipped our panniers on our bikes ready to leave while they strapped saddles and packs on to their horses. Only when we were seated on the bikes, turning the pedals to leave the corral for the start of a new adventure, did we risk turning to wave goodbye to the rogues. We need not have worried because they, too, were deeply engrossed in the work of the new day. Yesterday was a has-been.

Nick. Day 21.
Dawn looked promising in the half-light, but clouds came before the sun. It was icy cold and even clad in *all* our clothes we'd got numb feet and hands within one mile. The landscape was desolate. Brown hills maybe 1,000 feet high, desert-like valley bottom, through which crinkled the young river. We found an excuse every twenty minutes to stop. From the map, we could see that the small river, here flowing northwards, later

turned into a larger valley and then swung south to become the
headwaters of the Dudh Kosi which runs down past Everest
through Nepal. Three hours later we came into that valley and
the warmth of the sun brought us back to life. Caldo jacket and
over-trousers came off. We were getting lethargic from lack of
food. Earlier there'd been a few villages with flat-topped buildings painted red on the corners, hard up against the mountain
slopes. This main valley is painfully barren. It's nearly three
kilometres wide and the sides are brown, rounded, dry hills
nearly 3,000 feet high with sand dunes marching down their
flanks, blown by the constant westerly which is pushing us
onwards. After about forty-five kilometres this morning, we
came upon an Army barracks, and this low building. We're
eating tsampa and salt tea with yak butter again. Much as I'd
like to say how much fun it is to eat such ethnic food, and how
tasty it is, the truth is that it's the most hideously revolting
gunge that I have ever eaten. The young man next to me has
curly shoulder-length hair and a blue earring. The old woman
in charge has a finely etched brass clasp at her waist.

They haven't got any yak yoghurt here today. Dick's discovered that by going 'Moo', miming milking a cow, picking up
the imaginary bucket and drinking non-existent dairy product
with a big slurp! The old women think it's outrageously funny
and don't understand. So he's been through it all again, this
time also stirring it with a spoon, and finishing by looking
questioningly and pointing to all the different pots in turn,
doing an upturned twist of his hand which in this part of the
world seems to indicate 'What?' Their response this time is to
say 'Oma', which is presumably milk or yoghurt, and then the
old woman in wraparound skirts of floor-length red- and black-
striped blankets held up by an elaborate silver buckle said with a
sad smile, 'Mayta,' which seems to mean 'No' or 'Not now' or
similar.

Moving on, the landscape was mostly empty, though there were occasional
villages. A truck or jeep came past every half-hour or so. We stopped at
one point to attend to nature and from nowhere a knot of terribly dirty kids
in layers of patched rags appeared. The wind was behind us all the time,
excepting for fifteen disgustingly difficult kilometres across the plains at
Tingri where the wind blew so strong from the south that billows of dust
swirled across the plains. Though we leaned our bikes many degrees to the
right, like speedway riders banking round the oval track – the wrong way –
our bike tyres slipped sideways over the gravel. We were forced to pedal in
bottom gear despite being on level ground.

Our consolation was seeing Everest from the north – the back of the
highest mountain in the world. From the Tibetan side it's called Qomo-

langma Feng, 'The Mother Goddess Mountain'. It was difficult to spot at first glance because the familiar black triangle of the south-west face was on the other side. However, the king is a squat and heavy dinosaur from any angle, dominating the minions around it. A hundred kilometres away, we could also supposedly see Cho Oyu, and possibly Makalu or Lhotse, but it was a risky business trying to identify mountains we've never climbed! There was a small sense of frustration at seeing these grand peaks because they reminded us of our huge dog-leg route: we'd been forced to cycle west across Bangladesh and India along the front of the Himalayas to get to the only open border-crossing to China. Now we were cycling all the way back east along the rear of the mountains to reach Lhasa. Then, and only then, would we be able to turn north towards the Centre of the Earth.

It was a long tiring afternoon. The valley continued wide and stark. All the views were foreshortened in the thin air at this altitude, though the colours were crisp: oranges, browns, reds, purples and ochre. Bare hillsides as naked as the day they were born. It was imperceptibly downhill all the way, but being a dirt road we had to push the pedals all the time.

'It's certainly the most extreme pedalling I've ever done,' Nick said grimly, and followed it up with: 'I take my hat off to anyone who's ridden a bike over this.'

If he'd had a hat he'd have had to take it off – hardly had an hour elapsed before we cornered a shoulder of the mountain and there in front, wiggling down the centre of the road, like a drunk walking a white line, was a mountain-biker. Eamonn Wallace from Kilkenny was the epitome of the seasoned traveller. He had screwed-up eyes, sunburnt nose and tufty hair on top of the leanest, wiriest body you ever did see – like he'd lived on lettuce for a lifetime. His bike was a travelling haberdashery stacked up with countless, no doubt useful, bits and pieces. Nick and I were absolutely astonished to see him. We'd never for a moment expected another cyclist. He by contrast was so well baked that he was totally unfazed by our presence. To him it was normal but, then, whereas we'd only been out from home for a month, he'd cycled alone for two years to get here, so probably 'normal' meant something quite different to him. We three sat down in the lee of a big boulder for a good natter. Eamonn had some hilarious stories, and for half an hour the empty mountains rocked with laughter. He was generous enough to share his only packet of biscuits and some cake he had carried for a week over the passes from Nepal. In those circumstances there could not possibly have been a more selfless gesture. We cycled on, him at his pace, us speeding on at ours. It had been such a strange meeting. Ten minutes later, he'd disappeared behind us, behind a bluff. We couldn't truly remember if we'd seen him. Was he simply a figment of our imagination? When we developed the film would it show Eamonn, or would it only be a blank space?

We completed 129 kilometres on Day 21, struggling the last few kilometres, praying for some shelter, and to our dismay finding a police checkpoint. This worried us at first, but the young soldier seemed unperturbed by our bikes and merely wished to see our visa stamps. On our maps this place was meant to be an old village called Shektar Dzong, but he said it was new and called it Baiba. It was of no real concern to us what it was called. We only wanted sustenance. Having had no more than a few handfuls of tsampa and EW's gift for 200 kilometres, we seriously pigged out on pork stew and noodles from the Army's ration-house. Perched nearby were the outdoor facilities – when I dashed out at midnight, under the stars, I had a beautiful view of Everest. It seems many travellers overnight here, and we were joined by two Danish girls, Meta and Marion, trekking from Tingri to the Everest Base Camp beyond Rongbuk Monastery. In deference to the lightness of our gear, they left behind both toothbrushes and one towel. Shektar Dzong marks the departure from the desolate valley we'd followed all yesterday and the start of the fifty-kilometre climb up to and over the Jia Tsuo La to reach the Brahmaputra valley which is relatively densely populated – relative to the valley we'd been in, the Sahara Desert is densely populated!

Nick. Day 22. Jia Tsuo La.

I have to write now, in the exposure at the top, lest the extremities of the moment slip by for ever. After breakfast of biscuits and tinned mandarins, we set off up the hill at 12.30 p.m. having spent a couple of pleasant hours cutting zips off anoraks and modifying panniers to save a few ounces. Almost immediately things got difficult. The road had been heavily corrugated by speeding trucks. The worst we've been on. A long steep pass for maybe fifty kilometres. Both have headaches and sore guts from the rare meal last night. The jolting of corrugations – spaced at nine-inch intervals – is absolute purgatory. There was a hut and outside on a chain a huge dog that roared and barked. D fell asleep while the man got some water. Later we had a splendid view of Everest proud above all else. We wanted a photo of it but each time we looked it seemed the view would be even better from higher up, then when we were eventually ready Everest had disappeared for ever. Sometimes the corrugations changed to large loose cobbles like big ball-bearings that have us slipping, sliding and swearing on the road. We were reduced to walking pace – sought any excuse to pause: drink some water to soften parched tongues, take thermal top off, adjust snow-goggles, put gloves on, have a pee, simply take a deep breath of the thin sharp air. We have to stop to give our pounding brains a rest. This is the most cerebrally taxing stuff we've come up against. Alan Deadman would have loved it. He's a friend from Oxford who is Sergeant in Charge of the Stolen Cycle Squad and a keen time-triallist. Etched into the handlebars of his training bike, so it stares him in the eye each time he crouches to pump the pedals, is the motto 'No pain, no gain'.

After the atrocious climb through large valleys, we came out more quickly than we'd anticipated on to the summit of the Jia Tsuo La where there were small rounded knolls similar to the ones we'd seen two days ago on the top of the Lalung Le at 5,214 metres. The Jia Tsuo La was a similar height; the sign at the top said 5,220 metres, yet we had a note from a map of EW's which had it at 5,252 metres; either way it was well over 17,000 feet. Amazingly, hardly 100 metres from the summit cairn and prayer flags was a man all alone nonchalantly digging some sort of square trench in the knobbly turf. One kilometre back we had seen some yaks across the slopes and some structures like summer shelters. What made it particularly striking was that for the last fifteen kilometres, maybe 1,500 feet of climbing, there had been big snow patches on the slopes. To compound our astonishment, we free-wheeled off the smooth initial slopes of the other side, barely two or three kilometres, losing very little height, and there, on a facing slope, was a tightly clustered village of dark stone houses with plumes of smoke and some children playing outside. It must have been 16,000 feet above sea-level. I'd always thought that a farm at 15,000 feet on the slopes of Cotopaxi in Ecuador nearly on the equator was the highest habitation in the world, but here they're even more extreme!

After the open upper slopes, the road wound down into a tight cleft too narrow for the sun to penetrate. Then for twenty exhilarating kilometres of steep descent the road fell away in front of us under black cliffs and we were twisting and turning on the gravel track, snapping our brakes on and off, following every bend of the mountain torrent as it ripped down the ravine. The devil-dark gorge debouched us into the glorious humanity of the flat agricultural expanses of the Brahmaputra river valley. Sparkling-white villages and bright-green copses of trees were dotted every kilometre across the fields. Thin grey telegraph wires stretched across the plains, and with relief we joined the main east–west road of Tibet. This leads from Lhasa all the way to Kailash and eventually on towards Kashgar, running along the north of the Himalayas, up this massive ten-to-fifteen-kilometre-wide valley. It marked a significant step in our journey. The river here in Tibet is strictly called the Yarlung Tsangpo Jiang, but higher up near its source at Mount Kailash, where also originate the Indus and the Ganges, it's got the Chinese name Maquan He. Only where it reaches the eastern end of the Himalayas and turns south is it officially called the Brahmaputra, and even then it seems quickly to change its name to the Dihang and last of all the Jamuna before it joins the Ganges near Dhaka where we crossed it seventeen days before.

Dick. Day 22. Brahmaputra Valley.
All around here are pleasant rural scenes – ploughing, harrow-ing, sowing; in some fields fine new shoots push through the

soil. The farmers in the fields, men and women, are all in heavy black and red clothes. Yaks and oxen do the work while the men sing to them. The animals trot briskly along the furrows jangling their bells, flicking the crimson plumes on their horns like African fly-whisks and sending great clouds of dust in the air.

There had been very little traffic south of here. Now, on the main road, vehicles go past ten or twenty per hour. They put us off our track, slowing us for a moment then enveloping us in another cloud of dust which blinds and stifles us.

We stopped for a few minutes to photograph and tape some farming, but a large crowd gathered quickly then started tugging at our bikes and clothes. They got very aggressive. It seemed that, although we thought we were getting on well with the locals, we really didn't have any idea what upset or excited them. A small man held my wrist with an iron grip. It was extremely frightening, we were near panic, thinking they wanted us to hand out all our possessions. Then, to get them off us, I raised the camera, and instantly they were calmed. All they had wanted was for us to take away a photo of them. Tibetans seem particularly boisterous and jolly, and in spite of their tough life, or because of it, they enjoy high spirits and high jinks.

We spent the night in Lhatse, which was a sizeable town, the biggest we'd seen in China, and nearly as big as Gretna Green. It had many Han Chinese inhabitants diluting the original Tibetan villagers. It must be strange for the new Han 'immigrants' who've grown up on the fertile low-altitude plains and hills of eastern China. That's often called mainland China, in contrast to the isolated islands of humanity in Tibet and the Gobi. Lhatse also had proper streets, some of them tree-lined, telegraph-wires all around town and a proper hotel barracks for truck drivers and passengers. The town was well organized, clean and friendly. The hotel rooms all had numbers and electricity, glass in the windows and doors which fitted. There was clean linen and a clean towel for each of us, though the floor was clay. We shared with a Chinese businessman in a suit going to Nepal. The only disturbance was noise pollution: my pet hate. Loud-speakers around town blasted out music and advice continuously. We tucked into delicious fried-egg soup with bean shoots and Tibetan fungus followed by a meat, green bean and green pepper stir-fry. The Chinese certainly know how to cook. Nick proclaimed it 'the best food ever' – but, then, nearly all the food we had was that. Many youths came into the café for the evening; they set about serious drinking, their preference being a whitish fluid looking like chang, the Nepalese beer made of fermented grain. Being curious I ordered some 'matechita pinga'. What a surprise when I tasted it – sweet milk tea!

Nick. Day 22. Lhatse.

It's just about sunk in that we're actually in Tibet. The delayed reaction is, I think, partly because I never expected to make it this far this safely; partly because the change of culture and geography across the Himalayas has been so dramatic, so sudden that it's been like watching a movie of ourselves passing through this alien landscape rather than actually feeling it at first hand. Maybe the shock of the new has been so great that I've subconsciously suspended for a while that emotional involvement that comes with travel. Like all new journeys this is the most exciting of my life. Looking back over the last twenty or so days, Bangladesh, India and Nepal seem now like a rather tame cycling holiday. I had a thrilling image today: racing down the ravine; dirt road and bends, two clean bicycles and silver-jacketed figures leaning and speeding in tandem. It's the very first mental picture I had of this trip and it was like looking back to re-live a perfect anticipation. Aside from the minute-by-minute treasures we find along the road – the people, their land – it's fantastic to travel through such a 'tough' part of the world with such minimal gear. The few other travellers we've met are (pleasingly) amazed by our tiny bags.

For the next two days of the expedition, Days 23 and 24, we followed the Brahmaputra valley westwards to the city of Xigatse. Eventually we'd be able to branch off north to Lhasa, which is fifty kilometres up a tributary valley about 300 kilometres west of Lhatse. However, it wasn't quite as simple as just following the big river for 300 kilometres then turning left, because the two maps we had, one being the southern half of our route torn from Bartholomew's map of the Indian subcontinent, the other being the northern half of our route torn from Hildebrandt's map of China, overlapped in this area and they both showed different roads. We could either turn south halfway to Lhasa at Xigatse and hit the city of Gyangtse which Younghusband had captured and turned into a British trading post, then sweep around past the tourist attraction of Lake Turquoise and once more regain the Brahmaputra to cross it close to Lhasa, or we could press on past Xigatse and some distance further turn north over the big river and complete a loop up over high mountain-passes, sweeping around and entering Lhasa from the north. Both seemed much longer than straight along the main valley, yet there was no road marked on this obvious route. Why was that?

We had to get to Xigatse first where we might get some more information that would help us decide between the three possibilities, so we knuckled under and rode hard all day. We stopped once for food but the old lady, who incidentally was charmingly friendly and introduced us to all her family and a few others, offered only salt tea and tsampa. Seeing Nick's hesitation she produced sugar mixed into hot water. Later we crossed a 4,600-metre pass literally racing each other in our enthusiasm. It was a good day. The sun was sharp, the air crisp, bold bare slopes all around us, farmers with yaks in the fields below. The only real incident was a puncture, my first since Patenga Point. Then we got caught by the dark, thirty kilometres short of Xigatse after a 124-kilometre day. It was a beautiful clear dry night. Nick, the world expert in free camp-sites, found a rock gully. We smoothed the gravel and lay down our bags. There was scarcely time to worry about dogs, wolves and brigands before we were fast asleep. And then in a flash it was dawn.

We pedalled thirty hungry kilometres to Xigatse for breakfast at 11 a.m. in a Chinese café. This is the second-biggest city in Tibet, and has a famous monastery stretching like a gold and red card-house in many steps up the mountain-face overlooking town. It's one of the few not destroyed by the Red Army in the fifties. At one time there were several thousand monks. The number dropped to a couple of hundred twenty years ago, but now, thanks to the new policy of enlightenment, the numbers are increasing. This was no doubt good news for the café where we were, because not only were several young Buddhist scholars spending their pocket-money on tea and a game strikingly like the shove-ha'penny we'd seen in the chai house in Bhainse in lower Nepal but also it brought tourists and all their money to town. We talked to two laid-back, long-haired American girls but it was difficult for us two, bent on the earnest reality of our race, to tune into their metaphysical dilemmas about the meaning of life.

The Gyangtse route was scrapped on the grounds that it was the longest of the three routes to Lhasa, although all passenger traffic uses it. Leaving until later the decision on which of the other two routes to take, we cycled out of Xigatse on the metalled city roads, along the central boulevard with ornamental flower-beds and past two-storey office blocks and department stores. Market stalls lined the streets. On the outskirts we passed a municipal refuse-dump, then green fields, and soon were back into the Brahmaputra Valley proper with a patchwork of small fields dusted green covering the floor where they could be irrigated. The road lay down the south side of this and beyond it nothing except bare diluvian rock-slopes in subdued pastel colours, cracked by the cold, beaten by the wind and strewn with sand dunes blowing from west to east along the valley and clinging like barnacles on to the sides of the mountains.

The road we followed was clearly meant to be a main road: it was well smoothed, and all undulations were filled in with sand and gravel, but there was hardly any traffic on it. For three hours there was no traffic. Despite the strong wind behind our backs, it was extremely heavy pedalling because our wheels sank one or two inches into the dry sand all the way. It was like riding through a bowl of semolina. In places crescent-shaped barchan dunes, blown by the wind at a few metres per week, had slid across the road leaving a particularly sandy trail and we, for almost the first time on our 'Journey to the Centre of the Earth', had to walk. This was our first chance to enjoy the open desolation on the plateau:

we were able to feel, as Peter Hopkirk says, 'Trespassers on the Roof of the World'. We weren't the first to come this way because beside us, marching down the valley, were funny clay pillars. Later we found out they were the clay telegraph poles erected seventy years before to link Younghusband's Gyangtse to Lhasa. On the Plateau there is no wood for poles.

Eighty kilometres past Xigatse, in the late evening, we reached the ferry-crossing for the northern route, the second of the three possibilities to Lhasa. The big blue river was squashed in between two mountain shoulders and a hawser stretched across the narrowest point. Attached to this was a metal pontoon big enough for a couple of vehicles at a time. On our side was a dirty little set of houses and some frighteningly boisterous children who came running around laughing and shouting in their ragged clothes with mucus oozing from their nostrils, yellow tear-sap caked on their eyes and nodules of tsampa and grime stuck around their mouths. Their hands and hair were as filthy as the soles of their feet. I don't know if they ever washed or changed their clothes. It didn't look like it. They were no different from many other children we saw in southern Tibet. I do wonder if, at the altitude they live, they are forbidden to blow their noses in case they damage the nasal membranes. Nick and I both were having problems with nose-bleeds after blowing our noses.

The attitude of the men was as off-putting as the hygiene of the children. They said they needed to look in our bags, and told us firstly we couldn't go further and secondly there was no food or bed for us in their village. We took no time to decide against pausing a moment longer in this unsavoury village to ask about a route straight down the valley. In order to find some peace, we forked out several yuan to get them to ferry us quickly over the river. The men were at first unwilling – they didn't want to start the engines up unless they had two vehicles. We showed more money. When we got to the other side the ferry-driver seemed so pleased that he wanted us to stay on board and come back with him so that we could do it again. We wanted otherwise – and scooted.

On the north side of Detsukar Ferry, two girls in their late teens had a makeshift chai stall pegged into the hillside where the truckies stopped to wait for the ferry. They wore heavy cumbersome-looking black skirts and shirts topped off with a colourfully striped red, green, blue and black shawl worn like an apron. So many layers of clothes that we wondered how they moved. They lived in a little green canvas tent where they also kept their stores. Customers sat on upturned boxes under a white tarpaulin which gave shade from the sun. It was a pleasant place to sip tea and local beer in the late evening as the sun turned the surrounding high mountains red. That, a bowl of tsampa, and a big blob of rancid yak butter were supper. We got four kilometres up the stony road leading to the big passes over to Lhasa and then we needed bed. Nick did his gully trick again and sussed out a dry stream-bed 100 feet above the road, out of sight of the village opposite. We quickly laid out jackets to lie on, and bags to lie in, as the light faded away.

We woke early, keen to blast on to Lhasa. At the thought of those two big passes on the northern route I balked. An hour was lost discussing the relative merits of the certainty of 170 kilometres of the northern route, versus the 80–100 kilometres of unpredictability straight down the Brahmaputra. Nick liked the purity of the *direttissimo* but pointed out that by the northern route Lhasa should only be a day away – even if it would be hard work. Along the unexplored backwaters of the Brahmaputra, we wouldn't know if the river would be too twisty, too rocky, or too deep in sand for vehicles. However, logic eluded me and, fearing the heights – being stubborn and opinionated (sometimes) – I forced the decision to go into the unknown. I feel Nick's view at the time was that it was better that we were both committed to whatever we chose rather than having one of us sourly dragging his heels. Much later, when this distasteful episode was all but forgotten – as forgotten as a crucial incident can be – he told me that this was where for him all the team-work, built up since 30 January, self-destructed. In his eyes we were both then at odds and our whole joint commitment had to be rebuilt. Perhaps because I forced the vote, I felt no fracture.

To start the day, we back tracked four kilometres to Detsukar Ferry and got across with no problems. We ignored any possibility of getting breakfast and rode straight off the pontoon and round the corner out of the village without a glance sideways at the horrible children. We intended to pedal hard and silently to get some miles behind us before the first stop. The trail became very rough and twisty. We had to strip off our early-morning clothes leaving only salopets and cutaway T-shirts, plus of course snow-goggles for our eyes and balaclavas for our foreheads. The wide alluvial plains of yesterday had vanished completely and we cycled along a tortuous track carved into the mountainside with the big river constricted and foaming several hundred feet below us.

The track got worse. I started to get very worried that I'd led Nick off on a wild-goose chase into a dead-end valley and that we might yet have to backtrack out the way we came in. There were a couple of possible alternative side-trails, but none better than the one we were on. There were a few farms, and the first farmers seemed to think that we should go back the way we came to Detsukar Ferry to get to Lhasa. After a while our route seemed to be leading us up a side-valley. There appeared no way to get around the steep headlands easily to stay close to the Brahmaputra, and we wondered if the track was going to lead up over a 3,000-foot shoulder in this massive topography and back down to the river. Unfortunately it continued up the tributary. A farmer walking a herd of sheep seemed to indicate that the route to Lhasa was indeed up this small valley. Slowly it dawned on us that we'd been side-tracked up this river. It was marked on the map as the Rong Chu. It led all the way up to Turquoise Lake where we would be able to rejoin the main transport route which had come via Gyangtse – the route we had abandoned two days before. I started my apologies to Nick and made them especially profuse since there were no villages marked up here – and hence no food. Nick wasn't pleased. However, I did point out that the valley was only about thirty kilometres long in a straight line so we had time to get out today and find some food. Nick was even less pleased.

The track didn't improve; in fact because it was now going uphill it got worse. There had been absolutely no other road-users all morning except yaks and sheep going to pasture, so it was an amusing relief when we spotted a cyclist ahead. As we caught up with him we could see he was wearing a blue Mao cap and blue suit. He indicated he'd been to a farm down below to collect something in the can strapped on the back of his bone-shaker – a model called a 'Flying Pigeon'. With him we rode the level bits and walked the steep ones. He had the best news we'd heard all day. He promised there was food ahead. Nick managed a smile! We couldn't wait to find where or what, thinking that in this empty valley it could only be tsampa, but to our great surprise and delight he was heading for a quite developed town, Rinbung Dzong, not marked on any maps yet possessing at least two streets, a market-place and a large hydroelectric scheme – not large by European standards but big enough for some pipes to be seen on the hillside and to have two low huts as control houses supplying electricity to town. Our friend directed us to the café. We arrived at 2.30 p.m., having had no food all day. We ate heartily. The chai house proprietor was a chubby middle-aged Chinaman supervising his wife, daughters and granny, who prepared the food before he himself frizzled and tossed up the stir-fry, then dished it up with a flourish on to our plates and laid brightly painted chop sticks on the table. Everyone sat down to watch us eat. When we'd finished, the boss wrote on lots of little scraps of paper and laid one beside each bowl, then presented a slightly larger piece with the total bill – twenty-two yuan (about five pounds).

Two hours slipped away in Rinbung Dzong: writing diaries, studying the maps to see where we'd gone wrong or simply gazing into space telling ourselves how lucky we were. We were both well and happy when we set out to continue our odyssey up the Rong Chu. It was a nice day. We cycled for a while in a more open valley with green fields. There were small trees by the track and dry-stone walls, the spitting image of my own dear Cumbrian countryside. We passed a train of donkeys laden with thorn branches and tinkling with bells. Soon we entered a tight gorge. Then it opened out to give a thin green strip by the bubbling river where sheep were grazing. Likewise the sky was overcast. We were pedalling all the time over a poor-quality farm track in our bottom two gears. There were more small fields looking prettier and more fertile than any we'd seen elsewhere in Tibet. Then there were castle-like villages built above us on rock spires. All the time the clouds grew thicker and darker ahead. The breeze became cooler. It began to rain lightly. We clothed up fully and pressed on hoping to reach Turquoise Lake. Each time we rounded a corner of the valley, we hoped to see it all flatten out. Each time, however, a new shoulder would be hemming us in. We felt increasingly like mice stuck in a maze: someone above could see where we were, but we couldn't. We knew our prison on a map of the world, we knew where we were on a map of China, but we didn't know where we were in the windings of this valley. It got colder and the wind gusted down on us. We adjusted balaclavas, gloves, leggings, and did our hoods up tight. We were pedalling in bottom gear hoping to grind ourselves out of this ghastly mess. The mountainsides were all the time steep on both sides. There was no sensation of being able to see anything beyond our tiny enclosed world. All we could do was follow each twist and turn hoping to escape before too long. Though we saw occasional buildings and walls, there were no people with whom to share our misery. It was becoming more and more of a dungeon. Then it started snowing, at first gently then more heavily like damp Christmas snow. Dusk was coming on. We started looking for shelter for the night. Twice we saw small farms on the far side of the stream about 100 metres from us, but to save the detour we pressed on promising ourselves that soon we would find a place on our side. It never came – but darkness did.

Snow fell thickly on the night of Day 25. We were some part of the way up the Rong Chu, having left the Brahmaputra and Rinbung Dzong behind yet not having reached Turquoise Lake. We didn't really know where we were, not that it mattered very much as we couldn't go on. It got dark very quickly. The clouds closed in and mist came down. We could no longer stay on the bikes. We were forced to stumble along the very rough trail searching for any sort of shelter. Nick spotted a tiny rock overhang, maybe two feet off the ground, three feet deep and rising an extra foot inside its roof. We bent to examine it in the darkness. It would be our haven for the night. We would have to lie tight side by side, parallel to the rock. Nick set about finding rocks to build up a small stone wall keeping out the worst of the wind and snow. I got water from the stream and added Puritabs to make it ready for drinking – that would be our supper. We drew straws for sleeping position, I lost and got the outside. I reached in on all fours to feel for and flick out dried grass, insects and animal dung. It was so tight that only one of us at a time could sort our gear. My sleeping-bag was laid on my wind-proof jacket and trousers. With my gloves pulled over my toes, I slipped into my bag. A cold wind blew on my cheek. Nick passed in all his gear, then lay half outside the cave, half on me, to prepare his bed. When he had squirmed into his bag we could start to finalize our positions for the night. My feet were hooked into a forked rock and my head was wedged into the narrowest part of the cave where it plunged to the ground, leaving only one inch breathing-space above my nose. Cold rock touched my forehead. It was extremely claustrophobic. I had tucked my shoes and pannier-bags under me to stop me rolling down on Nick. He was jammed with shoulders between my hips and the rock wall. Nick's feet stuck past my forked rock into the cold 'outside world'. Neither of us could move without the greatest effort. Luckily the floor was earth so our hips weren't too painful, but we each needed to shift every

The start at noon on Day 1 by the Mouths of the Ganges

Vying for roadspace with waves of rickshaws in Comilla

Bangladesh is one of the most densely populated countries in the world

*Goalundo Ghat, Day 4, on the west bank of the Ganges,
there were only four punctures on the entire journey*

Dick drinking 'daab' – green coconuts. Note use of balaclava as sun visor

The odyssey across the Ganges from the ferry to Monghyr Ghat: rush-hour in Bihar State

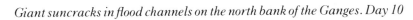

Giant suncracks in flood channels on the north bank of the Ganges. Day 10

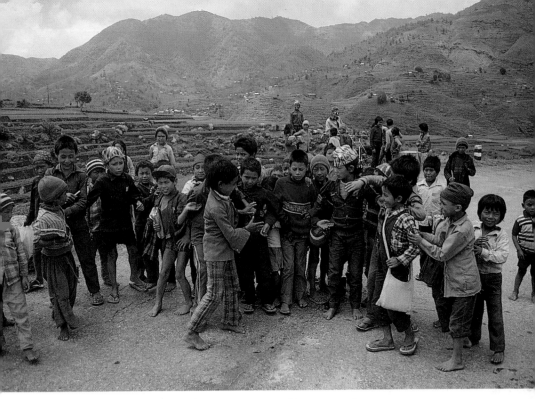

*These Nepalese children came rushing across the terraces
to get their picture taken*

Nick on Day 13 near the top of Simbanjyarg Pass in Nepal

Nepal's original green forest is dotted with terraces and bright specks of farm roofs

The Chinese had opened the road through the Himalayas barely two months before we crossed

Tattered prayer flags in the wind on the summit of the Lalung Le at 5100 m (17,000 ft) in the late afternoon on Day 21

Tibetan farmworkers between Lhatse and Xigatse, 11,000 ft above sea-level

In the Brahmaputra Valley; barchan dunes pushed westwards by the wind

Stirfry, noodles and omelette in Rinbung Dzong

The second of the uncomfortable cold caves where we survived the night of the 25th day in the Rong Chu valley

The miller on the morning of Day 26

Whiteout at Turquoise Lake; "The most miserably cold day's cycling in our lives"

The Potala Palace, seen from the roof of the Jokhang in the centre of Lhasa

Tibetan yak nomads somewhere between Damxung and Laqudiqu

The longest day's cycling in northern Tibet was 212km

A moment's respite in bright sun at 17,000 ft just below the summit of the Tanggula

Golmud market

Nick on the Qaidam Pendi, lost in a freak dust storm

Xing-Xing-Xia, for centuries a major border post on the Silk Road

Nick on Day 43. The dirt tracks which wandered over the sands of the Gobi almost defeated us

The infrequent trucks on the Silk Road always stopped to offer water

Waking on Day 44 after a night in the emptiness of the Gobi Desert

The sum total of our bike tool kit. Note holes drilled in spanner and spoke key sawn in half. Map of Urumqi, Dsungarei and Taklamakan underneath

hour. Our tiny digital watch was not luminous. We had no torch. The Kampas had nicked our lighter. We could only judge the time of night by our senses; by the change of the wind, by the tiredness in our heads, by the snow and the rain and the glow in the sky.

It was a long night and I was very frightened. Being so close to the sub-zero weather outside, and not having had any food, made us fearful. Hypothermia and exposure threatened. The darkness made me shiver. Snow fell lightly on my sleeping-bag. At first I couldn't sleep. I was locked in my channel beside Nick and I thought of grub – nothing special – all I wanted was fish and chips, then I decided I only wanted tsampa and salt tea. After a while I was so tired, I dozed fitfully. I dreamt I was stuck down a hole with my head jammed into a crevice. I shivered and prayed for dawn. I slept fitfully. It was terrible. I had the second-worst nightmare of my life: I was doing cyclo-cross with my dear brother Ados – he went racing ahead then I saw him hit a rock and go spinning in the air to come down choking blood. I woke in a cold sweat. Eventually it grew light and we agreed we could rise. Joyfully we crawled out into the cold snow, thankful to be alive. We packed our bikes and set off gaily to stop at the first house for breakfast. It was still quite dark, not yet fully light enough to cycle, but we were happy to walk a short while over this rough ground to warm up. Our footprints and bike wheels left a dark trail through the snow. The mist was low and the air heavy with moisture.

Nick. Day 26. Very early. Valley of the Rong Chu.
It was a creepy walk full of shadows. Ethereal mountains in half-light. Mist close and damp. Gloom surrounded us. A lot of snow had fallen while we'd been in the cave. The ghostly curve of the valley cocooned us. No wind, no noise. Stepping-stones on streams. Suddenly huge black animals were coming at us barking and howling. D yelled: 'Are they wolves?' I didn't know. Ten or fifteen. Demented black beasts charging us. Dark shapes from all sides, across the walls, across the snowy fields. D asked: 'What do we do?' I said: 'Pack tight, walk slow. We'll look like a bigger animal. Slowly, bikes outside: between them and us.' They came to within a few feet, from all directions, lunging at us. The noise was deafening. It was like trying to step through a nightmare.

The swoon of relief when the dogs retreated left me in need of a sit-down and rest to recover from the burnt-up adrenalin. Equally we needed to move on in case they came again. Common sense ruled and we plodded on in semi-darkness. Why did it not seem to be getting lighter? We tiptoed past two more hamlets terrified of waking the dogs. A good half-hour elapsed and we walked two or three kilometres before we realized that it was not the light of dawn. It was the glow of the full moon. Dimly I remembered that on the loo at Shektar Dzong in view of Everest it had been almost full moon. We looked up and scanned the clouds. Sure enough, there almost vertically up above us was a faintly brighter glow shining through. It was halfway through its arc but it would not be dawn for several hours. Tired and hungry, we were faced with the decision as to whether to walk on through the night and risk suffering more serious dog-attacks, or to find a new bivouac hole. Cold though it was, we decided on the latter.

There was a cleft like a half-cave in a tall chalk cliff. Tens of years of travellers had scratched away to make a seat carved tight to fit a small Tibetan body. Nick sat upright in his sleeping-bag, I lay at his feet half-in half-out of the cleft, and we joked: 'Let's hope this is nearly half as much fun as the last cave.' Snow was falling gently on the foot of my sleeping-bag because I couldn't hook my legs in close enough. To shorten the night we spent a lot of time getting our sleeping-bags positioned just right and adjusting our clothes for maximum efficiency. At one point I was busily adjusting my draw-strings to get ready to go to sleep then suddenly I looked up and found it was wonderful dawn. The last few hours of night had passed in an instant. I'd been so tired because of yesterday's efforts and the night's adrenalin that I'd slept without moving a muscle.

At dawn a man and his dog trudged through the snow. He was carrying a huge wooden plough over his shoulder. Seeing us dozing in the cleft, he stopped in shock and stared fully fifteen minutes without resting his burden while we got up, shook the snow off our sleeping-bags, took a photo, packed our panniers and left. Seeing this man in the cool morning light brought back a vague recollection of an incident during the night. It seemed at the time so much like fantasy that I wondered if I had simply imagined it. Just before we reached the cleft, when trudging morbidly through the dark, we thought we heard a bell. Coming the other way from out of the gloom shuffled an old Tibetan. He was leading his horse, which was head down, plodding into the mist. The man had yak-skin boots and a huge overcoat. Snow was stuck all down his front. His step didn't falter for a moment. We saluted each other cautiously, gave each other a wide berth and disappeared like comets on our own ways into the night.

Breakfast was paramount in our thoughts. We'd have to try to find food at the first place we came to. We set off leaving the man with his plough and dog behind. It was impossible to ride because the stony path was slippery and covered in snow. We walked briskly, mostly pushing our bikes but sometimes lifting them on to our shoulders for tricky stream-crossings. The first thing we saw was twenty minutes after setting out when we came upon a small windowless stone hut. It was clearly a grain mill because a stream had been channelled to flow under one side. It had no windows, we saw no smoke. Probably there was no one there. We yelled 'Hello' a couple of times, then to our relief a weathered face poked out of the door. He stepped forward with toothless grin and black woollen cloak like a film extra on *Planet of the Apes*. A minute passed. Another came out; fuzzed white hair, weather-lined face and draped in bundles of clothes. They both had yak-skin boots with typical red and green uppers. Then a little man with bright red nose and wide felt hat, and then a young strong man in green cotton jacket with flat Mao cap. All four at first were stony-faced then each in turn broke into a smile. To my simple question 'Cha?' there was an immediate welcoming beckon.

That breakfast in the millers' hut was a magical moment to be savoured for the rest of our lives. The food wasn't very special – indeed, it was exceedingly basic – yet that was part of its charm. The men were friendly and happy. Their hut was absolutely simple: a huge stone grind-wheel in one half whirring away, driven by the stream underneath, grinding the roasted barley grains which trickled from a rattling wicker hopper above. In the other half, a small glowing yak-dung fire in the middle of the floor. Bags and sacks around the walls and a scintillating shaft of sunlight slicing in through the smoke-hole in the roof. No windows, door closed to keep out the cold. We sat cross-legged on the floor. The strength of the occasion was our meeting, all six of us, together in adversity. They were there for a livelihood; the weather, they knew, was often bad. We were there by choice; the weather had caught us out. Together we all huddled into this little haven of warmth and sustenance. They will never understand our motives, we will never comprehend the reality of their lives.

The food they gave us (they absolutely refused payment) was the first food since the Chinese slap-up stir-fry in Rinbung Dzong. We had salt tea dished out of a huge aluminium vat boiling over the fire and topped up regularly with jerrycans of water. We had handfuls of tsampa to eat and the luxury of a knob of yak butter scraped out of one of their personal little tins. I think they had already had their meal because they didn't fully join in but just snacked occasionally, scooping up three fingerfuls of flour, bringing it to within a few inches of their mouth then throwing it in dry to be followed by a sip of tea. Every so often the eldest man, he who wore the wide felt hat, went to sweep up into sacks the tsampa flour which spun out from the wheel. The entire room – floor, walls, sacks, bags, people, even the shaft of light – shimmered in flour dust.

Refreshed, revived, with last night's fears forgotten, we decided it had to be time to move on. They would have let us stay, and equally they were happy to come and wave us off. They had patience and indicated their work could wait, yet they had no intention of imposing themselves on us. They had all of the timelessness of the Tibetan Plateau, and with timelessness a permanence and presence exceeding by far the transience of our busy rushing selves.

SIX

Lhasa and the Tourist Trade

The millers' breakfast lifted our spirits and we left with re-charged batteries, determined to make good progress. Feeling buoyant, we could take an overview of the situation. We would soon be out of the rough, winding valley and back on to a proper direct road. Lhasa and all its amenities would then be within our grasp, for we would have almost wriggled out of the bottle-neck in the route which I had forced upon us the day before. However, since the cumulative distance to date was only 2,230 kilometres, we both secretly knew that our target 100 kilometres per day was irretrievably slipping away. At this stage that target didn't seem particularly important because mere progress and survival were success enough. For the next 1,000 to 2,000 kilometres across the vast northern expanses of the Tibetan plateau, we would be hard-pushed for food and shelter every day. We hoped that maybe down on the Silk Road we'd catch up some time. However, there was a lot of emptiness before we got anywhere near the Gobi Desert. We were not yet at Lhasa.

Nick. Day 26. Morning. Turquoise Lake.
Day 26 is one of exquisite hardship. I don't remember how long we slithered over snowy rocks longing to find this lake. The trail was indefinable beneath the white. Maybe three hours before the small valley of the Rong Chu began to open out. Unbelievably a man with a yak was ploughing through several inches of snow. Then at long last, at right angles to our valley, a road – the main Gyangtse to Lhasa road, the southern of the three routes to Lhasa. Dick fell on his knees in the mud and kissed it. It marked our return to safety. We set off thinking we might make Lhasa today, but the shock of the first kilometre-post, 129 kilometres, stunned us both to silence. Added to that, there's a big pass, the Kamba La, in the way. Moreover, our miseries are compounded because the road is reduced to a gritty quagmire churned up by vehicles which spray us as they pass. Sticky mud cements itself all over our frames, chainsets and bodies. We

have quickly got soaked and cold. It is utterly, utterly grim.

I am monumentally hacked off at the thought of not making Lhasa today – we certainly would have done if we'd gone by the northern route. I didn't mind the tons of extra miles, cave-sleeping, wolves, extra climbing and all that. What really churns my insides is the way the initial decision was forced by Dick on that road after the bivouac by Detsukar Ferry. It's the principle not the result. However, the rocky Rong Chu has provided stacks of adventure which will be 'benchmarks' for a long time to come. So no regrets on that score.

We skirted any discussion of route choices and diverted our attention to the scenery. The road skirted what the tourists call Turquoise Lake, which like all lakes at high altitude beautifully picks up and intensifies the colours of the sky. And like all treasures it has its own name. It is Yamdrok Yamtso, Tibet's third-largest lake, an amoebic ingot of water turning and folding itself into all the shoulders of mountain and oozing up the valleys like mercury glistening on the palm of your hand. Above the shining lake, rounded hillslopes were dusted in snow. Though the sun tried to break through, as it does on a New Year's morning over Loch Cluanie, we never saw the full view because low clouds scooted around, obscuring the hills and dumping heavy showers on our heads. Lhasa lay not too far ahead. We were within reach of its tentacles of commerce.

Much of Tibet is today accessible to trade; we saw an increasing proportion of the men wearing the blue caps and Mao suits adopted after the Revolution. We stopped at a farmstead to get some more food, and once past the guard dogs we found the family, on a one-to-one basis, extremely friendly. Traditional salt tea and tsampa were the only food available ('Oh no. Not again,' said Nick) yet their modernization showed in the large radio, the numerous lightweight pots and pans, fancy torches and machine-made table-cloths. Further on we were excited to see a mini-bus of tourists coming down the road. They clearly saw us because all faces turned to look, but no one waved or smiled. They stared agog, with exactly the same gaze as Bengali boys in chai houses. Did they think we were odd? Maybe they thought all tourists were like them: cushioned in warmth and air-conditioning behind glass windows, looking out at a film of Tibet. The little children further up the road thought otherwise. They knew we were real, and they pelted us with snowballs. It took us by surprise and sent a wave of bristles rushing up our spines, so we rose up out of the saddles and raced away from their village as quickly as possible. These locals were bold and innocently aggressive, not amazed or cowed by foreigners, but ready to make fun of them – and why not? After all, it is, I presume, contact with foreigners which has created this atmosphere.

It was a long hard day's cycling, seemingly made harder by the proximity to Lhasa and the yearning for a decent rest and a bit of luxury. The weather tried its best to beat us down. The road was diabolical. A heavily laden local bus went past, and to our surprise we saw a mountain-bike complete with smart new panniers strapped on top. 'That's the way a mountain-bike does Tibet,' I said forlornly as we changed down one gear on our trusty 753 racers. On one occasion we had to dismount and push through the sludge. A fair wind got up across the open lake surface, seemingly climbing fresh out of a deep-freeze and intent on sliding down our necks. Off and on all day we had numb feet and frozen fingers. It was the damp cold which chills you to the marrow. An extremely depressing day of cycling. Later I wrote that we had 'struggled through almost the worst day of pedalling in our lives'.

Nick. Day 26. Bottom of Kamba La.

It took several miserable hours to get to the other end of Yamdrok Yamtso. The Kamba La rises above the lake as a smooth mountain slope with the road zigzagging high to a ridge. I am so sleepy and desperate for food. D stopped a truck to ask where we might get food. A chinless spindly youth with specs pointed a short distance off the road to a group of tents. Here we had the third overwhelmingly generous reception of the day. Under a pyramid of green canvas were three beds and maybe six or so men in working clothes and big boots. Han Chinese from a drilling site nearby. The 'boss', a laughing man with a green forage cap, poured us jam jars of clear sweet tea. Each jar had plastic net webbing for insulation and its own lid to keep in the heat. The boss patted his stomach enquiringly. My head nodded so vigorously it nearly fell off. Someone went and got four packets of dried noodles; they were tipped in with hot water from a Thermos flask decorated with gaudy red flowers, jungle foliage and birds. We slurped in earnest. My noodles disappeared so quickly that the boss went out with a big smile to get some more.

Most of the Han Chinese we meet are busting to please – maybe because for them this is an unpopular posting. They can sympathize with that 'strange land' vulnerability. Tibetans divide, on the basis of their attitudes, into several groups. In ones or twos out in the wildest country they're helpful and friendly – as they are when in a family group, or in a tightly controlled social circle like the miller and his entourage. But when they come in contact with foreigners a group of Tibetan farmers out in the fields or a gang of kids in a village are liable to get out of hand.

We left the work-camp with three hours of light to spare, turning down their offers to let us sleep there. The Kamba La we thought was 1,000 metres or more above us so there was some considerable work ahead. Nick's gear-cable snapped. Our first mechanical problem. It snapped just above the adjuster on the gear-mechanism and it took half an hour to mend by shortening it. We set off again. The weather was much clearer, but the gear-cable problem brought our attention to the thick layers of dirt on our bikes and the mercilessly grinding sand on the chain. We stopped again to scrape off as much as possible then cycled on until we found a truck-driver who could give us some sump oil for lubrication. The pass was steep and obviously put a lot of strain on the transmission. My bottom bracket had, for the past few days, been working loose again, so we used this as an excuse to walk our tired bodies up the pass. The first pass we'd walked. We felt we could relax a bit because Lhasa was almost in our sights.

Luck was on our side: the summit of the Kamba La, though at 4,794 metres elevation above sea-level, was not much more than 500 metres above the lake. It was an impressive exposed place where we could stop beside clusters of prayer-flags and cairns. This is the traditional boundary between Front and Back Tibet ruled respectively by Xigatse and Lhasa. We could look out in the direction the wind blew to row after row of grey hills stretching over Tibet. Close behind us, to the south, a few large white mountains blocked the view. Surprisingly, five urchins appeared beside us. They didn't seem to be doing anything; I presume that coming up to this windy hostile col of desolation was their idea of a day's play. They casually stood and looked. They were a real sight: dirty round faces, tatty black knots of hair, snot dripping from their nostrils (and, as they sniffed, darting back up their noses like marmots in burrows), open-mouthed, three or four shirts, open-necked, topped by tattered jackets ten sizes too big, broken zip-fasteners fixed by safety-pins. They wore clothes a jumble-sale would reject. They had chopped-down men's trousers filled with patches, flies so completely undone that it looked normal, bare ankles and broken shoes sewn by leather thongs. Lawless. Bare hands where we had special Black's thermal mitts with waterproof and windproof outer layer and fibrepile inner. Furthermore, we had a complete clothing system, double balaclava and comfort.

We set off optimistically down the road; the Brahmaputra could be seen shining temptingly far below us, and snaking off into the distance eastwards. We looked forward to an exhilarating free-wheel, but almost immediately it turned sour. Compared to the short four-kilometre uphill climb in the sun to the Kamba La, the twenty-four-kilometre downhill to the big river was dreadful. There was no sun. We started losing body-heat on the very first slope because rolling doesn't generate any warmth. The road was rough. We hated every jolt. A storm got up over a nearby mountain and we were stung by hail-stones. Thunder and lightning brought on freezing rain. Hoods tight round our heads, wearing all our clothes, we froze. Road corrugations shook us to pieces. We wound back and forth down and down into dark cold valleys. Our brakes were on almost continuously, making our fingers ache and numbing the palms of our hands. Our backsides were up out of the saddles and all the stress was taken on our crumpled toes. The wind gusted and buffeted, and we were very miserable. At times like this there is no point stopping for relief because that only delays the next disheartening section. We rolled on and on down to the Brahmaputra, and at the bottom we decided that, although the whole of the cycling for the first part of the day was the most depressing of our lives, it was exceeded in agony by the second half of the day.

The village Kamba Partsi down by the big river wasn't the crossing-place, we didn't spot any chai houses close to the road but we did notice that there was quite a lot of construction going on. We had to follow the valley a short distance. The road was new, half-constructed. There were many lorries and mechanical diggers. They'd chewed up the area in preparation for a lot of development. Further along, the Brahmaputra narrowed into a tighter valley, and here it was crossed by a new concrete bridge which led to smart buildings and office blocks on the other side. Haughty black sentry-boxes guarded the bridge. Just before the bridge we came upon, as a lovely surprise, the first tarmac road we'd seen in Tibet. Eighteen kilometres along this smooth fast morale-booster, over the river, hopefully leaving it behind for ever, we came sprinting triumphantly into the large town of Quzu Dzong where we unanimously and gratefully elected to spend the night.

Quzu Dzong was quite developed: street lights, trees, cars, painted signs and many new two-storey brick buildings. We stuffed ourselves full of meat, egg and vegetable dishes with rice, drank a bottle of beer in celebration of virtually reaching Lhasa, and peeped through the curtains at the building opposite where the loudspeakers were turned up to megadecibels, a lot of people crowded around and there seemed to be a disco going on. Chinese versions of English songs. This was a community busy destroying its identity. We were into civilization again. The hotel only had dormitory bedrooms – we wanted some peace so we bought all four beds in one room at two yuan each (about forty pence). All the food we scoffed cost eighteen yuan, equivalent to two small bags of fish and chips in Britain.

Nick. Day 26. Quzu Dzong (fifty-six kilometres from Lhasa).
The state we're in! I haven't seen a mirror since Kathmandu so I can only describe what Dick looks like and what I feel like: dishevelled matted hair, bloodshot eyes, lined thin face, stubble, burnt peeled nose, cracked swollen flaky lips. Pretty hideous. Our clothes are filthy, we haven't washed them since Kathmandu, and for three consecutive nights I've slept fully clothed. My gut rot has cleared up. Instead I have the heaviest cold; my nose tubes are blocked solid – my nose bleeds trying to clear it. Much of the time we're wearing T-shirts and balaclavas across our faces to keep out the dust and protect us from sunburn. Yesterday, Day 25, when it was wet and overcast we didn't bother and even then we got burnt split lips.

After a morning sitting eating stuffed momos (Tibetan dumplings), boiled eggs and a lunch of excellent stir-fry washed down by beer which lubricated the mental cogs ready for route-planning and the jobs ahead in Lhasa, we saddled up and rode on – a brilliant sunny day with fresh snow etching the gullies and rock-faces on rows of sharp peaks. Around us many people were working in fields and farms.

Nick. Day 27. Late afternoon.
Unbelievably the road was tarmac all the way – wide and smooth – and we creamed up the valley passing the odd vehicle. The breeze seemed to be behind us. It was very romantic. A lazy stream meandered across a wide grassy plain dotted with trees. Cows munched on the stream banks, and two Tibetans wallowed across the water in a yak-skin coracle. We passed a huge Buddha carved into a rock wall. White-capped mountains looked on. Then: two distant hillocks in the valley – like pimples – clearly topped by a building. Rectangular. Was this the Potala? Half an hour later we were cycling beneath those serenely sloping walls, brilliant white under the clear evening sky. It was 6.30 p.m. We'd arrived in the Forbidden City.

When Heinrich Harrer reached Lhasa forty years ago, he entered on an ass in a stream of pilgrims and caravans. He came to a great gate crowned with three chorten (Buddhist cairns), which spans the gap between the two hills and forms the entrance to the Forbidden City. A few beggars held out their hands for alms. His excitement was so intense that he felt inclined to go down on his knees and touch the ground with his forehead.

We pulled up at traffic-lights and whistled in amazement. There was so much happening. The first Spaniards into Cuzco could not have been more astonished. We took a deep breath. Exhaust fumes! Trucks, buses, cars. We were in a traffic queue. Horns hooted. The lights turned back to red and a wave of people flowed across the road in front of us. Then, on the green, a traffic-policeman waved us on and bicycles seemed to come from all sides, going in every direction. Lhasa is a modern city where the medieval lifestyle of Tibet is heavily over-printed, though not yet submerged, by the new China. It is busy with people and traffic, yet horses and donkeys are still ridden into town, and bicycles have plenty of room. So do the road-side kiosks selling sweets, cigarettes or home-made snacks. There are wide pavements, clean buildings and boulevards of trees. We cruised on, wide-eyed, following the main flow of traffic towards the centre. In order to find out where the gringo hotels were, we pulled up beside the first foreigners we saw. At the sight of us, they leapt back in fear. Then, regaining composure, they regarded us for a moment in stunned silence.

'Hello,' I smiled, and, by way of introduction: 'Is this Lhasa?' No answer. So, still smiling, I moved on to the business: 'You don't happen to know where the travellers' hostels are, and which is the best?' I'd put the ball into their court, and indeed they were now on home territory because if there is one thing that a tourist knows about a country it's where to find other tourists. There were several places to try; the first, the Taxi Stand, seemed to be full of jolly Americans buying cold beer and having hot showers. Furthermore it was full, so we went to try the Snowlands, which was much more our line: slightly dilapidated. It had a friendly manager whom we sought out in one of the dormitory rooms where he was chatting to four Japanese travellers. This hotel seemed to be populated by girls in long printed skirts who fed on live yoghurt and muesli, and read books like *My Journey to Lhasa* by Alexandra David-Neel, the first white woman into Lhasa, or by people who were either travelling 'for a long time' or had wanted to travel for a long time but had run out of money. Not to put too fine a point on it, being slightly eccentric ourselves, we fitted in well. The manager hired us the bridal suite. In this three-storey, probably 150-bed hotel, it was one of the only rooms which wasn't an eight-bed dormitory. We carried our bicycles in and hid them quickly before the rumours got started that there was a couple of mad Englishmen with racing-bikes in the room at the end of the balcony.

It was celebration time. On Day 27, after 2,391 kilometres of cycling, 761 of it on dirt roads, and having completed 14,180 metres of ascent up mountain passes, we had arrived at our first real target. We had averaged eighty-five kilometres per day, unfortunately not as good as we'd hoped, though in doing so we had cycled over the Himalayas from the Ganges delta and the heat of India to the heart of Tibet. Although we were not quite halfway to the Centre of the Earth – and it was only the easier half that we had nearly completed – the expedition, we agreed, was already a success. We could allow ourselves a well-earned break, get cleaned up, sorted out and start preparations for the next section. However, first things first. We went for some grub.

Downstairs, the eating-room runs a bespoke menu – you go into the kitchen, scoop out spoonfuls of diced veggies, sliced meat, peanuts, bits of fat, beanshoots and anything else you want, then give it to the cook, who hurls it in a wok roasting on a white-hot fire and the whole lot explodes in a sizzling frenzy doused for a minute in spicy oil then swished on to your plate. You take a bowl of white rice beside it and sit down with chopsticks to talk in English to all the other inmates. It's a fabulous place to swap gossip, learn up-to-date information about the area and occasionally relate stories. Travellers all over the world seem to be like this: more interested in preparing for the next exploration than reminiscing on the last. I suspect all of us are a bit the same and we think that today's the day to do things, there'll always be tomorrow to tell tales.

We found out many things; for instance, the Snowlands doesn't have showers so you wash in cold water in the yard. The lady selling yoghurt comes at 8.30 a.m. for thirty minutes. There's a wonderful view of the town and mountains from the roof of the hotel. We found out that the

Australian girl on the second floor had a Walkman so we could borrow her headphones to replay the tapes we'd recorded on the journey to Lhasa. Slide-film could be bought at the posh Lhasa Hotel a short distance out of town. Chocolate could be bought in a lot of the little shops. We raced off to get some – a couple of samples of each different type and a few handfuls of other sweets. The other travellers also had ideas about which monasteries to visit, which views to go to see, where to buy souvenirs and trinkets and who did black-market money-change. One constant source of interest was the drugs and illnesses we travellers carry or carried.

The great benefit of meeting up to exchange gossip is that travellers will have come from all the different directions and hence be able to forewarn others of difficulties or pleasures ahead. Excluding the majority of people who come by air to Lhasa airport, which is down near Quzu Dzong where we saw all the new development, people come overland into Lhasa from three directions. The least-used route is the one we'd come on over the gravel roads from Kathmandu, then there is a main road climbing over hills and valleys from the lowlands of Chengdu in eastern China. This used to be the principal route into Lhasa, but it has been overtaken by the northern route, which comes 1,000 kilometres over the high plateau from Golmud which is in a basin at 10,000 feet and is the rail-head linking the Tibetan Plateau to Beijing 3,000 kilometres away. We had assumed the road to Golmud would be dirt, so our ears perked up when someone who'd travelled it in two days on a bus said: 'It was fast and not at all bumpy, though I don't know what it was made of. All I remember is long boring stretches of emptiness. Desolation. Every time we stopped it was cold and windy.' This information, albeit scanty, was very useful in building an impression of the terrain ahead, though when I tried to imagine a picture of 'cold, empty, windy, boring desolation' my mind went blank. Few people could tell us more because, for the majority of travellers, the sections between the tourist sights and cities seemed to be nothing more than one or two days of inconvenience on buses, trains or planes. Cyclists get a very special view of a country, in many ways more intimate because they are forced to take the rough with the smooth and see both the basic life of the locals and the luxury of the visitors. On the other hand it could be said that cyclists never know any one aspect well because their travels are composed of an endless series of separate mini-adventures.

We found that there were, to our surprise, quite a few other cyclists in Lhasa. There were smart mountain-bikes on show on the landings of several of the hostels, so we started asking questions. Where from? Where to? How long? They'd come from Chengdu, Golmud and Kathmandu, sometimes in very quick times, and we thought this was all rather amazing until a Chinese American, Robert Goo, was bold enough to say: 'Oh, I didn't cycle. I came by bus. So did most of the others.' We met or heard of twelve other people with bikes in Lhasa – only three of them had cycled. A Frenchman whose name I've forgotten was unintentionally on a world tour: he'd started down in Africa five years ago aiming to do that continent then go straight home but had got side-tracked to the Americas, then the Far East and now seemed to think the easiest way home was to continue on around the world. 'After all', he said, 'there is only Afghanistan and the Middle East between me and France.' He'd cycled in from Chengdu. A short while after him, but along the same route, had come the Belgian, Marc Noël, who was making a portfolio of Chinese photographs. Both separately intended to cycle on to Kathmandu; Marc Noël, being a working man, was in a rush and would leave in a couple of days, the Frenchman in his own words 'in a short while: when it feels right'. Both these two had heard rumours of other cyclists who had been over these routes, but no one had heard of any others who'd tried cycling the northern route; indeed, there was a suspicion that the Chinese police might not let us out of Lhasa in that direction.

The third person who'd cycled to Lhasa was a most amazing Kiwi who on paper was as innocent as Snow White yet in practice was as capable, adaptable and *laissez-faire* as Passepartout, the intrepid valet of Phileas Fogg in *Around the World in Eighty Days*. Brian Williamson was fresh out of New Zealand. On his first day away from home he'd landed all alone in Bangkok, spent a week there, flown direct to Kathmandu, then on the spur of the moment bought a second-hand mountain-bike and blithely set off into the midst of the world's greatest mountain range. He didn't quite know what to bring, so he pedalled up to Lhasa in three weeks with packets of dried soup, a bike-stand and a big smile on his face. He also had an impressive range of what we considered to be rather heavy bike-tools: bottom-bracket spanners, crank pullers, spare chain, three different types of sticky tape, spare cables, etc. He confessed he didn't know how to use them but thought they looked good. We enthusiastically agreed – and got to work on our bikes. Brian was very helpful and we had a lot of fun together. Robert joined in; he was an expert bike mechanic, and had set off cycling with a team of three others towards Mount Kailash, but stomach problems and deep sand somewhere west of Xigatse bogged them down and they'd split up. Nick and I cleaned our bikes lovingly, not only chains, sprockets and chain-rings, but also spokes, rims, hubs, brakes, frame-tubes, lugwork and decals. The premiss being that a clean bike is a good bike. Our free-wheel blocks had bedded in and each needed a shim removed. We greased all our cables and checked absolutely everything. I had known since the Kamba La that the ball-race in my bottom bracket needed tightening. Brian's tools didn't fit, so I went down the street to find a street-corner bike-mender with all his tools and spares laid out on sacking on the pavement then borrowed hammer and punch. In contrast to open-air puncture-mending at Goalundo Ghat beside the Ganges this operation in Lhasa aroused scant interest from the locals. Indeed, during all our little excursions into town, a crowd never gathered. This is possibly the result of Lhasa being a reasonably busy tourist venue where foreign faces and funny clothes aren't unusual.

The place to head for tourism is the Potala Palace; we went there twice

to see the Buddhist treasures and walk the hallowed chambers floating
in the sky high above the city. Both times we were thwarted. It had closed
for the day. The gate was locked, and Nick climbed the railings for a clear
view. We can report that it looks splendid from below! However, that
didn't depress us because Lhasa is so rich in local colour and custom.
Barely three years ago, since the first visitors flooded in, modifications
have been made to accommodate them, but basically it's unchanged.
Numerous Tibetans wear yak-skin boots, the Kampas from the country
come in heavy black wool jackets with their hair wound in bright red braids
over the tops of their heads, daggers in their waistbands. Up one alley in
old Lhasa there is a line of street dentists standing by their chairs, proudly
displaying boxes of gold teeth. For a small sum they'll get a whacking great
big pair of pliers on to one of your teeth and replace it with one of theirs.
There are women at stalls selling countless different goods: foodstuffs
cooked or fresh, clothes, blankets, trinkets, and now there are souvenir
stalls. Often Tibetans from the country stop you in the streets and alleys to
sell, at ridiculously cheap prices, their family heirlooms: beads, money-
belts, silver spoons, knives and jewelled pins. The export of antiquities or
cultural relics from China is prohibited. I'm pleased to say that in the case
of the only person we knew who was illegally trying to mail heirlooms
out of the country we heard that the package had been slit open by
Customs officials in Beijing and sent on to its destination with the message
'We regret that this package contains fewer items than intended by the
sender'.

The most wonderful travel moment for us in Lhasa was visiting the
Jokhang in the middle of the old market. You don't have to pay an entrance
fee, you don't have to go out of your way to get there. It's the central
temple, quite uninspiring from outside yet you're drawn in by the mass of
people flowing around. Gradually it dawned on us that they were all
circling clockwise: devotees doing the rounds. This human tide makes it a
problem if you want to investigate a stall ten yards anti-clockwise because
you've got to go all the way round again. Its outside walls are blank; inside
are various gilded rooms, and huge red wooden pillars. In the entrance
hall, the nucleus of all Buddhist pilgrimages in Tibet, the floor is polished
to a high sheen by the repeated supplications of the faithful. Some have
come hundreds of miles, prostrating themselves at every step, wearing
knee-pads of bandages and holding flat smooth boards in each hand to slide
along the ground as they go down full length then rise again for another
step. This is the end of their journey; the score we watched going down on
the floor of the entrance hall moved no further forward than a foot in half
an hour. When we visited, on as far as we know an ordinary day, there were
forty ochre-robed lamas in attendance. They sat cross-legged on the floor
in two rows in front of the images of Buddha. Like forty titled toads with
low chants building up from the depths of their stomachs, they were
motionless except for the murmur of their lips and the flick of their eyes as
individuals from the crowd stepped forward to offer gifts to each lama –

sometimes pieces of cloth which each lama casually put behind his back, sometimes a bowl or twist of food put by the lama in front of him where he could see it, sometimes a gift of money which instantly vanished as though snipped by a fly-catcher into the folds of red wool.

Yak-butter lamps flickered to highlight the shadows in the half-light. We stepped through some doors and up some steps, out into the harsh bright sun on the roof 3,607 metres above sea-level (11,830 feet). Some parts of the roof are tiled and sweep down from pinnacles to dragons, gargoyles or intricate red and gold designs on the trusses. Other parts are flat and we could walk around, removed above the noise and business of the city. All around the mountains looked cold and close. Over to the west, reserved on its pinnacle, the Potala Palace, at one and the same time both heavily solid, showing no moods from its high-flying battlements or regular windows on flat-faced walls, yet delicate and timeless; impressive, impossible and impenetrable. Lhasa is the most exotic city I have ever visited. We didn't do it justice. Both of us want to return one day, one day soon, for a proper visit. We'd like, like everyone else, to understand and feel a few of its uniquely special secrets before it's swamped by the likes of us.

We had a few other preparations before we were ready to leave. We hoped to get them all done ready to leave at midday on Day 29 so that we would only have lost one whole day in Lhasa. However, like the other two big cities where we'd stopped to overhaul the gear, Dhaka and Kathmandu, we got ourselves bogged down with expedition minutiae. In each case it seems that we just couldn't cope with organization – out on the road life is simple: you pedal, you eat and you rest. We wrote a stack of postcards to friends, sent a missive to Steve Bonnist, and found an English couple to carry our films back home. We wanted to telephone Steve because a personal message is the best way to get things moving, but though we queued at the post office and went twice to the austere Lhasa Hotel we had no luck. One bonus was that we got so tired walking there that we unanimously decided to pay an extortionate price for a posh ride back to Snowlands in a black Mercedes. We sat in our room late on the night of Day 29 putting the finishing touches to our gear. We had been carrying three courses of Flagyl (for amoebic dysentery or Giardia), but now we reduced them to two courses. One course is fifteen tablets, taken three per day for five days. We reduced our Septrin Forte (broad-spectrum antibiotic for lung and internal infections, but also to sprinkle and spread on festering skin) from four courses of ten tablets to two courses. These were carried in small pieces of knotted plastic. We also had a roll of sticky plaster and a small tube of antiseptic cream. We did some intricate calculations as to how many Puritabs would be needed to finish – two each per day on the Plateau, five each per day in the desert. Based on 100 kilometres per day, that's 220 in total. Meticulously we opened up all the little squares of foil and popped all the tiny tabs into a minute plastic pill-pot. Using a large Swiss Army penknife lent by Brian Williamson, we cut off numerous buckles and clips from our panniers. We slept, then woke up on Day 30 intending to leave early, but weight-saving and fine-tuning continued into early afternoon, then lunch took us another two hours and we set off from the Snowlands mid-afternoon. We tried once more to visit the Potala but failed, bought a huge bag of tiny chocolate Easter eggs as consolation, and took a couple of photos with the Pentax MX balanced on a park bench and us smiling into the seven-second-delay timer in the incongruous setting of a concrete walkway and fountains in front of the Potala.

Nick. Day 30. Lhasa Valley to Yangbajin.
We were going to leave early morning but too much got in the way. At 5.22 p.m. we actually set off to leave the Snowlands. Within ten minutes we were totally lost up a dirt track and had to lift the bikes over the back wall of the boys' toilet in a children's school. It was a mildly disgruntled pair who eventually found the main road at 5.44 p.m. Committed, ready for the Plateau, we pushed off. Then we spotted the first kilometre-post: '1,929.' Where to? We didn't know. Somewhere on the far side of the Plateau? There is a huge emptiness ahead.

Despite all, we rode the eighty-four kilometres uphill-all-the-way in under four hours, arriving at our target Yangbajin before 10 p.m. The valley we rode up from Lhasa was a pleasant scenic contrast to the buff deserts of the south. With a rushing river for companionship, we passed green sprouting fields and numerous villages before the valley narrowed – to be floored in cropped grass – just a narrow band each side of the water. The green, and our road, channelled northwards between two rows of bone-dry peaks. Near the top of the climb, the road twisted through a gorge which shut out all the light. Yangbajin sits in a broader, flatter upper part beyond the gorge – treeless and much bleaker. There are meant to be hot springs. There is a large Army camp.

We found ourselves a room in a barracks-type Chinese lodging. The beds were Army issue made of plumber's pipe. It cost three yuan each, there were no loos, and we got water only by going into the manager's room. He was huddled close to his coal stove in the middle of the room, metal-pipe chimney to the roof, a couple of other men sitting with him. Nothing much in the room except a bed, his desk, two chairs to sit on and two upturned buckets. It had a concrete floor, no carpet and no decoration on the walls except flaking green paint and a curled calendar with a picture of the Shanghai water-front.

Yangbajin is at the furthest limit of the Lhasa tourist trade; tour groups come to visit the geothermal power station nearby. It's well beyond the limit of the Lhasa sprawl, and at the final edge of good cultivatable land.

Therefore the roads to here are well kept. We had guessed there would be accommodation here not only for this reason, but also because this is the point at which the road divides. The branch we aimed to follow goes north across successively higher plateaus divided by successively more hostile mountains then drops into Golmud for the rail-head connection to Beijing and east China; the other branch goes west over two high mountain passes and down to the Brahmaputra heading for Xigatse and crossing the big river at a place well known to Nick and me – Detsukar Ferry. That was where we had had our informal dispute: if we'd come by Nick's northern route we'd have eventually reached Yangbajin. Here the signposts showed us that the total northern route Xigatse to Lhasa is 335 kilometres; the southern route via Gyangtse, we were told, is 360 kilometres; and the route we took down the centre we know is 280 kilometres. Moral victory to me on distance, to Nick on time, to both of us on adventure. That's all behind us now; our eyes are turned northwards to we know not what beyond Yangbajin – beyond the safety of the commercial arena of Lhasa.

SEVEN

Cycling Out to Desolation

We slept like rocks on the night of Day 30 in Yangbajin. Despite the management turning on the lights at some unearthly hour, waking in the morning was extremely difficult. Eventually, we put on our jackets, gloves and balaclavas, wheeled our bikes out into the yard, had a pee, then walked across to one of the two chai houses. The nicest lady with the loveliest smile went to great lengths to cook up the hottest stir-fry breakfast we have ever had the misfortune to be fired by: pure chunks of ginger laced with red-hot chilli, enlivened by a liberal spattering of soy sauce. The only joy was picking out the hunks of pork fat. We needed energy for the journey ahead. From now on there'd be no pick and choose. Neither of us knew how far we'd get, nor where we'd be able to find any sort of food or shelter. Each day would be a test of stamina, each meal an adventure, each night in safety a success. We had found no one who had travelled this route except as a necessary evil to reach Lhasa overland from the north. Those few had journeyed in long-haul trucks or buses, stopping hardly at all, their only recollection being one of 'barren monotony and bitter winds'.

Our map was a map of all China. It had place-names marked every hundred or so kilometres along the route to Golmud, the first proper town. We hoped these were points of habitation. We expected to find nomads at intervals across the plains wherever there was sufficient grass for their animals. If we did get stuck, then retreat was an alternative, yet it was our unspoken code of honour never to backtrack. We hoped we wouldn't be put to the test. It was over 1,300 kilometres to Golmud, the longest section so far – and the most unpredictable. We were extremely apprehensive.

Though Yangbajin is 4,300 metres elevation, we set off uphill. To our delight, it turned out to be one of the most beautiful days' cycle-touring so far. We climbed gently for the first twenty kilometres, pushing big gears. The breeze was strongly behind us, and the sun was most pleasant. The valley was warm, becoming more expansive with every kilometre. Big green plains – not bright green, but the khaki green of mildew – stretched out like Peruvian altiplano to snowy mountains on both sides. How many

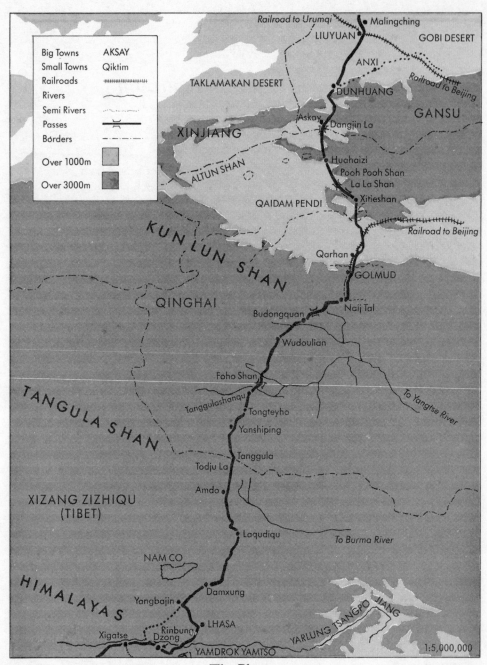

The Plateau

of those were unclimbed? We didn't care because the road surface was
tarmac. It was smooth and fast – a joy to ride. Our tyres were pumped up
rock hard for minimum rolling resistance. We cycled past huge herds of
grazing yaks and a busy stream wiggling its gravelly channel across the
openness. Huts and dwellings were few and far between, nomads' tents
more common.

The yak is a big chunky animal, incredibly timid on short thin legs. Its
illusion of bulk comes in part from the mass of thick black hair draping it
all around like the many tattered oversize shirts and jackets piled on each of
the herdsmen's children. The yak, which provides for nearly all human
needs, is at the nucleus of existence on the Tibetan Plateau. It is one of the
few animals hardy enough to withstand the weather and survive on the
scanty grasses. It gives milk and wool – and dung which is dried as fuel. It
provides meat, and leather which is used for boots and coats. Furthermore
it is a nimble pack-animal able to struggle through deep snow. Yaks are
mostly black – white ones are prized – some are crossed with cattle and
called dzo. Its horns are fairly impressive: wide, upturned and broad
across the skull. Its shoulders are high and muscular like the North
American bison yet it holds its head low to the ground like a dog with its
tail between its legs: cowed and afraid of being scolded. Jet-black eyes
seem oblivious to all around.

Twenty-six kilometres out from Yangbajin, where the valley had
become very wide and the hills relatively low on the sides, we seemed to go
over a col and for several kilometres flew downhill at what seemed like a
hundred miles an hour. We timed ourselves between two consecutive
kilometre-posts and did it in exactly one minute – 60 k.p.h.! This is the
way to pick up a decent mileage, we thought; it'll redress the balance of our
daily average, which has fallen very low. We timed a further twenty
kilometres, did it in thirty-five minutes and forty seconds, and computed
that we were doing 34 k.p.h. The bikes were so smooth. All the work in
Lhasa had made them feel good. It was difficult to tell if we were riding
uphill or downhill. Slopes were completely illusory up in the thin crisp air
and intensely clear views. Our bikes rolled fast yet when we turned to look
behind us we could see down the slope we'd ascended. Only the small
stream running in the opposite direction proved we'd cycled uphill all day.

In the mid-afternoon, we came to Damxung, a cowboy town. The
tarmac road ran straight down the middle of two rows of shacks. There
were tin roofs, telegraph wires humming in the wind, and men and kids
hanging about. There were dusty verges to the road where trucks drove off
to stop. Quite a few chai houses. The one we dived into had walls made of
tin sheets nailed on to a wood frame, with two big tin flaps fixed only at the
top hinged open as windows and propped with sticks. The door was a loose
movable large metal panel. The roof was branches of wood, overlaid with
sticks, topped with polythene and held down by large rocks and turf. It
was thirty feet long, eight feet wide, had three tables covered by plastic
table-cloths, thin wooden benches to sit on and a dirt floor. At one end

were a few shelves which served as a shop doing business through one of
the tin-flap windows. It had two types of biscuit, one stale, the other rice
crackers. Big bags of peanuts, bars of soap, three boxes of sweets, a few
bottles of liquor, tins of pork meat and bags of hard old bread rolls. The
cash-till was a large cardboard box full of Chinese notes. Down the other
end of the chai house was the cooking: bowls of food, pressure cooker
(necessary for cooking food at this altitude), and two huge drums of
water.

There were about twenty people gathered around us. Principal dress
for the men was blue Mao suits or scruffy Western slacks and jerseys.
Mostly the young lads were in layers of over-large jackets. There was one
Kampa, tall, handsome, with round face and long hair plaited up over his
head in red wool. One older man in wool breeches, white shirt, waistcoat
and straw hat, another wrapped around in yak-skin rugs. There was a little
girl, big eyes, black hair down her back. She shyly peeped around the
corner. The little lads had the whole history of China on their heads; some
had Mao caps, one had a toy Army officer's cap with red star, another was
in a fur Cossack hat and several had baseball caps.

Nick. Day 31. Damxung. Elevation 4,400 metres.
We have dived into an eat-house with the bikes. The management were surprisingly obliging considering the bikes blocked
the walkway – and for the whole of our sojourn kids hung
through the windows watching and staring. But all this is very
low-key hassle compared to Bangladesh.

We were served the most extraordinary tea: beautifully
presented in a china bowl with saucer and lid, painted in a rose
design. Big green tea leaves like seaweed, a huge lump of crystal
sugar like a piece of shattered quartz and two berry/crab-apple
things the boy called 'yoh'. They floated up from the bottom
when the hot water was added. We called it 'bollock tea'. The
bowl had at least eight to ten refills of hot water and the taste
kept developing; the sugar-rock gently melted and the leaves
and 'yoh' released their flavour. A totally dynamic, organic,
deliciously refreshing drink.

We also had a bowl of noodle-and-pork soup – simple and
enjoyably bland after all the rich greasy stir-fry of the past few
days. Then I had a second bowlful. This is stocking up because
it seems likely we're back to salt tea and tsampa tonight.

We both topped up on rice biscuits, sweets and peanuts, throwing the last
handfuls into our mouths as we mounted our bikes and pushed off into the
late afternoon. The prospects were grim. The bright blue sky which had
been sporting light white clouds in the morning had become overcast. The
wind blew colder. We could no longer cycle in only salopets and T-shirts
but had to cover up with jackets and long johns. To the south-east, on our

right, the hills were brown and smooth, rounded like the Cotswolds, but on our left they rose up to a sustained chain of snow-capped peaks linked by knife-edge ridges forming an Aonagh Eagach of nearly 100 kilometres length. For much of the day they were topped by mist and later they held swirling snow and rain in the corries. After forty kilometres we thought we'd reached the high point of the road because we came upon a mass of cairns and prayer flags, so we stopped for a few moments' solitary celebration, but after a couple of kilometres downhill it started going up again and darkness began to close in. Having seen no habitation for a while, we had to press on, eventually clocking up the 160th kilometre of the day – at altitude. We felt sufficiently weak that our bodies knew it, too. Nick said sincerely: 'I'm so exhausted. I'd give £100 for a packet of choccy biccies and a pot of tea.'

I upped the bid to £150.

From the depths of his heart, my cousin yearned: 'I'd give £150 for *one* chocolate biscuit and *one* cup of tea.'

We set off again. Then, after a short distance, luck came our way.

Nick. Day 31. Evening looking for bed.
We spotted two nomads' tents across the valley and dragged our bikes over. We were met by a stone-faced youth in a brilliant blue jerkin and colourful felt boots. The woman of the encampment (his mother?) in heavy skirts and shawls came out and greeted us warmly like long-lost friends – though stranger friends cannot be imagined: D and I in skinsuits, they looking like they've stepped out of the Museum of Mankind. We put on a fine display of shivering and hunger pangs. She waved us into the tent: three metres square with a mud-brick wall one metre high and a smoke hole at the top of a ridge of yak-wool fabric woven so openly that light shone through a million holes. We sat on thick rugs of detailed maroon design and she gave us salt tea – topping up our bottles each time the meniscus disappeared. The stove in the middle burnt dried yaks' dung – glowing bright and warm like peat. When D rubbed his stomach and made plaintive sounds, she produced two bowls of mashed rice (like rice pudding without the milk or sugar) and offered chilli powder (refused!) as a flavouring. Instead we got worm-like jelly things of uncertain origin with tiny bits of dry black yak's meat. This mix was poured from a big tin mug. Spotting a tall cylindrical cask in the corner, D then asked for whatever was in it – tangy liquid yak's yoghurt which the woman ladled into our bowls. The resultant wormy goo was mouth-watering – the most tasty Tibetan meal I've had. Shortly, the man of the tent, and another woman, came back from herding the yaks, penned them in the corral and stooped into the tent. The man quickly made it clear we could eat with them but not sleep – the tent was

too small. This was a blow. Eventually we were literally ordered
to leave – with plenty of smiles.

We paid our dues and waved goodbye, then headed northwards into the
cold and darkness, vowing to stop at the first place we found – praying it
wasn't too far. Eight kilometres of emptiness under black storm clouds
into the red sunset, we found a brick hut and outhouses in a walled yard.
There were no lights and, it seemed, no people. However, when we
stopped to investigate, two dogs affirmed habitation. Venturing into the
dark yard, we saw two shapes disappear and a door thudded behind them.
Then some low nasal singing led our eyes to search again. A man in tatters
sat on a cold stone step looking blankly into the hills. We were chilled to the
bone and needed to get inside. We asked 'Cha?' and then indicated 'Bed?'
No reaction at first, then after several tries the madman disappeared into a
room, closing the door behind him. Our hearts fell. Luckily a moment
later he came out with tea, but he wouldn't let us inside. He sat down in a
huddle on the step and started his incantations again. We wrapped up tight
and shivered – honestly. One of the women came out on an errand, then
went back in leaving us marooned. It was pitch black, and somewhere a
few feet from us the two dogs prowled. We pleaded with the madman for a
bed, and we tapped on the doors, but soon they told us in no uncertain
terms to 'Go away'. In the cold and dark we were going nowhere. So we
had to persevere until a sense of pity broke their resolve. They may well
have had a right to be fearful of us because for a lot of these folk the
memory of the 1950s Chinese takeover is still fresh. Furthermore they
were brought up with the traditional Tibetan antipathy to all foreigners.
We felt we had no choice but to lean on their human weakness. Eventually
they relented and gave us yak-skin coats and piles of rugs and led us across
the yard to a cold outhouse. It was a shed. We peered around in the light
of the petrol wick lamp they'd brought and saw we had to sleep on a tiny
patch of dirt floor below precariously towering piles of dried fuel in this,
the yak-dung store. It was difficult to stretch out and difficult to get
comfortable on the lumpy floor. We slept fitfully – fearful that the Great
Yak Goddess in the sky would drop something on us. Being several
thousands of feet higher than on previous nights, we had altitude sickness.
We were also scared the madman would come and get us in the night.
Worse yet, we thought that if this is what it's like on the south of the
plateau, still close to Lhasa, what will it be like in the remoter areas?

We were up at the crack of dawn. Unfortunately, no one would give us
tea in the morning. The first few kilometres were icy cold in the shade
before the sun rose over the eastern horizon. By and by we left the valley
and the snowy ridges of yesterday behind and cycled up and out into a
completely different topography. We were on undulating plains, no real
hills to be seen, everywhere was thin green pasture. For the first time we
were on the wide open expanses like pampas which we had imagined made
up all of the Tibetan Plateau. There were some sparse nomads' tents, and a

few distant square white flat-roofed houses kilometres apart, but no walls and no tracks excepting this ribbon of black tarmac – our lifeline.

We stopped for breakfast when we saw a nomad's tent close to the road. They thought it was great fun to entertain us in their well-appointed home. Their tent was twice as big as last night's. They had carpets, a central metal stove with chimney pipe, treasure chests covered by ornate rugs to sit on, and a chest of drawers with a couple of candles, faded family photos and a transistor radio.

> *Nick. Day 32. Morning.*
> An old man with glasses sat in the corner, making the band on a ring smaller by wrapping it with cord. The little girl in shaggy skins smiled when he fitted it to her finger. A kettle (full of tea?) boiled away. But the drink we were offered first was hot yak milk – a bit watery but solidly sustaining – and quite sweet. Next came the tsampa – a particularly nutty mix which went well with the hot yak milk – though the woman poured salt tea over it, too. I must be getting tuned in to tsampa because I actually didn't mind eating that lot. Maybe I'll even like it soon!!

The women had colourful beads woven into their hair and several large bangles. Their pride and joy, the teenage boy, clearly felt a certain bond with us since he also was a bike-owner. In fact he was mending his pedal when we cycled up. His bike was a big, black, very heavy-looking roadster. He went to show it off and cycled around over the grass totally ignoring the nearby tarmac. It is rumoured that some of the nomads use bikes for herding yaks and sheep. It may be true. Certainly there are intensely competitive bike races at the annual September festival of wandering tribes in Damxung.

Onward across the undulating plains, still 15,000 feet above sea-level, we didn't know for several hours if we were going uphill or downhill. At some point we must have crossed the very important watershed where, behind us, streams flow down towards Lhasa and into the Brahmaputra to be carried around the eastern end of the Himalayas and then down into India to join the Ganges. We had waved goodbye to the Brahmaputra for the last time and hence severed our last connections with the Bay of Bengal, our start point and source of all the fun in the first few days. Ahead of us was the drainage of the Nu Jiang which veers out eastwards and then turns south to become the Salween which passes through Burma and debouches into the Indian Ocean near Rangoon.

We had fifty kilometres of downhill to the Nu Jiang itself, where there was the first town since Damxung 160 kilometres ago. It was approximately in the right place on our map to be a place called Nagqu, though the locals seemed to think it was called Laqudiqu, which wasn't on our map. It didn't really matter what it was called because there wasn't anything else very close. Apart from yaks, nomads and the odd brick hut, we'd seen nothing since Damxung except a bridge a quarter of an hour before Laqudiqu and beside it a signpost which said nine kilometres to Laqudiqu and 290 kilometres to somewhere up a dirt track. The whole issue of finding where we were or where we were going was complicated because few people except the Han Chinese seemed to use kilometres even though there were kilometre posts all along this trade route. Furthermore some towns had several names and we needed many many attempts to convert the written names on our maps into an acceptable pronunciation. The best approach was usually to show that we were trying to talk place-names by repeating the few we knew well, like Lhasa or Damxung, and also the last one or two we'd come through. They then usually caught on and helped us play the game of guessing which names we meant on the road ahead.

Laqudiqu was just like Damxung, a ramshackle modern monstrosity thrown up like an oil-boom town in the wastes of Texas. It was a main road with rickety chai houses indistinguishable from those at Damxung, with a square mile of single-storey corrugated-iron buildings: home to the several hundreds of people who presumably based their livelihood on the huge open-cast mine nearby. Beyond the town were empty rolling plains. We scoffed Chinese stir-fry and wrote a couple of pages of diary about nightmares in backyard fuel dumps. The diaries were our escape. We could shut out the world around us and immerse ourselves in our own thoughts. They provided a predictable safe channel, like radio, newspapers or telly, which rested us from reality and wouldn't answer back. On to them we could pour our woes about the misery of the riding, the fear of the desolation ahead, the irritations of our cousin. Whenever we stopped to eat, and waited for food to be served, we'd write. Then we'd set off again.

Day 32 had started well with seventy-two kilometres before Laqudiqu. We capitalized on this and turned it into a megaday by powering on through the perishing cold over the undulating plateau, all the way averaging 14,000 feet (4,500 metres) elevation, and joyfully cracking the 200-kilometre barrier before falling into the town of Amdo at the same time as darkness and a vicious squall fell on to us. It swiped through the tinpot town without so much as doffing its cap. Our hair stood on end with its ferocity. Dust whipped up into our eyes and a flash deluge tipped from the sky. It was gone in minutes but it left me in tears. I was fatigued by the cycling, frustrated as we searched for a bed and at the same time jubilant at the huge distance we'd covered. We had reason to be pooped because for all the last 137 kilometres from Laqudiqu we'd had no food and only our one litre of water each. When the storm dumped itself on me it was all too much and I hobbled behind Nick hanging on to his pannier rack for guidance as we felt our way in the dark over dirt heaps and rubbish, past wildly barking dogs, in search of the shelter they told us was 'over there'.

Nick. Day 33. Amdo. Noon.

A very good night's sleep – 11 p.m. to 10 a.m.! Last night we talked the barracks cook from his bed to do a stir-fry for us. This morning, with very thick heads and slow motions we've stumbled back to the main road where we piled into the first tea house with the customary 'Cha, please'. A good stir-fry for breakfast, then three double packs of 'cream sandwich' biscuits, a bottle of pears and a million 'cha' refills. We're very cold. Our feet are freezing.

It had snowed quite heavily in the night. Two inches covered everything. As we walked from the barracks to the chai house, the muddy pocked landscape at the back of town looked like a First World War battlefield – bleak, with the promise of worse to come. Blizzards periodically drive past the door here, and cloudbase is hovering about 200 feet up the hillsides. 'Why don't they ever close doors?' says D gazing at the big white aperture that's letting in a howling gale. If this is what it's like in June – what's it like when the weather gets bad?

From our maps, it seems we have ninety kilometres to the next town over a 5,130-metre pass, the Tanggula. There are some lorries so they'll keep the road clear of snowblocks, but it'll be wet all the way because we'll be soaked by our own wheel spray. I am deep down apprehensive; not desperately keen on tackling that pass in a blizzard. Feeling weary from the last few days. A bit worried, too, because with our 'minimalist' gear we've no back-up should things get really difficult. If we're wearing all our clothes in a tea house, what will happen on top of a 17,000-foot pass? Neither of us is too keen to make the first move to go out in the snow. Interestingly, there is no question that we should go for the Tanggula. We've not been stopped by the weather yet, indeed by anything. Once we use it as an easy excuse, it can be called upon again.

At 1 p.m. we plucked up courage and started. Within literally two minutes, we were lashed by a blizzard of hail and snow – luckily from behind, so it kept our eyes clear. It set the scene for the day by soaking us to the skin. There was nothing to do but tighten the toe straps and make progress up the pass. Half an hour later the storm had gone to be replaced by blue sky and sun – and a tearing freezing wind. Our feet went numb. We agreed that a short day was in order, and that it would be quite enough to battle the weather to the heights of the Tanggula and descend to the next town, which we thought was Wenquan. We thought it would be a small day. We should have known that on the Tibetan Plateau nothing is that simple!

Forty-seven kilometres out of Amdo we hauled ourselves to the summit of a pass. We assumed it was the Tanggula. A signboard said 5,165 metres,

rather than the 5,130 metres we'd expected. There was no view to be
seen and we were frightfully cold, but we had to stop because our feet
felt like thick sheets of frozen leather. They'd stayed wet all the past two
hours. They were painful to stand on. I sat down for a minute in the lee
of the summit cairn to take off my shoes and socks. I gave each of the
massive ice-boxes a quick massage before strapping them to the pedals
again.

Even in our misery, we rode with good spirits down the pass because
this was meant to be one of the major passes across the Plateau – tongue in
cheek we said: 'Downhill all the way to Golmud.' Half an hour swooping
down brought us out on to a flat plain with snow-fields and small tarns. It
could easily have been thirty kilometres of Rannoch Moor in winter. The
wind blew hard and we took it in turns to be the leading rider leaning with
left shoulder into the wind while the other sheltered. Joyfully, we spied a
road-worker's cottage and stopped to enjoy shelter and tea and dry bread.
Within a minute of stepping over the threshold, I had my shoes and socks
off and was gently warming my toes on the fire. We explained where we'd
come from, pointing back along the road and saying 'Lhasa', 'Tanggula'.
To our horror they frowned and, pointing the other way, said, 'Golmud',
'Tanggula'. We hadn't yet crossed the Tanggula. This was a great shame
because we'd hoped to do only about forty more kilometres that day
downhill to Wenquan. The pass we'd crossed they said was the Todju La;
furthermore it was 160 kilometres to Wenquan. We set out again feeling
desperately unenthusiastic. Barely half an hour later, we found some more
huts by the road and dived in for food. This was a Chinese compound of
five cell blocks amid piles of rubble inside a perimeter wall. It must have
been 5,000 metres above sea-level; we were right in the middle of
nowhere, all around us were snow-fields covering sandy high-altitude
desert. Not the slightest bit of vegetation anywhere – 'What a damn stupid
place to build a housing estate'.

We pedalled through the silent snow scenery. It was an open landscape.
None of the hills looked particularly big, no bigger than 1,000 to 1,500
metres above us, though of course they were way above sea-level. However, we weren't looking at the view but concentrating on forcing our
weary legs up this pass. At times like this when you don't want to pedal you
have to treat each hill as your last. You must pedal up it mercilessly. We'd
both been wearing Chinese road-worker's face-masks which are intended
for dust protection: we found them excellent for keeping sunburn off our
lips and for moistening the dry air we breathed. However, at this altitude
up slight inclines, I quickly ran out of breath and ended up gasping,
ripping the mask from my face to suck huge gulps of air.

In bright sun, the summit cairns came in sight. This was a big-success
pass – the highest between Lhasa and Golmud. We reacted accordingly
and each started sprinting for the summit; we flipped up a gear, nearly
reached the cairns, ran out of steam, fell down panting and stood up
laughing. Then to our dismay we saw another two kilometres to go to the

real summit. Once there, the height on a concrete plinth was 5,231 metres (almost exactly 17,000 feet). The mountain-chain we were crossing was the Tanggula Shan. It's one of the principal dividing ranges of the Plateau. It threads east to west, separating the dissected mountainous areas of Tibet proper around Lhasa and Xigatse from the open high-altitude tableland to the north. The Tanggula is the boundary between the Tibet Autonomous Region and the next province, Qinghai, reputedly so desolate that it's nicknamed the Chinese Siberia. Rumours have it that it is the refuge of convicts, criminals and society's 'undesirables'. Significantly for us, the Tanggula is the watershed between those streams which run to the Indian Ocean, and those which flow out eastwards like the Moron Us He and Dam Qu eventually to join the Yangtze, which issues into the Yellow Sea. Thereby spiritually linking us to Bo Hai Wan, our second point of nearest open sea to the Centre of the Earth.

We were almost in the dead centre of the Plateau, and had clocked up more than 2,500 kilometres, putting us in theory halfway to our target in thirty-three days. We'd done 550 kilometres from Lhasa and were halfway to Golmud. We had a right to be pleased, though ahead of us things could get yet harder. Ever since Laqudiqu the number of yak nomads had decreased and most habitations were road camps. There would usually be something every ten kilometres. Villages of more than two huts only occurred every eighty kilometres. Nomads' tents had been seen maybe once every five kilometres, whereas before Laqudiqu, especially around Damxung, they were almost continuous. Since Damxung we had rarely if ever seen a village of the square white houses which grace the Lhasa valley and all of southern Tibet across to Zanskar and the Karakorams. It was as though this area was so high, desolate and snowy that only the road provides life-blood and only immigrant Han Chinese drive on it and maintain it. It was virtually uninhabited.

In the past few days, we had covered some huge expanses of emptiness. Riding the road was mind-numbing. A lot of effort was required for a little progress. We never knew how cold we'd get, nor where we'd get the next food. Dreams were needed. Food dominated our thoughts. When the weather was good, i.e. not snowing or raining, we'd fantasize on turkey dinners and chocolate cake. When we'd come too far without food, and our legs hurt and our feet were cold, we'd crave bangers and mash – fish and chips had been banished from our minds because the Chinese stir-frys had soaked us in grease. When life got really horrible, a plate of rice, or bowl of noodles, was all we desired. We were obsessed with food. Robert Swan, on his 1985–6 Antarctic Expedition in the footsteps of Scott to the South Pole, summed it up when he said: 'On the cruellest days of ice and cold, the fantasies of food were agonizing. We'd try to avert our thoughts from food. Anything which took our minds off food. For instance, I'd think of my mother at home trying to imagine her knitting, walking in the woods, or the books she'd read. But, in 1.2 seconds my mind had flashed up an image of her fridge – What's inside? My X-ray eyes would see chickens and pies. Then as I tugged at the door my dream turned sour – I'd find it locked.'

However, for us, for once, the Plateau treated us kindly. We came sweeping off the Tanggula in brilliant calm late-evening weather. The snowy hills were like the Lake District in winter sunshine. Barely ten kilometres down the pass there was a semi-derelict road-camp in the snow. There were quite a number of large white canvas tents, most of them fallen down. Lying about were many piles of wood, rock, scaffolding and oil drums. The camp was surrounded by a bamboo-pole perimeter fence and churned-up mud and snow where vehicles had driven. We walked in and hollered. A chap with a nice smile came out and, as calm as Farmer Giles's wife feeding the chickens, beckoned us in. The tent was ten by five metres in area and maybe three metres high – a full-grown tent. It was very dark because the heavy white canvas was lined with felt to keep in the warmth. The only light came through the door-flap and a tiny semi-transparent square of discoloured plastic. Dimly we could discern two beds piled with rugs; one chap was in bed snoozing. I climbed on the other bed, Nick sat on a crate by the door. The floor was mud, and there were stacks of sacks and boxes of provisions as though they had taken a leaf out of Captain Scott's book and were prepared for a winter sojourn. We set to making notes in our diaries while the first man started making some food. He definitely said we could have something to eat, but the options for sleeping were in doubt for a while. We sat fingers crossed because we'd have hated to have gone out into the freezing cold again. We allowed time to run its course, knowing that the guys in Chinese road-camps are usually very friendly.

Our water-bottles froze in the night. We snuggled warm and cosy inside our sleeping-bags under a huge pile of rugs and blankets they gave us. In bed, we felt securely isolated from the traumas outside. We'd come some distance from Lhasa but there was an increasingly inhospitable distance ahead. It wasn't an easy night. Because of the thin air of the 5,000 metres altitude we had a slight problem sleeping – we'd wake in fear every hour or two completely out of breath. I had a dream which I think was meant to be a nightmare of failure but evolved in to a comedy. I was cycling up a steep slope when the saddle, wheels and frame vaporized from underneath me. I saw Nick rush past. He was on skis, going uphill, doing telemark turns on a power winch.

Nick. Day 34.
A bad night – couldn't breathe. Felt 100 per cent lethargic. D forced me out of bed before the 'lads' next door had got up themselves. So, no tea to start the day. Just a very bleary stumble into a post-dawn frozen nightmare. Hard snow, crispy earth. Tired legs. Down the mud-bank to the road. We curled downhill, losing height fast. Within minutes my feet were blocks of ice. Wind cutting through jacket, shoulders covered

only by thermal layer and jacket were particularly cold. We thought it was only fifty kilometres to a place called Wenquan, but it was an invisible place. This was the most empty part of the Plateau we had seen so far. The flattish bowl where Wenquan should be was fifty kilometres across. Our road hugged the hills to the left, distant mountains on the right. We saw only two road-huts, one nomad's tent and a herd of sheep. We never knowingly found Wenquan, though two road-camps, twenty kilometres apart, both claimed to be it. As always the people are exceedingly friendly and they're sitting quietly and proudly watching us eat. They find our lightweight chopped-down chopsticks fascinating. We've got noodles and a few bits of tinned pork meat. It's surprising how tasty simple boiled noodles are for breakfast when you've had to cycle sixty kilometres to get them! They said we were at Wenquan already, but also that it was around the corner (wildly flinging their arms). Finally we found an exit from this plain when the road dived off left into a valley mouth and we began a long gentle downhill ride. Thick mist and rain came down. A while later it left. The river became big and fast and brown. Despite the tinge of green in the landscape we saw no animals excepting several dead yaks. Epidemic?

Further on we came to Yanshiping, the first village since Amdo, 190 kilometres ago. It was a scrotty little hole with a single row of ramshackle cottages 100 yards long squeezed between the stream and a hill. There was a stench of rotting flesh. Very unusually for the Plateau, lots of refuse lay along the street and there were several dogs eating it. All of them looked mangy. There was an outdoor market stall selling bright Draylon cardigans and black plastic gumboots. Several men were sorting through the goods. Barely six feet away, a dead dog lay tangled in wire. The chai house was very cold.

We pressed on, not because we wanted to, but because we had several hours of daylight left and, however much we might dislike it, the only way out of this adventure was to get to the end. It had stopped snowing by the time the valley opened out on to yet another huge wide plain. It was the widest, flattest, *emptiest* place we had ever crossed. There was exactly zero sign of habitation, excepting one dead yak, one bird in the air, the strip of tarmac we rode on, and the line of telegraph poles to show the way. Everything else was a flat smooth uniform void. Huge expanses of plain earth devoid of humanity. A blade of grass and nothing else. Never before on this journey had there been such emptiness. The second worst was the ride that same morning over the Wenquan bowl. It seemed the further north we went, the more extreme the environment. Yet this plain was covered by a tinge of grass, and a big braided river flowed over it. We were only 13,000 or 14,000 feet above sea-level (4,000 or 4,500 metres). Why were there no people? Possibly winter was too severe for nomads, possibly everyday weather was too harsh.

The weather was intolerably fickle. It could swing in half an hour from wet, wild and windy to warm, calm and sunny. By early evening there was thunder coming on and it was snowing heavily. We had set off from Yanshiping in firstly a dry powder snow storm, then driving sleet. Big black columns of rain swept over the plain as we rode. The weather was a climatologist's dream. At one point late in the afternoon there was on one quarter bright blue sky and cotton-wool clouds over rounded brown hills, on another snowy peaks under a solid grey gloom. Behind us was a black tower of rain and in front we saw shiny green grass under cirrus sky. All in all, the most spectacular area for weather (excepting maybe Bangladesh!).

Despite the gloriously wild beauty, it was the first day when the journey really became a chore. We decided it was no longer as much fun as it was meant to be. It was a drag. The camera was broken. We'd ripped the inside toecaps out of our shoes to see if they had restricted circulation and kept our feet cold. Our feet remained cold but at least we'd lightened the load. We were wearing all our clothes all the time, and were cold all the time. Snowstorms and rain alternated with powerful winds and also moments of peaceful calm and sunshine. Because there were fewer and fewer people, it had become increasingly difficult to find shelter for the night. The Tibetan Plateau was serious.

I took to singing a song to myself to keep me going. It was suitably morbid:

> Well, how do you do, Young Willie McBride?
> Do you mind if I sit down by your graveside,
> And rest for a while in the warm summer sun?
> I've been walking all day and I am nearly done.
>
> I can see from your gravestone you were only sixteen,
> When you joined the fallen in 1915,
> Oh, I hope you died quick and I hope you died clean,
> Or, Young Willie McBride, was it slow and obscene?

Plopped down in the middle of the plain, forty kilometres from where we'd entered it and so far from the sides that no mountains were visible, was a corralled settlement called Tongteyho. We decided to stop early for the evening to give ourselves a chance to calm down, take stock and get a good sleep. But Tongteyho was a disaster. Inside the walls, there were four rows of one-room huts and a road-works compound. The huts seemed to be populated by loonies: cross-eyes, juddery movements, gammy legs, totally electrified hair and one girl with wild eyes and horrible stuff like flour all over her face. As we came in to start asking for lodgings, the first few doors slammed in front of us. It was very scary. We had no alternative but to stay here. A middle-aged woman in an apology for a mini-skirt came running out, laughed in our faces and disappeared. The next place was fifty kilometres on, the last proper village was forty-eight kilometres back. It was most unsettling. We had to persevere and hope that someone inside one of the doors was agreeable. We went to a door which looked like it might be the manager's room. When we knocked, a head did stick around the fractionally opened door, but with drawn eyes he shooed us off.

Mentally we rehearsed the procedure for scooping out a hollow in the desolation of the plains, and wrapping anoraks around our sleeping bags. We hoped it wouldn't get that bad. Luckily, reason was on our side and three rather strange men took us into their room where they sat on armchairs around the walls gnawing meat off bones. We sat on a settee, feet on the cold stone floor, and a woman who looked like she cried all the time poured us endless enamel mugs of hot water. It was certainly a peculiar place. Their first offer of bed was under the tractor in the shed outside. We would happily have slept there if we could have locked the door to keep them out. However, they had our best interests at heart and miraculously conjured up a spare room with double bed all to ourselves.

Nick. Day 34. Tongteyho.
I tried counting how many more kilometres to Urumqi; it's nearly 550 to Golmud and another 1,800 from there. The prospect was just too much for my hope and energy to grasp. I've been cold for most of the time since leaving Lhasa, continually uncomfortable, unable to sleep properly, stressed by the risks we're taking (both familiar and unfamiliar), stressed by not knowing where the next food or shelter is coming from, stressed by the unpredictability of the weather which could make both of us exposure cases if it wanted to. Also I guess the cumulative tiredness of the trip is beginning to show. Dhaka, Kathmandu and Lhasa proved that there's no rest until the journey's done. We're running down the whole time. Now we're stretching.

I know how hard I'm finding it, because for the last few days I've been escaping into fantasies in order to take the strain off what's going on. One of my favourite fantasies has me sprawled in my flat, with a big pot of tea and a packet of chocolate digestive biscuits. Penny's there. Friends come by and I've all the time in the world to do nothing. It's totally warm, secure and comfortable.

Other fantasies have me designing furniture – I've created the ultimate item: a computer work-station cum L-shaped bed doubling as settee with portable hi-fi module and swivel book-shelves. Life in a sitting-position; no motion. Other miniature dreamettes have me with the family in Norfolk and Coventry, or sitting by the fire in Cringleford eating toast and jam (this is an historic re-enactment fantasy – one of my favourite after-

school treats). Sometimes these daydreams are almost frighteningly vivid, and I make half-hearted efforts to banish them
lest I'm detaching myself too much from reality. Trouble is that
reality is so awful!!

The next day the same plain continued twenty more kilometres, the road
was as straight as a die, paralleled by the telegraph wires. It was dull and
overcast, cloudbase 1,500 feet above us. We had icy toes and cold hands,
and we pulled our balaclavas tight round our faces and tightened up our
hoods. For the whole of the first hour, during which time we pedalled off
the plain and back into hills, we saw nothing except, for some strange
reason, eight road-workers digging a trench. Having ridden off the
Tongteyho plain, we could confirm it was the most inhospitable we had
ever seen. The hills included a minor pass which took us a little over an
hour. There was no evidence of nomads, yaks or goats, though we did pass
two small stone huts, from one of which some children in yak skins came
running. We had our hearts set on Chinese stir-fry for breakfast, forty
kilometres further on in Tanggulashanqu, so we didn't stop. Quickly we
were on to the next intermontane basin. This one was almost bigger than
anything before. To the west it narrowed to a width of twenty kilometres
as the low hills bounding north and south vee'd in. But to the east it
stretched off in an unbroken flat expanse and we could not see any hills at
the end. I sensed that, like a yacht on a calm ocean, we could feel the
curvature of the earth.

Part of the ride over this desolate plain so closely resembled the Solway
Firth that my homesickness wanted to bubble over. We rode along a more
or less straight open windswept road like the coast road heading south past
Silloth and Allonby. Off to our left were ten to twenty miles of grassy
green, then beyond them some low round hills like the Lake District above
Cockermouth where Charles, Sandy and my sisters live. Off to the right,
the ground dropped down to the wide plain braid of sand, gravel and
expansive snow-fields that stretched thirty miles, like the width of the
waters of the Solway Firth, across to a single group of snowy mountains
under cloud like Criffel. A lump welled up in my throat and tears came to
my eyes. I wish we could have baled out.

Halfway over the plain we were treated to the surprising sight of a line of
ten yaks loaded with packs heading across the plain. Their destination
must have been the same as ours: Tanggulashanqu, the largest town we'd
seen since Amdo, nearly 300 kilometres behind us. It was composed of 200
to 300 low brick or tin huts mostly with corrugated-iron roofs. There were
several gas-tanks and a couple of things like water-towers. It was strung
out for 500 metres along the dry river and the road cut straight through it at
right angles with green glass bottle shards littered all along it on both sides.
It was a really basic town but had the advantage of serving an unexpectedly
good breakfast of onion omelette, followed by egg and onion soup, and
main meal of pork-fat cauliflower and onion stir-fry with rice, plus a bowl

of 'bollock' tea. I then nipped out to scrutinize the town and find who sold sweets and biscuits. An excellent prize was jars of fruit; we had two of apricots.

Further into Day 35, we pedalled northwards off the big plateau around Tanggulashanqu, over some minor hills, across a small basin, and then a white-out snowstorm engulfed us. It literally blew us without realizing up and over a major pass at 5,010 metres which we later learnt was called the Foho Shan. By this time we were very cold, wet and miserable again and ready to grasp almost the first sustenance we came to. That was after ninety kilometres. It was an isolated roadman's cottage of the sort to which we had become accustomed. A nice bouncy woman and her family lived there. She had a warm metal stove in the middle of the single main room. We made a beeline for it. She gave us hot water and bread, which seem to be the staple offering to guests in these parts. Various framed photos on the wall, a bright Buddhism Thanka calendar and some home-made tin ornaments. The bouncy lady, who incidentally when we came had been, like my late Mum, barefoot, sitting outside on a chair keeping an eye on the weather, brought out a radio and spun the tuning knob through a multitude of crackly bands and a predominance of static to find, to her great joy, the BBC World Service with age-old favourites Frank Muir and Denis Norden doing 'My Music'. Everyone laughed heartily and thought it was very funny – 5,000 metres up on the Tibetan Plateau – very funny indeed. When we looked outside again the sun had been replaced by sleet driving across the doorway. We elected for another mug of hot water and roasted our socks a little drier.

The sun kindly broke through half an hour later so we started again in good spirits with almost dry feet. We got about forty kilometres across another flat plain and were rolling well. As dusk came the wind grew extremely forceful so we could hardly pedal. Once more we were very tired. There was an unpleasant prospect of nowhere to sleep because distances were now so great; often forty kilometres between buildings. We clocked up in excess of 160 kilometres on Day 35. We'd broken the 100-mile barrier once again.

Around one corner we had the great pleasure of seeing a huge herd of sheep – the first animals *en masse* that we'd seen for days. Then over one more hillock and we came upon a tented road-workmen's camp. As always we approached slowly, making a big show of getting off our bikes and staggering slightly. We paused to peel off headgear, balaclava, goggles, face-mask, gloves, then stepped painfully forward with big grateful smiles uttering the words 'Hello', 'How Do?', 'Nice Weather'. The first young man to see us behaved normally and walked straight past into his tent. The second walking towards us was transfixed, then a third came and, seeing us, stopped momentarily before turning to rush and get his friends. With ten or more in front of us, then twenty, they broke into smiles and shook our hands, welcoming us into a tent. A couple of lads were earmarked by the leader to look after our bikes outside, but we didn't think this was a good idea so we lifted them into the big tent. We were given pride of place sitting on the edge of the big wide sleeping-platform which filled half the tent. The more important, or elder, or maybe simply faster, men sat beside us on the bed. Others at our feet. All in blue Mao suits and caps. Yet more filled the door.

Our timing was perfect because the sun had set, darkness was coming on, the men had finished work and food was cooking. As guests we were served first. Out came our short chopsticks and caused a laugh. Big bowls of noodle soup. They brought us seconds, and fed us strips of twisted bread buns. We felt totally stuffed but found it difficult to refuse more and more. Then big mugs of black tea. They were fascinated. After food we recited the nearest thing we knew to a story in Chinese – the list of place-names through which we'd cycled. You always find each name is known by someone in a crowd. They come up with a big smile when they know it and you give them a cheer so all their friends approve. Next thing is to try the places you're trying to get to, but that's harder because you rarely get the pronunciation right. We tried talking distances, e.g. from Lhasa or Golmud – that was too difficult and not a crowd game because it entailed writing numbers in the dirt with the back of a spoon or with our finger. We got out our remnant of China map and tried home towns.

One of the best games we had for evening entertainment was the contact-lens stunt. This was sure to mystify the crowd. I'd lean forward and peer wide-eyed at everyone, then bending my head slightly, pop out my contact lens and hold it up with a big smile for them. Everyone would lean in close, staring hard and murmuring among themselves because they couldn't quite work out what it was. So I'd lick it clean and pop it back in my eye. Smile. Do it again with the other lens. Put it back in, then invite everyone to take a close look at my eye to see if they could see it. Once we'd satisfied them with that game, the next game was getting Nick to do the same thing. It would raise equal astonishment all over again! The other good party trick, very applicable any time it was dark and we wanted to go to bed, was the incredible expanding sleeping-bag. Nick perfected a certain Tommy Cooper nonchalance for this, so that even I was in stitches of laughter and could never guess what he'd do. He unshipped the nearside pannier from his bike, tossed it lightly in the air so we could all see how small it was, then, unclipping the top, carefully began pulling out his sleeping-bag, as though doing the Indian Rope Trick. Each time he pulled, it doubled in size until he had in front of him an immense Black's balloon of warmth. He followed this up by then trying to stuff it back in again, fighting the sleeping-bag like a snake which leaped around the tent and all but escaped from captivity.

It would be impossible to convey to anyone who has not experienced it what it is like preparing to lie down to sleep on a communal cot with six Chinese beside you, watched by twenty others all uniformly dressed chattering away ten to the dozen. 'Getting your knickers in a twist' becomes no longer a mere figure of speech. Not only do you get Velcro strips sticking to all the wrong things as you pull off jackets and open sleeping-bags, but slinky cycling salopets require unusual contortions at the best of times. Nick solved it by sleeping in his, but got equally entangled by trying secretly to unload the microphone and tape machine. However, once ensconced, sleep came very quickly because the exhaustion of the day and the excellent fill of food combined contentedly with the obvious safety in the young roadmen's camp. We were asleep with the lamp still burning before even the first viewers had crept away.

When we woke, they'd all disappeared to work. Only an old man on our cot and the two cooks in another tent remained in the camp. It turned out rather disappointingly to be too late for tea. We set off northwards and, round the first corner, saw all our friends from last night hard at work. They were moving with pick and shovel a mass of earth from a hole in the ground to fill an embankment so the road could be levelled across a dry-stream gully. We waved cheerily and then settled to our work of turning the pedals for another twelve hours.

The sun came in low and sharp from the east giving long shadows. It was cold. We were fully wrapped up and keen to press on towards Golmud. A rather menacing 36-vehicle army convoy came past. Almost immediately we had to climb a short col, maybe ten kilometres of uphill, but enough before breakfast to start the day badly. Down the other side, the town we reached wasn't any more inspiring. It was relatively large, nearly as big as Tanggulashanqu, or alternatively with about the same population as the National Portrait Gallery on a quiet day, though not as well appointed. It was as awful as Yanshiping. A truck driver said it was Wudoulian. The chai houses – we tried three of the six – were freezing cold, and the staff most unfriendly. We met two gringos who were excitedly bumming a lift off a tour driver with a smart minibus. They told us all about how rough the ride was, how cold they'd been, how desolate it was. You tell me! We kept silent.

Wudoulian wasn't marked on our map, though with about sixty buildings and two things like gas reservoirs it was quite big. There were actually two towns forty kilometres apart marked on our map, and since we never found either of them Wudoulian was probably one or both. Its name was unimportant – a cad by any other name would still be a cad.

Nick. Day 36. Wudoulian.
We pigged out on stir-fry (meat and mushrooms), rice, onions, a jar of peaches, lots of biscuits . . . at which point I suffered a violent stomach cramp, rushed for the door and a derelict building. Too late. Horrible, horrible, horrible. Back at the chai house twenty minutes later, I ate the last of the biscuits. Slowly.

Further up ahead we decided our target for the day would be a place called Budongquan. It appeared to be about 100 kilometres away. Importantly, it seemed to be the last place on the far side of this last huge desolate plain before we crossed the Kun Lun Shan. This range of mountains stretches right across the Plateau from the Karakorams and Pamirs in the west to the lowlands of eastern China. They are a northern equivalent of the Tang-gula Shan, in this case dividing desolate but faintly green intermontane basins in the south from a forbidding area of barren salt desert called the Qaidam Pendi in the north. Once over the Kun Lun Shan, we'd plunge down into Golmud, which had been, for a long while, the light at the end of our tunnel.

Despite the cold wind, we set off enthusiastically. Seeing the kilometre posts clicking by (they'd been with us ever since that 1,929 marker outside Lhasa) we were excited by the imminent arrival of the one marking 1,000 kilometres. Counting down the distances single-mindedly we built up a lot of adrenalin and started sprinting for this unusual target. Each of us led for two kilometres: crouched down into the headwind, the other tucked in behind. When within six kilometres of the post, we shortened it by unspoken mutual agreement to one kilometre each. Thus we arrived fully burnt out, exhausted and laughing halfway over the final plain. We photographed ourselves and taped some comments, then gaily set off again. This plain turned out to be eighty kilometres wide. The biggest flattest plain we'd seen. At a stream a little further on, Nick stopped to attend to the results of his earlier misadventure. I took a stroll away from the road, out over the emptiness.

Dick. Day 36. Afternoon. Qinghai. 4,000 metres elevation.
I've taken a walk out away from the road over the wide rolling plains. They are big. The only noise is the whistle of the wind and the sing of silence in my ears. The road disappears many kilometres away in both directions over the brownish undula-tions of the plains. There has been very little to record on tape in the past few days. This area is so devoid of life. Only wind and fickle weather.

I'm lying in bright warm sun. The ground is soft gravelly red-brown earth. Every few inches there are tiny tufts of half-brown, half-green grass. Once every foot there is a nodule of moss. The ground is completely pock-marked by inch-deep footprints of sheep and horses. Horse dung is scattered every ten or twenty feet in every direction. Obviously there is a lot of activity here some time in the year. We haven't seen any of it. Maybe prints last a long time because there is little soil activity to destroy them.

This desolation stretches fifty to eighty kilometres in every direction. On the one side to snowy hills, on the other to the black jagged mountains of the Kun Lun Shan. In other direc-tions to emptiness and rolling plains, or to low brown hills or to the dark thunder cloud chasing us from the south. The silence is both eerie and friendly in the warm sun. It is so empty and so expansive that in the thin air you feel you can see hundreds of kilometres in every direction. There is much more than 360 degrees of horizon. As I look and turn, it keeps unfolding. . . .

EIGHT

The Big Descent

By the end of Day 36, we were coming up to finishing the last of the ultra-high-altitude intermontane basins. We had been cold for five days. We had had five days of snow interspersed by high wind and stark sunny intervals. The altitude had hovered around 4,500 metres all the time, leaping to 5,000 metres in order to cross the small ranges of hills which we encountered every sixty or seventy kilometres. There had been fewer and fewer people until for two days there had been virtually nobody and nothing for stretches of thirty to forty kilometres. In the distance, across the open plateau, a hard grey band of mountains topped in white had been getting closer all the day. They were the Kun Lun Shan, marching west to east across the middle of the Asian Plateau. We had cycled 1,000 perilous kilometres from Lhasa across the little-known Tibetan and southern Qinghai mountain terrain. On the other side of these mountains, to the north, was the unknown Qaidam Pendi salt plateau. Fortunately, just across the Kun Lun pass, barely 200 kilometres further, was the very large town of Golmud. Justifiably, we called it 'safety'. The optimism which tends to build up when you can see the glint of gold in the distance began to warm our spirits. We were sure there would also be some sort of habitation this side of the Kun Lun. A name, 'Budongquan', was marked on our map, though previous experience told us not to hold out too many hopes. All we wanted was a little sustenance and shelter before tomorrow's grand entry to Golmud.

We hacked on over the plain. It was eighty kilometres wide – a large hunk of real estate which would have been equally valuable, and probably equally interesting, if it had been at the bottom of the Pacific. I can imagine the advert, 'Undeveloped building site – Immense potential – Would suit fanatical time triallist – Private 50-mile straight!' Lake Bonneville salt flats: eat your heart out.

Nick. Day 36.
The clouds came closer and our energies depleted. The snow came thick. The road a long straight line of black. Just mindless

cycling. A strong headwind. Slowly the kilometres ground by. Damp, cold feet, dead legs. I was zigzagging in low gear. No life left at all. Budongquan came in sight. It was silent and white. A small group of white buildings sheltering by a small hillock, crushed by heavy cloud. Budongquan looked deserted.

There were a couple of roofless buildings, some sort of barracks, a couple of corrugated-iron sheds and a reserved walled compound. By the road, three whitewashed huts with red Chinese characters down the sides of the doors. Several oil drums were on one side and, in the snow, leaning on the wall of the middle hut, was a wicker broom. The door opened and a rotund jovial Chinaman leaned out. He had a round red face, glowing fresh in the chill, and a beaming smile. On our watch it was two hours to dark, but we decided to stay because dusk was beginning. Luxury on Day 36 of JCE was his concrete hut. Though it was small, he indicated we could eat and sleep there. It had a roof of criss-cross wood topped by tin, and no windows. There was no heating. We were at 14,000 feet (4,500 metres) with a gale howling outside. Our host and his wife (she was as chubby as him) were a happy young couple who looked like Michelin men in their thickly padded blue Mao suits and smart blue caps.

> *Nick. Day 36. Evening. Budongquan.*
> It is so cold inside that for the first time we are wearing our emergency thermal wear: sleeping-bags worn inside our jackets. The man and his wife are touchingly friendly. This is their home. The eating room: one table, the blow-torch cooker and hearth, bowls of veg and meat. No electricity. They've done us seaweed and dried shrimp soup followed by veg and pork noodles. Really very good indeed. It's the cleanest room we have ever been in and they take pride in cleaning it up. It's been swept twice already while we've been here. It's got a stone flag floor as polished as the entrance to the Jokhang.

We relaxed into the evening and, with much pleasure, sipped black tea from enamel mugs with matching lids. What made this so homely was firstly that we were pooped and secondly that the young blue-eyed Chinese couple seemed so much in love. They seemed so happy looking after us in that oasis in desolation. Clearly foreigners were new to them, and the idea that some people didn't speak Chinese was an alien concept. The man jabbered away in Chinese telling us all sorts of things about his hut, the village and where they came from. He had a big smile on his face and his short hair was all sticking up like caterpillar hairs sprouting out of a radish. We wittered away to him about our route, our home, our luxuries. It didn't matter that we didn't know what each other was saying: we were all just having a good time.

Nick. Day 36. Evening. Budongquan-in-Desolation.
The wind is tearing at the walls. Outside it's spectacularly cold.
It's snowing. For D and I this is luxury: good food but, most
importantly, totally hassle-free. Nice and secure and relaxing.
We've been able to sit at the table for two to three hours with no
disturbances. Just the flickering paraffin wick lamp to see by.
Never before have we sat at a table and had no visitors leaning
over our shoulders. I just can't believe how harsh this place is,
and how this couple make a living from the rare travellers.
We're too close to Golmud to be a major truck halt. Why have
they chosen to come to this isolation?

When we finished eating the man brought out a tin bowl of water to wash
in. Not only that but he produced some soap. Nick went berserk. More
than that the big surprise was that it was hot water. I submerged my hands
and gently turned them for ten minutes. Sheer luxury. We'd been cold for
five days so external warmth was intensely pleasurable. We made the sign
language for sleeping and he looked happy. It wasn't quite clear at first
where we could sleep because the hut was so small. He and his wife slept in
the room behind the stove. The only other room was behind a curtain: a
small storeroom with lumps of wood, sacks and boxes on the floor and
shelves of stores and vegetables. He made a generous gesture with his arm
indicating we could sleep there. 'Great' we thought sarcastically, and
imagined Nick lying on the stone floor, me wriggling in on top of four sacks
and a petrol can. Our host had better ideas, and with a loud chuckle lifted
all the stores off a huge shelf, swept it clean and looked proudly at us. We
both slept extremely well wearing all our clothes in bed and suppressing all
thoughts of having to go out in the cold for a pee in the night.

Nick. Day 37. Budongquan. Morning.
Dawn exploded into the house when the young man unhooked
the door and fresh sun lanced into our storeroom. It had been a
great sleep. As with all five-star hotels, all we had to do for
breakfast was saunter through a door – though we were clad in
every stitch of clothing including sleeping-bags! The day began
with a big meal. Our host was on as good form as last night. It
was a pleasure to wake up and see his short spiky black hair and
round moon face. His crinkly laughing eyes disappeared
altogether when he found something really to his liking (such as
the prospect of a ten-yuan tourist FEC note with which we
offered to pay him).

Outside it was phenomenally cold. It had snowed in the night. A pretty
two-inch layer covered everything and made it very bright. The wife had
already swept the snow away from their door. As we pushed our bikes back
to the road, they stood at the door waving like wartime wives at the

dockside sending their loved ones off to the Front. It would be true to say that we weren't all that certain how much longer we'd survive. The chances of us ever getting back to Budongquan were zero. It had been a most beautiful interlude in an otherwise alien journey.

Nick. Day 37. Kun Lun Shan. Morning.
Out in the bitter snow. A monochrome grey morning once the sun had gone. We pedalled stiffly swaddled in all our clothes. The scene was so like Scotland – we agreed we were on the road from Crianlarich to the Five Sisters of Kintail, with rounded and sharper snowy peaks 2–3,000 feet above us on each side. The colours – or lack of them – were identical: the streaks of snow and exposed patches of rock and earth so reminiscent. Even the temperature was Scottish, a biting breeze at just below freezing, and a wetness on the road from new snow. Big mountains ahead – entirely snow-covered, like Cruach Ardrain from a distance. Impossible to see where the road will find a gap in the range of the Kun Lun Shan.

We'd done twenty-one kilometres when the road took a left, climbed and dropped, climbed to a right and another left. Suddenly we realized we were at the highest point. We had ascended maybe only 300 metres in height from Budongquan to reach the summit of the Kun Lun Pass. This was the big divide between the exceptionally high-level basins behind and the high-level salt desert ahead. We could wave goodbye to the drainage system of the Yellow River and the China Sea, because ahead of us all the rivers were internal drainage – disappearing into shallow lakes and evaporating to leave a crust of salt.

Nick. Day 37. Kun Lun Pass.
It was freezing cold on the col in the snow. We were still wearing our sleeping-bags wrapped around us under our jackets. We pulled on our over-trousers and were thus clad in every single stitch of clothing which we had: 'All we've got left now are the spare tyres to wrap around us and the pannier bags to put over our heads.' We gazed with slight trepidation down the other side. The tarmac went only down. A huge column of new green Isuzu Chinese army lorries was grinding up the slope. There was nothing to be seen excepting more gentle slopes and it was difficult to imagine that we had a couple of thousand metres of descent ahead.

With all the rigours of the emptiness behind us forgotten, we tipped over the edge of the pass to roll speedily down what was at first a pleasantly small-scale valley in gentle snowy hills. Beside us, a gay little stream slipped away from time to time under shelves of snow. We could have been

in any one of the nondescript valleys since the Tanggula. Further on it
steepened a little so that each time we released the brakes our bikes seemed
to try to pull away from underneath us. The gentle slope looked as though
it didn't really lead anywhere but merely lent relief to the monotonous
high-altitude plateau. It turned east after ten kilometres into a much
bigger valley, quite different from anything on the high plateau. This new
valley had a kilometre-width of unusually green grass in the bottom, and
sides which rose up more than 1,000 metres. To our left they were well
eroded and roughly rounded, yet to our right they were black and jagged
with rock faces and snowcaps reaching up into the clouds. They were the
spine of the Kun Lun: confirmation that we'd crossed to another world.
This was a big valley of the sort we hadn't seen since Lhasa: we were tiny
specks wallowing in a trough of majestic scenery.

We veritably flew down the eastward-trending valley in top gear,
turning the pedals gently to assist the thrust of the gradient. Tufty clouds
floated around. Intermittently, the sun shone through to warm our backs.
Twenty kilometres from the top of the pass, the first habitation was a smart
clean new-looking Army camp of eight concrete hut-blocks, a water tower
and two fuel reservoirs. Apart from a small hut, it was the only habitation
since Budongquan, forty-one kilometres back. Then there was a road-
camp hut. Then nothing more and we charged on downwards. The road
veered over to the left for ten or more kilometres to a low point where the
valley seemed to level out in a flat bottom three kilometres wide. On both
sides the mountains continued above us. We sat up straighter on the bikes,
holding the tops of the handlebars, taking the breeze on our chests. The
flattish area ahead was hemmed in by mountains to the south and north,
our valley came smoothly down from the west and a mirror-image valley
sloped in from the east. There appeared to be no route out. It seemed to be
a closed depression. We thought surely this should be a lake? Were we
indeed riding into a black hole? As we closed in, a ragged tin village
became apparent at the low point. Then we discerned a narrow cleft
leading out north through the hills to the left. There were a few huts and
chai houses in this place called Shedatong. It would have been nice to stop
to drink tea and relax in the excitement of our return to Lhasa-type
Himalayan scenery after the barren emptiness of the high plateau, but
we'd set our hearts on Golmud for bed. That was 150 kilometres
away; we'd identified lunch as the place on our maps marked as Naij Tal
which seemed to be at the confluence of two big rivers and therefore ought
to have a good choice of food.

On the corner, as the road turned left into the cleft, we stopped briefly to
ablute. We congratulated ourselves on crossing the Kun Lun, then set off
thinking all the dramatic scenery for the day was over. We could not have
been more wrong. Big changes awaited us. The cleft was the beginning of a
long winding corridor of steep sharp mountains which soared up above us.
The road was caught tight between crags, scree and the tumbling torrent.
It was a magnificently savage gorge of torn naked rock faces and mountain

shoulders with multicoloured strata; browns, reds, blacks, greens and tints of purple climbing and crumbling all around us. Above that – snow. The river was a fighting braided stream twisting and turning like a demon trapped in a pit. We were losing altitude quickly and, as the temperature rose and the sun shone, we stripped off over-trousers and sleeping-bags, then rolled on happily doing very little pedalling. We enjoyed a penetrating warmth which we hadn't felt since Lhasa. Things were changing. The scenery continued to amaze us. The river in the bottom part of the valley cut down into its own gravels to form a mini-Grand Canyon with vertical cliffs fifty metres high beside the white water. The mountains stood bare and fresh like the newest mountains in the world, thrown up and broken down the day before yesterday, reminiscent of the entry into freshness of the Peruvian Cordillera Blanca up the road from the Atacama to Huaraz and Yungay.

By the time we were halfway from Shedatong to Naij Tal, our heads were spinning with the superb convolutions of the scenery. Yet there was more to come in the remaining twenty kilometres. The valley trended north-east. We came into semi-desert scenery with grass tufts one foot tall and scrubby bushes in clumps. The first big vegetation for 1,000 kilometres. Flash floods rushing in from side-gullies had cut deep scars in the soft gravel shelves beside the main river. Still there were no people. We saw only one small roadside hut. Suddenly we realized the air was warm, almost hot. The last few kilometres to Naij Tal we could cycle without anoraks for the first time in many days.

We reached Naij Tal mid-afternoon after the best-value day of cycle-touring we have ever enjoyed. Our pleasure was accentuated by the preceding days of desolation. In this single morning of ninety kilometres, we'd come from bleak cold snows and small hills through grand barren mountains to semi-desert vegetation in a crudely etched landscape similar to the harshness of Sinai. The only possible parallel to this ride would be the descent from the snow peaks of the Lalung Le going south through tight white timeless Tibetan villages in bright sun to the Himalayan forests by Khasha and then lush green Nepalese hill terraces. Alternatively, for the newcomer, exotic and startling in its own way, would be the London–Brighton Bike Ride from the majesty of the Houses of Parliament, through the vitality of Brixton and Streatham, over the beauty of the Downs, to the fun of Brighton. There you could stand and stare at the open sea – we hadn't seen any for thirty-six days and were still riding away from it.

Naij Tal was not big. In fact there was no chai house. It was a large Army encampment and nothing else. It took us ten minutes to find this out and by that time we'd been apprehended and escorted into the camp. Nervously, we were shown into a waiting-room for an audience with the commander. Was it good or bad? We didn't know. We had to wait. They brought us tea in china cups. It was a clean bright room with concrete floor. We sat on a floral-patterned sofa – soft seat for sore bottoms!! The officer in charge was a nice bloke in smart uniform; he was cordial without being unduly sociable. He sent an order for food, then left us in peace to wait. In due course we were summoned to the officers' dining-room. A round table had been prepared with tablecloth, flash chopsticks, water jug, mugs and, quite unbelievably, wine glasses. A soldier offered us a choice of beer or wine. This was luxury. The cooks served many dishes of excellent food. They watched and smiled. We tore into it with a vengeance, feeling a little guiltily that we should have more respect for their generosity – we needn't have worried because afterwards they made us pay. However, it was very good value even at the exorbitant price of 30 yuan: bean-curd soup, chicken and ham stew, grease-free courgette and pork stir-fry, cauliflower pork and soy sauce stir-fry, plus oodles of noodles. The beer went to our heads so we were both a bit tiddled. Our calves went weak and tingly. We were well fuelled. Sitting on a bike was going to be difficult for an hour or so until the food settled.

Golmud was 100 more kilometres, thankfully mostly downhill. In the officers' mess we'd seen their clock and found our watch was losing time – it was one and a half hours slow! That's why it got dark so early. We had four and a half hours' daylight left. We climbed on our bikes. A stiff northerly breeze had got up. It did its best to hold us back and we had to crouch low over the bikes to make progress. The first few turns of the pedals boded ill for the ride. Then our luck changed in a most amusing way.

Dick. Day 36. Late Afternoon. Confluence of Rivers.
Helluva way to go cycletouring! We've sprinted twenty-one kilometres into the headwind behind dumper truck 23-00452 driven by a lass in pigtails. It turned on to the road from the back end of the Army camp and it chugged all the way here. Epic journey for a dumper truck. We really had to battle to stay with it. Fought to keep our food down, yet hated the idea of having to struggle alone into the wind. All the way slightly faster than we could manage for a short sprint by ourselves into the gale. Up the few slight inclines, it started to get away from us. Gritted our teeth and forced our legs to turn. Big problem holding down lunch! Had to rip our face masks off at times. Exhaust-pipe right under our noses. On the outside of the yellow putt-putt was an old guy in blue tunic and cap. He's probably the foreman. In the middle seat, a girl in pale blue tracksuit spattered with paint. Interestingly this shows the work equality in the Chinese system – seemingly no discrimination. That's more than can be said for me: I naturally assume that the old bloke is in charge because he's a man.

The scenery for this sprint was very grand. Austere mountains ran steeply up both sides. The valley bottom was narrow. The river increasingly big.

It got steadily warmer. Bit by bit the scrub vegetation faded away. At twenty-one kilometres where 23-00452 pigtails left us, was a confluence with another big river and a second Army compound. We carried straight on. The route had turned due north. The wind blew straight at us and we wondered if we'd make the rest of the distance to Golmud. Luckily the clouds of bad weather had been left behind: stuck on to the Kun Lun. As we cycled the valley grew wider. Its central part becoming a wide flat sand and gravel expanse filling the valley bottom. The big river cut a deep vertical groove. Side-streams trickled in from their own small notches. The mountains on both sides became smaller and smaller. As with the bigger mountains before, they had freshly eroded barren slopes with jagged teeth along the tops. Their multicolour structure enhanced by evening sun. The sand plains of the valley became more and more extensive as though the big peaks of the Kun Lun were sinking down beneath the sands, submerged by their own alluvium.

Finally the mountains disappeared altogether and we cycled out on to a plain as flat as a pancake. Close to where the mountains finished, there was a cluster of huts and factory units and accommodation still partly under construction – not so much a new town as a transplant of the worst of early twentieth-century industry. Beyond it, the road stretched straight as a pencil over the flat sand plain. The biggest topographic feature was the line of telegraph poles. Golmud was no more than thirty more kilometres so we assumed we were as good as there. But a freak turn in the weather grabbed us. A black turmoil of clouds filled the sky and blocked out all light. For fifteen minutes a wall of wind hit us full on. I wanted to stop to let it pass, but Nick quite rightly urged me on. We fought forward in bottom gear. Not much faster than walking pace. Leaning with our left shoulders into the gale and rain. We took turns to shelter in the wind shadow, 100 metres each. Then, as soon as it came, it went. Suddenly we were free to race to Golmud with a pleasant following breeze.

Nick. Day 37. Evening. Golmud. 3,500 metres elevation.
Despite being supremely knackered I just managed to absorb the drama and significance of this abrupt transition from high cold plateau to lower flat desert. The bleakness was all that remained unchanged: a strip of tarmac laid over a buff desert. The ubiquitous line of telegraph poles for company. After the storm, the bikes bombed along the tarmac, each in the lead for one kilometre, at maximum revs. I just couldn't turn the pedals quick enough, we were going so fast. Slightly downhill with a following wind. Very exhilarating. Heightened by the lower altitude, which is allowing each breath to draw more oxygen. Despite it being the end of a long day I feel ridiculously strong. Already I'm dreaming of making the 527 kilometres to Dunhuang in three days.

My thoughts weren't quite as far ahead as Nick's. I was busy enjoying the sprint to town. It felt like a return to civilization. That's not to say it wasn't a strange civilization we were entering. It's an oasis of dreadful Chinese architecture and big messy compounds in the midst of many hundreds of kilometres where even a nuclear bomb would feel lonely. It seemed to take a long time actually to get into Golmud, but that may have been because it was the first place with any sprawl since Lhasa. Golmud had always been for us a mark of success; if we could get to Golmud, then we dreamt we could complete the trip.

We cycled through eight kilometres of suburbs to get to the roundabout in the middle of town. It added up to a very long 179-kilometre day including the fabulous Big Descent from the Kun Lun to Golmud, losing 1,200 metres of elevation in 159 kilometres. In town, the biggest buildings were six storeys high, most were two or three, all were uninspiringly square. The air seemed full of wires and poles. There were droves of vehicles and lots of vehicle-mending shops. At the bus station we found good clean accommodation in a spartan room with clean sheets, metal beds, a chair, a table, a concrete floor and a tin washing-up bowl. To our immense delight we had a tree right outside our window. Equally exciting, we were on the first floor: we hadn't been this high off the ground since Lhasa. In a daze, we sat on the beds, munched tinned apricots and chewed some mass-produced ammonia-flavoured bread. It was very difficult to assimilate everything that had happened – either on that day, or in the previous eight days from Lhasa.

Nick. Day 37. Late Evening. Golmud.
We laid out our map of China on the bed. For the first time since leaving the UK, we could see the Lhasa–Golmud section in the context of the whole trip. Now that we'd done it, it became a reality. We could see it in relation to the entire geography of this area. We had crossed the bulk of the highest part of the Tibetan Plateau – furthermore we'd done it by bicycle. It was a significant journey on a world map. Having been through it, we wondered how we'd done some of it so quickly. We could glance back and see some of the incidents: the night in the yak-dung store, the blinding sweeps of dust and rain in Amdo, the desolation of Tongteyho, the emptiness of the final plateau, the nights of fun with the road crews, and the jovial smiles of our chubby Chinese friends at Budongquan.

NINE

Sprint to the Gobi

We met a few other tourists in Golmud. They almost unanimously said it was ghastly; someone had stuck a note in the corridor of the hotel that said 'Golmud equals glum, mud, mold, dog, dul, ug!' We thought it was fabulous. We found lots of things to eat, plenty of places to mend bikes, hot water for washing, and a café with a telly to watch World Cup football in Chinese. It was a godsend and a gold-mine.

There were many jobs to do before we could set off across the last section of the Plateau. We allowed ourselves one day only in this warm cowboy town. The elation of having finished what we thought should have been the toughest part of the journey sent our minds racing on Day 38. It was a day of tidying up, checking gear, going shopping and stabilizing our thoughts in preparation for the sprint to the Gobi. In the space of two hours in town we ticked nearly everything off our shopping-list: new notebooks, pen, razor, new face-masks, washing powder and sweets. We ate so much chocolate that our mouths hurt. We found the office of the Public Security Bureau – marshals of law and order, feared by tourists in the same way that the Germans invading France feared the French Resistance. It was rumoured you had to get a special stamp from the PSB to be allowed to travel north to Dunhuang. If this was true, then we had no idea how we'd persuade them to give one to us. However, our luck was in and the lady in charge explained in good English that no permit was needed for bus travel to Dunhuang. We smiled and promised to go and buy a bus ticket *tout de suite*.

Three days previously the light meter in our camera, which had been overhauled at great expense by a supposedly reputable camera-workshop in London, had failed. For three days we had had to guess the exposure and take three shots of each photo. We had half-hoped that we might be able to buy some sort of camera – any sort of camera – in Golmud either from a local luxury-goods shop or from a fellow-foreigner. It was a bit of a long shot but you never can tell until you've tried. In our investigations we stepped into a photo parlour where customers were getting themselves photographed in front of a gaudy mural of the Potala Palace. Two particularly solemn soldiers had their photos taken. Nick observed that the glaring arc-light gave a flatness which really made them merge into the painting. The photographer wouldn't sell his camera – it wouldn't have suited us anyway because it was as big as a wind-up gramophone and every time a photo was taken the photographer disappeared under a voluminous black drape. However, Golmud came up trumps in half an hour. Nick spotted a traveller with a bulky camera-bag so I went over to engage him in conversation. He was a Japanese called Kenji Aoyagi, now a good friend of ours. Without much ado I turned to the subject of cameras and, truly amazing, he just happened to be carrying three Pentax bodies. By way of establishing our credibility, we showed him the covers of our *Cycling in Europe*, *Running the Himalayas* and *Bicycles up Kilimanjaro* books; then, following fifteen minutes' friendly discussion, he sold us his spare body for 140 dollars. A super bargain. What, we wondered, are the chances of finding a Pentax body in Golmud? Or, for that matter, Tibet or even the whole of China? Let alone finding someone to sell it? On Day 38 our luck was *in*!

In the middle of town we found the market. There were tables of fresh vegetables, trucks full of cauliflowers, huge piles of spinach. Some stallholders had baskets of chunky red tomatoes, others sold acrylic sweaters. There were two stalls of mini-magazines, which looked a bit like picture flick-books. These were not for sale but for hire. A knot of men and boys immersed in the stories squatted on the pavement on small stools. One area of the market was devoted to meats: pig's ears, pig's trotters, bits of cows. Those stalls were all tables with large umbrellas overhead. For some reason the fishmongers in another corner all displayed their wares on sacking on the ground. There was a group of soldiers in smart clean uniforms walking about looking slightly taller than the average Golmudian. When we brought out our new camera for a test shot, they quickly turned away.

En route back to our beloved bikes, we stopped for an hour's fun drilling holes in some of our equipment to lighten the load further. We surveyed a row of similarly ramshackle yet well-used garages and selected the one which had plenty going on. The workshop seemed to be centred on a welder working on a lorry chassis. Behind his back someone was shoving a hand-plane along a six-foot board balanced on two trestles. Three other men were holding a large wooden panel for the side of a lorry in place while a fourth whacked it with a large sledge-hammer. The work spilled out in front of the shed and coalesced with the neighbouring repairs. There were several other lorries in various states of undress, many large, precariously piled slices of sheet metal, a fine old green ex-Army motor bike and sidecar and, all over the floor, various bits of wire, wood and wood shavings. Chained to a stack of boxes of nails, rivets and bolts, an immense black shaggy guard-dog which leapt at us apologetically. It looked painfully sorry for itself.

Nick simulated drilling a hole in a specially toughened Campag cone-spanner with his finger. A wrinkled and very short old man watched sympathetically. He didn't seem to have any concept of safety: he selected a drill bit which appeared to be totally blunt and then shoved the two wires from the massive industrial drill-stand into the unearthed variable switch housing. The drill started up and was clearly off-centre. That seemed no worry to Steptoe because it simply made a bigger hole. He held the spanner steady in his hand, disaster was a thumbnail away, and he proceeded to bore three holes by high-pressure friction. While the men did their deeds, I used our penknife to grind a couple of little holes into the handle of my plastic teaspoon.

Back with our bikes, we spruced them up and checked all bearings. Both bottom brackets and both rear wheels needed tightening. We did the first job but the cones on the rear wheel were so tight that we feared cracking them. Therefore we left them alone, telling ourselves they were only slightly loose. I didn't really know the significance of this, but Nick on an early trip to southern Europe had found to his cost that a loose bearing quickly leads to much heavier shock loading on bumps and a snapped axle. On JCE that would be disastrous. We had no spares and no way of getting anything to fit, save sending back to Britain for more.

In the early evening a new group of travellers checked into our hotel. To our great surprise the one in a pith helmet was pushing a bike. He turned out to be Mark Skinner, an Englishman doing a World Trek for Charity and he'd come on the bus from Dunhuang that very day. We talked a few minutes then he took off his helmet and, looking inquisitive, he said: 'You're not the Crane Brothers, are you?' Nick blushed. We'd heard this question several times before. We said: 'Yes, more or less. We're trying to cycle northwards to Dunhuang and then Urumqi.' Mark had come that way. He said Dunhuang down near sea-level was a good relaxing oasis where one could rest up and recover from arduous travels. It was a fairly large town so a wide range of luxuries were available, yet it was not so big as to be impersonal. There were trees and fields and little streams. Altogether a very nice place to find on the edge of the Gobi Desert. Urumqi, he said, was huge and industrial – not pleasant. He tried cycling out from Urumqi to Turfan and onwards but it was too depressing. In another industrial centre, Hami, he'd been arrested. In his travels, he'd had some fun and indeed had been one of the first people, and obviously the first cyclist, to enter China from Pakistan to Kashgar over the Kunjirab Pass when it opened on 1 May – exactly the same day that Nick and I waved goodbye to the open sea. He'd been on the road for two years, mostly Europe, some Africa, plane to Pakistan. Ahead of him another two years through Asia, the Far East and America. Halfway through an epic like that he was understandably depressed: unable to see the end, unable to believe the beginning.

By late evening we were nearly ready for our early departure in the morning. We wanted to put everything into the next section of 547 kilometres to get to Dunhuang quickly – weather, drinking-water, terrain and the omens permitting. The area is called Qaidam Pendi. It's salt desert. The few rivers which exist are internal drainage. They flow into themselves and disappear in the sands or shallow lakes encrusted by salt. Our guess was that it would be quite flat like an extension of the plain of Golmud. The road, we had thought, would be a continuation of the tarmac we'd had all the way from Lhasa. Just before Dunhuang we would reach the Altun Shan mountains and there we would cycle over the lip of the last part of the Asian Plateau leaving behind 3,000-metre elevations once and for all. At this point in the expedition, we both thought that the worst was over and it would be plain sailing from here on in. We calculated three days to Dunhuang, hopefully four or five to Urumqi, one more to the Centre of the Earth. We'd be finished in under fifty days. Things were rosy. Suddenly the accumulated stress of the past few days and weeks unloaded in a barrage of pent-up fears aimed at Nick: always leaving a few mouthfuls of water in his bottle as reserve, eating too much, having a different view on how to tape-record, sleeping too long, not having fought me tooth and nail at Detsukar. In Golmud, seemingly near the end of the journey, we thought external strife had finished, the pressure was off. Unconsciously my brain allowed me to criticize and complain: all the gristle which is normally poured into diaries, or written in letters to loved ones, this time was dumped on to the person closest to me. Nick took it quietly and objectively. Months later he told me that, although he hadn't noticed it at the time, overall he had the impression that it was my way of keeping up the pressure of our speed ride by falsely creating stress during times when the day-to-day business was easier. Nick said: 'I prefer to escape from the fears of the journey at certain points, and switch off to relax from time to time. Golmud would have been a good place!' A similar thing happened in Running the Himalayas, because when we got to a mere few hundred miles from Pakistan I let out several massive outbursts against Ados. However, on Running the Himalayas it did transpire that we were close to the end; out in Golmud we were unaware of the difficulties ahead. After everything we'd been through to date, we thought that we had seen it all, but Day 39 showed we were far from the truth.

Nick. Day 39. Morning.
Dawn crept slowly into Golmud. The light was grey. The sky overcast. Only the wind was busy playing games. Lost 3 hours getting ready. Departed Golmud elevenish. Straight fast road. Making good time. Tarmac. Dead flat every direction. Sand or baked earth. Strong sun. Railway on right. Telegraph poles (twenty-one per kilometre therefore 35,000 since Tibet border). Fast. Featureless. No veg. No nothing. Little traffic. Hot. Sweating. Snow-goggles and face-mask. Air very dry.

We sped out of Golmud on a very good road surface. Shanty development sprawled six kilometres from the centre, then there were a few tents in the scrubby desert up to ten kilometres from town. Then nothing. Flat sand-desert stretched away to the horizon. Twenty-five kilometres out of Golmud we came to the edge of a salt marsh with dragonflies and big fat mosquitoes which bit Nick on the bottom while he was relieving himself. Sixty kilometres out of town we came to a road-side settlement called Qarhan where the railroad turns east to leave the Plateau and start the long descent to mainland China and the city of Xian. In a tented road-camp, the men were extremely friendly and gave us hot water to drink, cooked up some soup, offered us momos left over from breakfast and wanted to ride our bikes. We each took turns to stand outside the tent on guard. A kind young man with a jacket brought us four dried fish. We were so hungry we devoured them head, tail and bones. Someone kept offering us spirits to drink. We spun out of Qarhan after thirty minutes, hearts set on knocking up a really good mileage on this fast road.

One hundred kilometres out of Golmud we stopped to gaze in awe at the emptiness. It seemed unreal that we had crossed such a large distance of totally featureless terrain. The road was essentially a continual straight. Though 3,000 metres above sea-level, all the way we saw no hills, no mountains and it was hot, dry and flat. Nick sat on the edge of the tarmac for a rest. In deference to the enormity of the cosmos, I took a short walk out across the hard-baked salt crust beyond the telegraph wires. There was nothing between me and eternity. For the benefit of anyone who might hear our radio tapes, I recorded the sounds that you hear in the middle of nowhere. There is no sound, except the blowing of the wind. The wind, the dryness and the heat of the sun are the only handles which give reality to the fearful void (apologies to Geoffrey Moorhouse).

Alone in the vast hemisphere of sky, I was virtually involved in a religious experience. Life was reduced to very simple components: earth, sky, sun and wind. They were the four dimensions. The wind marked time. I was at the centre of them all. I felt very important because they all radiated out from me; the earth in every direction equally flat and featureless, unrelenting; the dome of sky built so exactly over the very point at which I stood; the wind blew directly at me; the sun focused on me. I felt incredibly small and helpless. All these phenomenal forces concentrated on me. I was powerless to reach out and touch them. For an agnostic, I felt surprisingly humble. I knelt down.

Kneeling down I came close to the earth. I saw mud cracks, sparkling crystals and a tortured salt crust. Suddenly I was a giant again. In the minutiae of the terrain was a whole world of mountains and valleys, gorges and forests of shining salt crystals. The polygonal plates between sun-cracks were up to a metre across. Their surface was as rough as magnified cinders, dry as ashes. A well-matured block of Stilton breaks with similar artistic crenellations and leaves the same clammy dryness in the mouth. Fine, furry white dustings of evaporites lined some of the folds. Nick yelled: 'Hurry up, Moses, before the floods come.'

A short while further on, we started to climb steadily out of the middle of the Golmud part of the Qaidam salt basin. The road had been good fast tarmac, technically downhill all the way from the top of the Kun Lun Pass, 260 kilometres ago. The slope was imperceptible at first. Gradually the salt crusts were left behind. Low ridges appeared ahead. We pedalled into an area of golden yellow seif dunes which stretched east and west as far as the eye could see. The tarmac strip and telegraph wires were cut through twenty-metre-deep furrows. Sand spilled on to the road. There were plenty of signs of regular road-workers and dumper trucks which shovelled it away.

One hundred and thirty-three kilometres out from Golmud we topped the first line of low dry spiny hills. Far ahead, bare grey mountains could be seen. Everywhere was empty of life. It was more truly deserted than anything we'd seen before. The road continued like a gunshot straight across the Qaidam. The wind was hot and dry, veering around to face us head on. We set off again. Inexorable. Dreadful headwind. One kilometre battling lead each. Bone dry. Heat haze. Mirages – or hallucinations? What on earth next? We struggled on, determined that Dunhuang was close and we could do it, come hell or high water, in three days.

One hundred and thirty-seven kilometres out from Golmud, we met the cruellest blow. The tarmac ended. With it ended our hopes of making good speed. The next town, Xitieshan, more than fifty kilometres away, instantly became too far for that night. Also we thought our hopes of Dunhuang in three days had died. It was quite depressing. We couldn't even be bothered to get off our bikes to commiserate. In fact it was incredibly depressing – our belief that the Lhasa–Golmud section was the toughest was turned on its head. Here, in the Qaidam Pendi north of Golmud, the environment was more alien than on the Tibetan Plateau proper. It was almost totally empty. There was virtually no habitation. It was excruciatingly arid. Any ideas we might have had of finishing in under fifty days had completely dried up. Our only consolation was our own optimism that this might be merely a short section of dirt – good tarmac would reappear soon. It didn't. At times like this, when confronted with the unfortunate in the midst of adversity, there is no point in sitting down crying – the only thing to be done is to collect your wits together, take a serious cold overview of the situation, and get yourself out on to the next section. A couple of times in the past, similar circumstances have befallen me, twice being caught out on foot overnight, hungry, in the snows of Zanskar; once Nick and I with eight friends on the side of An Teallach in mid-winter. No one will come to the rescue – you have to do it yourself. We bottled our woes and got our heads down battling into the wind.

One hundred and fifty kilometres out of Golmud, having seen no colour in the emptiness all day, except bone-dry browns and greys, we cycled round behind the bare grey mountains, and saw to our surprise, in the next basin, a beautiful treasure shining in the evening sun – a royal blue lake, rimmed on the far side by white salt shores, and edged near us by rich green reeds and lush pastures with thick grass like the best in Britain.

Horses and sheep and a couple of white nomads' tents were far away in the distance. How on earth, we wondered, do they find their way to this secluded drop of sustenance? Their next neighbours must be a hundred kilometres away. We stopped and sat down to gaze for a moment. Like Lake Titicaca, it was a haven in the midst of awful hardship. Despite the immediate beauty of this jewel, in its entirety it was one of the most hostile environments I have ever seen. The greenness lasted only a kilometre from the lake. We had cycled out of alien desert; sand dunes crept up behind us to the edge. On the other side a steep bare mountainscape rose up black and evil to a snow-capped ridge. Triangular outwash fans rushed back down carrying erosional debris to the lake. All the elements of the scene were etched in severe contrast to each other. The colours were prime. Everything asserted its independence: the lake, the salt, the sand dunes, the scree, the snow and the unguarded sun. Even the hordes of biting flies. A fierce wind tore across the lake ripping out its share of the bounty.

The sun was low and we were tired. We decided to seek out a sleeping-place, even if it meant sleeping rough. However, as always, luck was on our side. We pedalled only about five more kilometres and found the road was badly dug up, being rebuilt. There, we came upon a tented Chinese road-workers' camp. There were thirty tents arranged like a corral, with a row of trucks, a tall radio mast and various stacks of equipment. The men were endearingly friendly and we were escorted to meet the foreman. He had shaven black hair, a cigar, a big smile, and he shook our hands. He wore a white open-neck shirt and baggy black trousers with a jangling chain of keys on his belt. His tent had a carpet, electric lights, and the walls were insulated with felt. It was a luxury tent with bed, spare chairs and his desk. On it were ink pot and pens, electric calculator and abacus. They brought us tea, and in our eagerness to rehydrate I spilt some on his desk. One of the ordinary road-men rushed forward to clean up quickly. I apologized profusely and wouldn't have been surprised if they'd kicked us out there and then but instead they brought us the most fabulous meal. We stuffed ourselves on four huge momos, a massive rich omelette, a luscious ginger-flavoured meat dish, mouth-watering fish platter and a couple of bottles of fizzy red pop. They would accept absolutely no payment for the food nor for the beds for the night. We entertained them with the sleeping-bag trick and the contact-lens trick. Also we recited place-names we had come through and hoped to go through. We slept in absolute luxury with a bed each in a heated tent and completely forgot about the Qaidam Pendi.

The next day, we rose early, at first light, and left before the cooks had breakfast ready. Most of the men were still in bed. We were desperately keen to make good progress and get off the dirt road and the Plateau as soon as possible. Physically, Day 40 was probably the hardest day so far. The details disappeared into an empty mash of rock and gravel. It was always dry, always deserted. Most days I can easily recall the details of food and drink, reconstruct the passes and the bends, enjoy again the scenery and the people, but for Day 40 on the Qaidam it nearly all vanished leaving only a bare skeleton on which to hang the day.

We didn't seem to stop at all. Pressing on along the dirt roads, we forced ourselves relentlessly, and took what food and water we could get in the few places we saw. Breakfast after thirty kilometres was greasy breadsticks and rice-water soup in the dirty, dusty and unfriendly new town of Xitieshan. We took hot water and stale momos in a hut below the La La Shan where the man was drunk and had his flies undone and the woman held her hand over her face all the time. We struggled on through depressingly thick gravel in chilling cold under overcast skies up the Pooh Pooh Shan 287 kilometres from Golmud. Last thing before darkness we time-trialled thirty-five kilometres, alternately one kilometre each in the lead into the wind and one kilometre each in the slipstream fearfully keeping upright in the gravel and frightened of the kilometre-post which signalled our return to the lead. That frenzy of single-mindedness spared no thought for discomfort and took us into the village of Huahaizi at ten. Huahaizi was our target and we made it. It was our launch-pad for reaching Dunhuang the next day and satisfying the three-day dash from Golmud to the Gobi. By the end of Day 40, we had covered an impressive total of 183 kilometres. This was a most creditable performance on a road which was dirt and rarely flat, 3,500 metres (10,000 feet) above sea-level, especially since the previous day, Day 39, we had cycled 157 kilometres. The distance reflected not only our aggressive determination to get to Dunhuang but also our high level of physical fitness after all the high-altitude days before the Kun Lun Shan. Day 40 was probably, on paper, our biggest physical effort thus far but it came without any significant points of interest or strife. It was the most nondescript day we had – simply one long soul-destroying power through emptiness. We each needed private thoughts of home to keep us going. Fourteen hours of daylight disappeared in a mindless blur of pedalling.

I was pushing for a dawn start on Day 41, but unfortunately I slept through it. This pleased Nick because he was of the opinion that eight hours' sleep were better to speed us to Dunhuang. One hour after dawn we went looking for food. Huahaizi was only small – a pin-point of habitation in the middle of another flat plain like Golmud. It had a huge radio aerial, three faceless white-walled compounds, an army barracks and half a dozen small white-walled brick huts. Some of these were locked, three were chai houses. We'd slept in a room in the army barracks though there was an official truck-drivers' compound where everyone was drunk. In the morning that place was strewn with litter and rubbish and the first drunks had already stirred to find their bottles of booze and continue destroying themselves. Nick dubbed it 'the filthiest hole in the whole of China'.

After soup and stir-fry, we headed north once more. The alien empty Qaidam Pendi ended with the same wide, absolutely featureless and flat expanses with which it had started at Golmud. There was only our straight dirt road, a row of telegraph wires and, nestling into the edge of the road, the small kilometre-posts which we eyed jealously – they already were linked to Dunhuang: we had a long way to go. After eight kilometres we reached a bend. This was a significant point of interest. We looked ahead, and the road continued straight into the distance. We buckled down to churning out the wheel revolutions. The kilometres slipped by. Each time I looked up, the road was endlessly straight ahead. It made my heart sink. I kept a statistician's tally of the distances. Three hundred and sixty-eight kilometres from Golmud we met another bend. After that it was a further twenty-five kilometres to the next. Luckily at this point the road was starting to climb noticeably uphill out of the Huahaizi basin, and bends began to come thick and fast. The basin had been ninety kilometres wide between the incline down from the Pooh Pooh La on the south side and the climb up to the Altun Shan on the north side. Last night we had pedalled hard along forty-five kilometres of dead-straight road into Huahaizi where there was a kink, so the sequence of straight stretches of road between bends was 45–8–20–25. It's not often that one finds only three corners in ninety-eight kilometres.

Over this plain there was, every fifteen kilometres, a solitary road-mender's house. Each seemed to supervise the care and repair of seven and a half kilometres of road on each side – marked by little notice-boards where the gravel surface would change slightly depending on the whims of the individual caretaker. The small tractors which dragged the road-levellers and graders turned around here leaving sweeping semicircular comb marks in the gravel and sand. To our great delight a hard black road surface appeared before we finally left the Huahaizi basin. We stopped for a celebration rest on the tarmac – real tarmac – and assured ourselves that surely it must be continuous to Dunhuang. Only 147 kilometres to go. We desperately wanted to get there that same day.

The last section of the plain was slightly less empty than preceding areas. There had been barchan dunes and later there were some brownish fields to the east of the road. On the west no vegetation, only dry land. Ahead the Altun Shan mountains were not particularly impressive as scenery but they were an exciting marker of the end of the Plateau – our escape from the Qaidam and our final farewell to high altitude. They were large but unimposing, slightly rounded brown massifs. One or two peaks had snow summits. We could see our road lead up to a large cleft and disappear into its mouth. Our excitement was building up and despite the uphill gradient we silently began to pick up speed. At first we rode side by side, both feigning no interest in a competition. First one, then the other, would pull a wheel length ahead, then a bike length ahead, winding up speed, testing each other for stamina. By this time we had covered five kilometres and were thrashing a largish gear, sometimes pulling twenty metres in front for a couple of minutes until the other summoned up courage to turn on the taps. No race was mentioned. We were both tight-lipped, yet gasping for breath. Each thinking to ourselves, 'I'll show him.' We powered on, draining our legs in a frenzy of excitement at departing from the Plateau. It hurt. Eventually I cracked and yelled: 'Stopping to look at the view at that corner ahead.' We both sprinted like mad, then collapsed in heaps of laughter and agreed a dead heat. We were nearly into the mountains. Behind us the Huahaizi plain stretched off in the distance back beyond sight to the hostile black mountains and the few royal blue lakes, behind that to busy little Golmud. Far away now were the Kun Lun Shan. It was difficult to imagine the existence of the lovebirds in the snows of Budongquan. Anything before that was a dream.

Large alluvial fans washed out of the front of the mountains. We pedalled into the steep valley and, five kilometres later, at 13.48 hours we were sitting at the summit of the Dangjin La, the pass out of the Altun Shan and away from the Plateau. Big Celebrations!

Nick. Day 41. 1.48 p.m. Dangjin La. Altun Shan.
Sitting on a sunny bank at the top of the pass, the most northerly limit of the Tibetan Plateau. Brown hills rise 500 metres above us. There are some clouds. Around about us are the high serrated ridges of snowy mountains. Our road will lead down through them in a huge valley. A blue water-tanker is grinding up towards us, its bonnet flaps open for cooling. Just a short distance over the pass is another lorry with its sump in pieces spreading a huge pool of oil on the road. Fine pale grass is dusted over these slopes, and a short way below us some horses are grazing. It's quite peaceful here. Just at the moment it's hard to believe that we've actually crossed the Plateau – that big purple weal on my school atlas that looks so big; so impenetrable. I wonder if anyone else has made this journey? We've been at an average 4,000 metres above sea-level nearly all the time from the Lalung Le and the Nepalese border 2,500 kilometres away. It has been a struggle. Now, as always, it's impossible to get an overview of the ride because the details of daily survival outweigh the pleasures of basking in achievements. There's always the worry of food and water. We're hoping to get to Dunhuang tonight. Then we worry about the heat of the Gobi Desert (a radio broadcast in Golmud last week said it was 39°C). Will we get arrested in the closed towns of the Silk Road? Can we find the Centre of the Earth? Etc., etc. But one thing we no longer have to worry about is crossing the Tibetan Plateau. We have done it! WE HAVE DONE IT!!

The descent started. Our bikes fairly leapt away from us. The tarmac was smooth and fast. Beyond the first few bends, the road was steeper than an Alpine pass. We flew like birds. We had to touch our brakes on and off all the time. No pedalling needed. None was possible. We had to concentrate hard to get around each new bend. The air temperature was barely above zero. The wind chill factor was something extraordinary. Wisely we'd togged up fully in all our clothes before whistling down the descent. The well-rounded gentle brown slopes where we'd started soon closed up. We dived in between the higher mountains. The road was hemmed in by steep fell-side interspersed with rock-faces. Ahead we dared to glance out from the gorge, not to foothills and distant desert, but to open blue sky. Down and down we went. Our road snaking through the gully. The air temperature increased all the time. We plummeted thousands of feet from the austere heights of the plateau towards the sizzling desert.

We issued from the mountains after twenty-four kilometres in hardly more than twenty-four minutes to Aksay. It was a small cluster of buildings, satellite to a much larger cluster several kilometres off to the west snuggled up under the front of the Altun Shan. The formidable black rock walls of the mountains came plunging down from the dizzy heights above then vanished straight on down deep under the ground. A mantle of alluvial fans overlapped and interlaced all the way along the front of the mountains and stretched out northwards towards the desert proper. It made an extensive flat apron tied all the way around the base of the Plateau like an enormous skirt on a cosmic hovercraft. On a smaller scale, it was bouldery and rubbly, made of large gravel and small cobbles brought down in flash floods. There were abundant scrubby bushes like they have in Westerns, and little knots of tufty brown grass. Aksay was at an elevation of maybe 2,000 metres, just the right height to guarantee a lovely temperature and sun from the Gobi, combined with, from the Plateau, all the scenery and breeze you could hope for. We dived into the first chai house and wolfed down fabulous flat-noodle and vegetable soup, freshly steamed momos – Nick said, 'Four of the *best* momos I have *ever* had' – with pork and onion stir-fry, and bowls of tea. A most satisfying blowout. Beside us a bus-load of Chinese officials were slurping in appreciation of their gourmet meal.

It was four in the afternoon when we left. We knew we should be able to make Dunhuang because, although it was just over 100 kilometres further, it was theoretically downhill all the way. The piedmont gave us twenty kilometres of fast straight slope. We careered along, no brakes, no pedalling, racing each other using a variety of aerodynamic racing positions. Nick, keen Tour de France follower, let me into the secret that the fastest position seems to be that used by Greg Lemond and the Colombians – backside high, nose on front wheel, elbows tightly crushed – it's extremely uncomfortable.

At the foot of the piedmont, the road veered north-east for a while and we had to get our heads down into the wind and pedal. The gravel terrain changed to sand. The vegetation vanished. We were down to 1,500 metres elevation, and the wind-proof jackets, thermal tops and leg warmers we had worn since the summit, and during the lunch stop, had to be rapidly discarded. The balaclavas which we'd worn as head-warmers for virtually every single one of the 3,000 kilometres from Kathmandu were turned inside out and converted back to sun-shades, as they had been in Bangladesh and India. Our perpetual worry about keeping warm on the Tibetan plateau had been swapped for fear of the heat and dryness of the central Asian deserts. To us, returning to low altitude after weeks in the cold, the air was thick and our legs felt extraordinarily powerful. We had it in our heads to do the remaining seventy kilometres to Dunhuang in a sprint. We persevered for fifteen kilometres into an increasingly strong wind, then we got into the first of many areas of roving sand-dunes. They were very large, dwarfing us and the few trucks which came past. Behind us we could still see the wall of the Altun Shan holding back the Qaidam and Tibetan Plateau. On the top of it, snow peaks were visible. Our road in the heat channelled through the dunes beside an almost dry stream bed. The wind funnelled straight back whipping sand into our faces. Our enthusiasm waned. The remaining fifty kilometres looked a very long way.

A tractor and trailer trundled past. I shouted: 'Tractor – Get on, Nick.' We sprinted like Six Day riders at a prime. I led out into the wind after it. I faded, Nick took over the chase. He faded, saying: 'We can't catch it.' That gave me new strength and I tore past him, he powered for a moment to get into my slipstream, then I hammered away at the pedals for maybe five seconds and we sprinted into the slipstream of the trailer: one to two feet behind the vehicle so it broke the wind. It's an extremely dangerous way to travel. Out in the Gobi we were desperate. It was taking a chance, but it killed the kilometres.

This trailer, and the back of several trucks which overtook us, were loaded with coal, maybe from mines in the town near Aksay, going to Dunhuang. Several times we saw loaded coal-trucks going the other way – 'Coals to Newcastle'? After some kilometres the tractor stopped to cool the engine. We went out alone into the wind and sand squalls. It was increasingly hot and parching dry. We sipped sparingly at our water-bottles. They'd inadvertently been filled with cold tea in Aksay. Now it was lukewarm yet quite refreshing – but, then, anything is when you're that thirsty. Our feet were burning hot from pressure on the pedals, quite a change from freezing blocks of ice. There was no view except featureless plains, the strip of tarmac we rode, the line of telegraph poles and Nick's bum every two kilometres. We were taking it in turns to lead. We made good progress. Twice we were about to stop for a rest when a tractor came past us and we sprinted into the wind shadow to make a few more fast kilometres. As I wrote in my diary that night, it was an 'amazing way to enter an oasis – in the suck of a coal-truck!'

For forty kilometres from the edge of the piedmont there was nothing but absolutely level stony desert devoid of scrub but blown over by sand-dunes and blanketed by wind. It was exactly the same as the other side of the Altun Shan excepting 2,000 metres lower and ten to twenty degrees hotter. Just as flat, bleak and dry. Just as barren. Then suddenly, a short way before Dunhuang, 493 kilometres out of Golmud, nearly 2,000 kilometres from Lhasa, the first trees. They were taller than us, covered in

fine leaves and looking a bit sorry for themselves on the edge of all this
sand. They were irrigated by stream water running down from the Altun
Shan. Their green appeared to our green-starved eyes rich and deep, and
as shocking as a flashlight to a troglodyte.

The trees marked the first of several small oases which linked up to the
main Dunhuang oasis. Shortly we were riding past fields of lush green
maize, wheat, vegetables and fruit trees. There were avenues of trees by
the road, a brick-works, mud huts, small factory compounds, tractors,
donkeys and bicycles. There were weeds on the road-verges and the
singing of birds in the trees. We could smell the vitality. There had been
no smells for twenty days. Even our own body smells had seemed to
vaporize in the emptiness of the Plateau. Most importantly, around
Dunhuang there were people by the score: walking, riding, sitting,
working, planting, reaping, talking, playing. A donkey cart bobbed along
the road. A woman rode her bicycle with her kid sitting on the pannier-
rack. An old man was bent under a sack. A young man in floral shirt
emerged from having a pee in the bushes. Three children were shouting in
joy about a game of ball. All this life and the greenery, the smell of green,
reminded us instantly of Bangladesh. Of course to be truthful the fertility
of this place is to Bangladesh like a single dried flower is to a field of Dutch
tulips – but a single dried flower after two thousand kilometres of shades of
brown seemed to us like a bouquet of roses.

Five hundred and twenty-seven kilometres out of Golmud, we came
into Dunhuang. Physically we were extremely tired, yet we were jubilant.
We'd done it in three days. The major part of the journey had been on
hostile empty dirt roads at altitude. Dunhuang was big. It seemed the size
of Xigatse. There were wide streets, many many shops, roundabouts, a
bus station, down-town backstreets, neon-lights and ornamental flower-
beds. We pulled up at one of the larger tourist hotels where a cross
receptionist told us to take our bikes out of the hall: 'Lean them against the
railings outside. They'll be all right.' 'Not on your life,' we said under our
breath. With a little faffing around, she booked us into a four-bed
dormitory shared with a Frenchman. We rushed our bikes upstairs before
anyone could stop us.

Though it was nearly dark, we went out on the town to explore. It was
very busy, almost as though the locals go parading in their Sunday Best in
the main streets every evening. There were many street stalls selling
different snacks. We chose a large central restaurant already busy with
men having supper. There were no women eating. Most of the serving
staff were women, most of the kitchen staff were men. It was a bright
spacious place with linoleum floor, plastic table-cloths on tables and
freshly painted pastel-green with blue walls. We celebrated our return to
sanity with deep-fried fish served up in sweet and sour sauce. It was
superlatively delicious. We washed it down with a bottle of white wine
from the 'Great Wall of China Wine Co.' Nick also managed egg soup and
pork stir-fry. On the way back to the hotel, we took the opportunity to

stock up for the night: two bottles of fizzy pop, three jars of fruit, three large packets of biscuits, eleven bars of chocolate and seventy assorted sweets. Plus we found there was a late-night ice-cream shop next door!

Nick. Day 41. Dunhuang. Evening.
This was the start of a whole new adventure. At the Dangjin La we had left behind all vestiges of the mountain folklore. In fact poor Tibet evaporated way back at the Tanggula half-way across the Plateau – almost before we'd become acquainted. Powerful people swaddled in yak-skin clothes. Aggressively independent yet at the same time fun-loving. In contrast, Qinghai and the Qaidam were populated – if that's the right word for a place so empty and inhospitable – by people who were mostly torpid and sour – immigrants (or were they exiles?) from mainland China.

Down here in the desert we were into the great melting-pot of central Asia. Over fifty different ethnic groups merged together. Kazaks, Uygurs, Mongols and Turks are numerous, but the Han Chinese are officially in control. Animist beliefs, Taoism, Buddhism and a little Christianity have all been practised, though Islam is in vogue for this millennium. Every new wave of travellers along the Silk Road has left its mark on the culture of these oases. In its turn the Silk Road was due to leave its mark on us.

TEN

Depression on the Silk Road

Dunhuang in days of old was an important stopping-off place for the Silk Road. Caravans of camels and mules bound for the Middle East and Europe, and those heading back to Beijing and the rest of eastern China, would stop off to replenish supplies, rest their animals, and sell or barter some of their wares with other traders. These people were the bringers of news, the life-line linking all the individual oases which dotted the deserts of central Asia. Conversely they depended on the oases for their life-line.

Today Dunhuang is a busy market town, recorded in tourist guide-books as 'a three hour bus ride through the oblivion end of China from the Lanzhou–Urumqi railway line'. We are told 'there is little to see in the oasis itself . . . the main attraction is the Magao Caves – one of the greatest examples of Buddhist art in the world'. Nick and I never got there. Apparently an early British tourist, or explorer as they were called in those days, got there in 1907 and carted away a bounty of priceless manuscripts and paintings which had been preserved for a millennium in the dry desert air. Countless other foreign raiders followed him in the name of science. They've been up and down the Silk Road endlessly since then – we didn't expect to see any genuine *in situ* relics. It seemed to us that the Silk Road would today be a large modern highway with bounteous traffic and countless transport cafés.

We had set our hearts on it. We believed with absolute conviction that it was going to be fast and smooth, so we counted on it, ever since Kathmandu, for enabling us to claw back a decent overall average daily distance. Up to Dunhuang where we arrived at the end of Day 41 we had covered 4,077 kilometres from the Bay of Bengal. Therefore it looked like our average was nearly but not yet 100 kilometres per day. However, we had started at noon on what we called Day 1, so in truth we had only taken forty days and nine hours to get to Dunhuang. Furthermore, the time difference crossing the Nepal–Chinese border put our elapsed time down to forty days and four hours. That meant, I concluded with enormous pleasure, that we had cracked the 100-kilometre-per-day barrier. We had

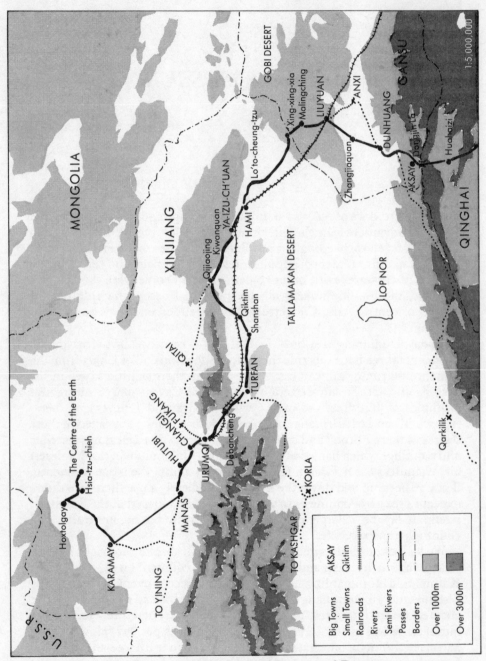

The Gobi, Taklamakan and Dsungarei Deserts

recovered from the lost time in Kathmandu and south of Lhasa. We now intended to keep on the right side of 100.

Assuming that the Silk Road was indeed fast, we thought we should cover the 1,000 or so kilometres to Urumqi in about five days. There was firstly a short section of side-road to get to Liuyuan where we would meet the proper Silk Road – marked by cartographers as a thick red line on maps of China. Then the road headed north-west, skirting the western edge of the Gobi Desert and the northern bounds of the Taklamakan Desert. It passed through the large town of Hami about which we were a bit worried because everyone told us it was strictly closed to foreigners. Further on along the Silk Road was the Turfan Depression, which was below sea-level. In a sense, that would mark our completion of flying over the hump from sea-level south of the Tibetan Plateau to sea-level in the north. After Turfan it was a short hop over the Tien Shan mountains to the big city of Urumqi and somewhere north of that to our target in the Dsungarei Pendi, another desert, at the Centre of the Earth. Fifty days was once more a feasible time limit – we thought.

We would, of course, be travelling a lot faster than the conveniently accepted pace for Silk Road travellers of three miles per hour across the desert. The centuries come and go, yet camels, horses, donkeys, mules, carts and those on foot all travelled steadily ten hours per day and covered thirty miles, hopefully the distance between oases. This had been going on for more than two thousand years, the first recorded traveller being Chang Ch'ien, who was sent out by the Han emperor Wu Ti firstly in 138 BC to make contact with distant Chinese allies, then later to establish a forward base for the silk trade with the West. According to Eric Newby in *The Atlas of Exploration*, as early as 100 BC there were twelve caravans per year, each with 100 men, leaving China for the West. The Persians acted as middle-men, buying the goods, controlling the supply, and trading them off to the Mediterranean civilizations. The Romans developed a craving for silk; indeed, it became a severe drain on the financial resources of the Roman Empire. Eventually two Westerners, posing as monks, smuggled the eggs of the silk-moth 'Bombyx' back to Europe. It was one of the first examples of industrial espionage. Many other goods were traded from China, particularly furs, ceramics, cinnamon, bronze mirrors and indeed, a fellow IT explorer, John Pilkington, tells me, rhubarb. In exchange the West sent gold, precious metals and stones, textiles and glass. As well as a channel of commerce, the Silk Road was an important artery for the dissemination of knowledge, art and religion. It had been busy with an endless stream of missionaries, scholars and invaders for nearly two thousand years. Over the last half-millennium, trade had been slowing down. It appeared that we were on the end of the queue. We must hurry before all that history disappeared into the shifting sands of the desert.

With all haste, we collected our wits together in Dunhuang, sorted over our gear, stuffed a lot more food down ourselves (we went back to the same place and once again had deep-fried fish in sweet and sour) and tried to get out of town before high noon. We failed. In the same way as Dhaka, Kathmandu and Lhasa in their turn had held us back in the grip of acute triviaetis, so did Dunhuang. Triviaetis is an as-yet-undescribed affliction of expeditioners which causes them, pre-departure, to flap around for ages, extending their deadlines, whilst they immerse themselves in the minutiae of life: each unnecessary titbit generates a plethora of new jobs, all seemingly important, but in fact trivial.

We fiddled about with rolls of sticky plaster perfecting dust- and sunburn-guards on our goggles. After much deliberation, I bought a new diary, and carefully trimmed the covers off. For a couple of hours we both wrote complete overviews of the journey so far. We delicately cleaned the logos on our bikes and measured and re-measured distances between the coming towns. Hami was 400 kilometres; in the old days it took three weeks to get there. We each bought Mao caps; they fitted perfectly yet we fiddled for ages adjusting them minutely and personalizing them. And of course we messed around selecting where to eat, what to eat, and indeed how to eat it. Eventually it was late afternoon.

'Do you think it's worth starting now?'

'What time is it?'

'Dunno. It's pretty late. Have you done your diaries yet?'

'I'm just noting down predicted distances and times to Urumqi.'

'Ooh, let's see.'

'The next decent town is Liuyuan in 128 kilometres. I've got it down as today's target. Maybe it's too far.'

'Maybe we should start fresh tomorrow?'

Time frittered away. Eventually our dedication to speed won through. Suddenly we were ready for immediate action. At 4.30 p.m. we set off, optimistic that we might make all 128 kilometres to the fabled Silk Road before dark. Our map suggested it was dead straight all the way; if so, then for us it would be a world-record straight road, eclipsing by far yesterday's burn-up on the Qaidam. At 4.35 we stopped to oil our bike chains. At 4.45 we had second thoughts and decided to turn back. At 4.55 we had third thoughts and decided to go a short way and see how the day looked. A following breeze blew us swiftly out of town to the edge of the oasis. It looked good. We committed ourselves and, in good spirits, got down to some brisk cycling.

Far from being a pleasant evening's excursion, it turned out to be an unexpectedly tough ride. Barely a stone's throw from the edge of the oasis, the tarmac ended. The road was thick with gravel piled up on the edges of the truck-ruts which cut deep into the surface. The base was hard and knobbly like riding broken pavement, and the loose surface was composed principally of inch to two-inch alluvial cobbles, rounded and smooth, slippery enough in a river and like ball-bearings here. We cursed and swore. Our hopes of an evening dash to Liuyuan were dashed. We even began to wonder if we'd get there the next day. But of course we could do nothing about it, so we bent our heads and worked at ticking off each 100 metres. Each revolution of the pedals required a controlled effort of the legs. We had to concentrate on the up-pull of the rear foot as well as the smooth push of the leading foot. All the time our eyes were flicking over the road a few feet ahead searching for better traction, firmer footing. It seemed to be only fractionally faster than pushing a shopping-trolley through a field of wheat. We couldn't understand why this road linking the large oasis of Dunhuang to the importance of the Silk Road should be dirt. Slowly the kilometres were forced behind us one at a time. An hour or more elapsed for the first ten kilometres. Then a strip of tarmac appeared and we yelled for joy. One kilometre later, the dirt re-started.

It was an uninspiring ride. The road was laid straight as a die on a slightly raised bed across a flat, stony plain. There was moderate scrub cover punctuated by holes dug by the men who were gravel-graders. They threw spadefuls of dirt at inclined wire meshes in order to sift out the pebbles for use on roads. There were some large roadworks going on and I imagine that if, Heaven forbid, we were to go back to that road again it would be beautiful bitumen.

Half-way to Liuyuan there was a small hamlet called Zhangjiaquan. Here we gave up. It had seven houses, several carts and tractors, a donkey tied to a telegraph pole and numerous trees beside a gurgling stream. There were many green fields around us and a couple of dusty tracks led off probably to other little farms. A flock of floppy sheep disappeared up one track and there were birds singing in the trees. This place was the small oasis at the lowest point of the basin between Dunhuang and the Silk Road at Liuyuan. Technically it was the end of the long downhill which had started on the Dangjin La 178 kilometres ago and about 10,000 feet (3,000 metres) above us. Half-heartedly, we ventured into one of the houses to see if it was a chai house. It was, and Zhangjiaquan turned out to be a great joy for us as we had time to unwind ready for an early start the next day. This was something we'd been trying to do for many days but had never achieved.

The place we entered was a single-storey brick-wall building twenty metres long, five metres wide, divided into two rooms. The middle section was a shop, with three bare walls and a glass-topped counter in front of the fourth where there was shelving. The main item for sale was booze. There were also glass jars of fruit and fish, boxes of sweets, a couple of boxes of biscuits and tins of meat, school satchels, a selection of auto parts and many different brands of cigarettes. We sat in the smaller room, which had a well-swept brick floor laid in a herring-bone pattern. There were three tables and numerous wooden stools, a central light on a string, a barred window, a transistor radio turned on low, a pile of boxes of shop goods in the corner and, behind me, several large clay urns in rope webbing. Our bikes stood under the window.

Nick. Day 42. Zhangjiaquan. Evening.

Well, I'm very glad we left Dunhuang – we could so easily have ended up spending another night there. The staff here are beside themselves with pleasure at seeing us. This road-house is the perfect place for us. Cosy, family atmosphere. It's clean. Since Budongquan, the chai house owners have shown an astonishing interest in cleanliness. Budongquan was the first with a swept floor. Golmud and Dunhuang were likewise. The chai house we're sitting in now is the most extreme of all – dangerously Scandinavian – they've sprinkled the floor to keep down the dust, and the owner is cleaning the individual bars of the window with a damp rag!! They'll have to be careful.

The gent in charge was helped by his son and his father. They all had blue suits and Mao caps and were friendly but discreet. They didn't oversee all our writings and eatings. The grandfather sat on a stool behind the counter and dozed or chatted with the few passers-by. He reminded me of a grand retired prime minister. He'd been through life and done his share. He was happy to rest and give his time to others. The gent and his son cooked food on a four-foot-square brick/clay stove fuelled with coal. There was the pleasant murmur of voices interspersed with occasional laughter and the sizzle of food. They used a wok frying-pan, a huge pot with lid and several blackened kettles. The vegetables and meat were in a partly prepared condition and were stored in a series of enamel basins under a sheet of muslin on a table by the stove. A side of pig fat hung by the back-door. They served us a gourmet meal based on fresh noodles, which seemed like they were the staple in this area. Nick wrote that it was 'the best meal we've ever had'. We finished the meal with sweets, including one which we discovered was like Turkish Delight and called very grandly 'Xianshgaliongynliaochang'.

Like Steve Bonnist, the grandfather leapt into action every time we asked for something. He showed great delight in leading us into the yard when we asked for bed. He showed us to an out-house with four beds. As we started unpacking our bags on the two we fancied, he jumped in to intervene. Apparently one of the beds was his, the other belonged to his grandson. Now that he pointed it out, we could see that there were a couple of neatly folded garments at the foot of the bed and a box of things underneath. We slept extremely well even though various different people did come and go in the night.

Dick. Day 43. 7.00 a.m. Zhangjiaquan.

This is a momentous day. The first reason is it's the first time since Bangladesh and India that we've got up at dawn. This should mean that we get to start cycling before the wind gets up. The sun has not yet appeared over the horizon but it's nearly there. It's still cool. Out in the fields a tractor is at work.

Otherwise it feels very early for China. I hope the food comes quick because we must be going soon. The morning is moving on and this will be the momentous day when we meet the Silk Road. We can speed to Hami and then Urumqi. All our worries will be over.

Nick also made a diary entry while waiting for breakfast. Whereas I was all dreamy about grandeur and the overview, Nick firstly checked on the essentials of life – in his diary, he drew for the proprietor a picture of a pancake, which is what he wanted for breakfast!

Nick. Day 43. 7.20 a.m. Zhangjiaquan.
Last night we had tea, omelettes, pork, courgettes, mushrooms, onions, apricots, sweets – the best meal we've ever had. We were up too early to get breakfast instantly today. I had a little walk outside. A green island in the desert. A grey haze coming from the east. Birds chirping – so fresh after the barren Plateau. This oasis has an isolated provinciality.
      This is the day when we begin the final section of our journey. I'm tremendously excited about meeting the Silk Road. Mongols, Kazaks, Marco Polo – the trade route of all time. I hope the mystique remains.

Everything started well. The dirt road quickly changed back to tarmac after Zhangjiaquan. The heat of the day had not come. Around us was the level gravel plateau. There were patches of golden sand-dunes. The air was very clear. We could see the fine line of low black mountains ahead. They marked the northern boundary of the basin. They were the spine of the Silk Road. Further west they joined up with the Tien Shan. After seventy kilometres the open desert came into black foothills. We reached Liuyuan – a dreary place where no one smiled. We had a dull bowl of soup served by a dull girl. Somewhere in town should be the modern Silk Road. We couldn't find it. The people said this was the rail town. The road to Hami and the west was back there – pointing to where we'd come. Dispirited, but not yet disheartened, we backtracked. We found nothing but a rusty metal signpost. It pointed along a dirt track no better than the road to the rubbish-tip outside Lodhwar. We sat down gloomily to wait for a truck to come so we could ask the driver what it said. It said: 'Hami – 298 km.'
      We could not believe that this was the Silk Road. We were stunned. We sat in a daze a while, then started walking.

Nick. Day 43. Near Liuyuan. Morning.
This was meant to be the big moment; the point at which we joined the Silk Road – that ribbon of smooth tarmac which would draw us magnetically, rapidly, towards Urumqi. In-

stead, we have a dirt track of indescribable quality. Is this really the Silk Road? The Silk Road – source of all those legends – the longest trade route in the world stretching one third of the way around the equator?

'Surely this must just be a short diversion around the outside of town?'

Two kilometres further the town was left behind. There was no other road. This was the Silk Road. It was also the road to the local rubbish-tip so when a tractor came past we stopped him and checked. He confirmed our worst suspicions and indicated that if he was going to Hami he'd go by railroad – only a few rare trucks go there. We thanked him courteously, though it was quite useless information because we could see for ourselves that only a few trucks went there – maybe even less than a few. We sat down to check our maps. We looked at them upside-down and inside-out but there was no way we could be anywhere else. Our only hope was that somewhere further on a tarmac road would appear.

'No chance, Dick,' said Nick objectively. 'That would be a miracle.'

According to our maps there was virtually nothing between Liuyuan and Hami except a few tiny place-names. We waited a while to check again with a truck driver but no trucks came. I wrote in my diary that this was 'hell of all hells'. Instead of a busy modern road with many cafés, we had no road, no food, and no traffic.

> *Nick. Day 43. Silk Road! Morning.*
> Suffering from shock we tried to cycle. It was nearly impossible to make the bikes move. Deep gravel sucked at the tyres. In some sections the gravel was so thick that we were forced to walk. Everywhere it was a battle. The track was ill-defined. Our toes were getting mashed from the down-thrust on the pedals, the up-pull on the rear foot, the struggle to keep the bike upright and moving through the grit – like cycling through a snowdrift. Not for one moment would the bikes roll. Always we had to keep up the pressure.

Bit by bit we made ground. The small black hills were roughly eroded, bare of all cover. In between, the track weaved over a gravelly pediment with sparse scrub bushes. There were many wiggles and corners, small ups and downs as the track found its way westwards. We still couldn't believe that this really was the fabled Silk Road. We sat down and studied the maps again. It took us two hours to make the first ten kilometres. We weren't making good progress but we were progressing. Goodness only knew where we would find food and water.

Presently, twenty kilometres out of Liuyuan, we were pleasantly surprised to come upon the railroad. We hadn't seen anyone since the tractor at the rubbish dump: not a vehicle, not a hut. There wasn't going to be anything ahead for at least the same distance again. Yet here at the railroad-crossing was a thin old man in a dandy black railman's waistcoat. He was sitting on an oil-drum smoking a pipe. His round tortoise-shell specs had flat glass which caught the light in the same way as theatrical specs. Behind him the kettle was on the boil in his tiny signal-man's hut. It was a quaint little scene which could have come straight from the pages of an annual like 'British Railways Before Beeching'. Railways all over the world have this quality of being totally independent of, and seemingly impervious to, the environment around them. Way back at the beginning of our journey, we'd stopped at a similar rail-man's hut to watch a steam-train pulling into Comilla. Years ago, I'd ridden the Guayaquil–Quito train and, though that's half a world away, I could swear I saw the same signal-man and the same kettle of tea. Too much desert does funny things to your perceptions. We'd only had twenty kilometres thus far. He filled our bottles with water and gave us some momos and cold cucumber stew. Sitting here in peace, the awful reality of the failed Silk Road began to sink in. We might have 1,000 kilometres of dirt to Urumqi! We could hardly believe that all our dreams had vanished.

The whistle of a train broke the silence. A huge locomotive on wide-gauge track chundered past. Our little old man got up and saluted. A kilometre of wagons rumbled by. Then they were gone into the distance and we were left with the silence of the desert. That was where the Silk Road had gone. All the commerce and trade bundled up into the railroad wagons. The railway was completed in 1963 and is reckoned to be one of the greatest achievements of the Communist regime. This railroad to Urumqi has opened up the interior. Later we saw passenger trains: long green coaches, big glass windows, people sitting at tables with lampshades and plates of food. No longer were travellers dependent on the oases. No 'three miles per hour' for them, but more like eighty kilometres per hour. One day from Urumqi to here. They'd seen the sand-dunes, the stones and the size of the desert, but had they felt the solitude and silence? If they had, would it matter? Nick looked wistfully in the direction the train had disappeared and said: 'Next time I go on an adventure – that'll be me.'

For the moment we were cyclists in the Gobi, so cycle we had to. The track we followed veered north of the rail, not to rejoin until Hami. The Hildebrandt's All-China map on which we'd depended ever since the Lalung Le was a bit devoid of detail and wayward on place-names in this area. Luckily we were getting so close to our destination that our US Air Defense Mapping Agency Operational Navigational Chart of the Centre of the Earth: Sheet ONC f-7, which we'd lovingly carried all the way from the open sea, came into use. Metaphorically speaking, we'd cycled on to the bottom right-hand corner this morning. It had a scale of 1:1,000,000 and showed contours every 1,000 feet. There were very few places marked in this area – probably because few existed. Some distance ahead was the name Malingching. We hoped it was a place, we hoped there were some people, and we hoped to reach it before sundown.

We came to a tiny deserted oasis. There was a patch of brilliant green grass no bigger than a pocket handkerchief and a minuscule pond of clear water. Also some beautiful lilac flowers nudging into the water. Beside it were the ruins of half a dozen beehive houses of baked clay bricks. Presumably this had been one of the watering places in the heyday of the Silk Road. There was nothing inside except piles of donkey droppings and hordes of vicious mosquitoes. Nick ran off flapping like a helicopter. I sprinted for the bikes chased by a swarm! The country was semi-desert. It was no longer hot but actually a little chilly, for we had climbed steadily up from the Zhangjiaquan plains and the altitude was nearly 2,000 metres. All the topography was small scale. There was no particular feature or mountain on the horizon to give us a sense of progress. There were quite large flat areas a few kilometres across separated by small dark hills. Vegetation up here was thicker than the scrub around Liuyuan. In fact in places there was almost a continuous ground cover of bushes. More natural vegetation than we'd seen anywhere on the Plateau. It was fascinating to see a living wilderness again and for a few minutes I escaped from the discomforts of the long-distance cyclist to the time, ten years ago to the day, when I had been a naturalist. There were two different types of bush, one with gorse-type little yellow flowers. There was a very low clump of something with white flowers and several different types of grass. There were flocks of birds like clouds lifting off the ground as we struggled by. Some birds were like pigeons, another was like a lark, one looked like a curlew. This was bountiful wildlife. We were excited to see four antelopes. The track continued in its terrible state of repair. It was as bad as a farm track. In places the sand and gravel were particularly thick but we strived always to keep up some momentum and continue pedalling. We were headed north-north-west across the slopes flanking the Taklamakan Desert which lay over to our left. We stayed at 2,000 metres elevation all afternoon and into the early evening. Malingching didn't appear when we thought it would and so we had to persevere more. Every extra kilometre we told ourselves was not purgatory but a bonus – because we wouldn't have to do it the next day.

When we came to Malingching, the sun was low, casting long shadows from the bushes and etching dark lines into the hills. There was a tall radio mast with the metal-work lit up red in the dying sun, and a white-walled workers' compound. It looked just like a small version of Huahaizi. There was a partially built new compound. Around here were quite thick bushes, some of them nearly trees, and various pools of dirty-looking water near the track. Luckily for us, there were people here – a construction team of about forty men and two women. The last section from the railway-hut had set us a new world record of thirty-six kilometres with absolutely no habitation. Never before, even on the Qaidam Pendi, had we covered such a distance without seeing anything at all.

The men were excited to see us, but didn't seem to realize at first that we were in need of food and a bed for the night. We laid the acting on thick. I made my legs fold so that I fell in a lump against the wall. Nick rolled his head, and his eyes spun up out of sight. They got the message. Possibly they were a bit too enthusiastic – we were mobbed until a man in a blue tracksuit, whom Nick dubbed 'The Godfather', took us under his wing. In next to no time we were all good friends having noodles and soup. Two men were asked to vacate beds and, despite the claustrophobic crowd, we both fell almost instantly asleep. I had the bikes tucked between me and the wall. The Godfather came and tucked a quilt over Nick, who was already in dream-land.

Nick. Day 44. Malingching onwards.
Eight hours' sleep meant it was a full-rounded sun which blasted through the windows on to my muzzy face. The old man and boy in the kitchen gave us a couple of cold momos for breakfast. They tried to get us to stop for a full-blown fry-up, but after losing time yesterday we were eager to get on the road – Hami and Urumqi are now a very long way away. We swigged as much water as our bellies would hold and set off. We headed north-north-west. Elevation remained 2,000 metres. Chill morning on dusty track. Crossing flat plain. The vegetation thinned out. Stony. Hard angular stony desert. Line of tele-graph poles. A lonely ruined rest-house, roofless.

The track was pitiful, worse than anything on the Plateau. We pressed on determinedly, heading for a place that we'd heard mentioned in several different sources. We were sure there'd be some habitation there. It had the wonderful name Xing-Xing-Xia, which means 'Gorge of the Starry Skies'. In the first three hours of the day we covered slightly more than thirty kilometres. There was nothing to be seen and no reason to stop. Any break in the monotony of this wilderness would have been a relief. We passed some rounded brown hillocks, then by and by we drew close to a range of low black hills and began to climb towards a crossing. This was going to be our exit from the high table of the last sixty kilometres. The track entered a narrow defile. It had smoothly rounded bare black rock on both sides, a flat buff sand floor thirty metres wide and, to our great delight, two small green trees like jewels in an empty cask. Well worth stopping for photographs. Blue sky, bright sun. An excuse to walk a little through the sand and relieve our poor bashed toes. However, Xing-Xing-Xia beckoned and we climbed aboard again for whatever short distance remained.

First we spotted a solitary ruin on a hilltop like a watch-tower. Then several more turrets and a broken tower. We came to numerous ruins, forty or fifty in total, in our small valley and the remains of a large fort. It appeared to be totally deserted. This was Xing-Xing-Xia. It was a sad derivative of what had for two thousand years been one of the important staging-posts on the Silk Road. The highest point on the route, it marks the boundary between the province of Gansu behind us and the huge autonomous region of Xinjiang which stretches from here for 2,000 kilometres to the Russian border in the north and to Afghanistan and Pakistan in the west. Over the centuries, innumerable camel-caravans have passed this way. All traffic from the waterless wastes on both sides was compelled to pass through this narrow defile in search of the brackish water of Xing-Xing-Xia. The bare splintered hills which line both sides were easily defended, and conversely easily sheltered bandits, rogues and rebel armies. Everyone was both relieved and alarmed to arrive at Xing-Xing-Xia. We thought of the early Chinese noblemen Chang Ch'ien and Hsuang-tsang, of the first Europeans Carpini and Rubruck, and of course of Marco Polo, Genghis Khan and the Mongol hordes who ruled most of Asia during the thirteenth century. We dreamt we could hear their ghosts in the castles and the souls of the travellers singing in the sands. All that had faded away during the last few centuries as China closed up. Modern explorers such as Sir Aurel Stein, Sven Hedin and Pelliot had come in the last hundred years to give Xing-Xing-Xia a new lease of life. The Chinese had garrisons up to a thousand strong merely fifty years ago. But sea trade, air travel and the 1963 railroad had finally killed it. These derelict buildings were a touching reminder of past glories.

Nick. Day 44. Xing-Xing-Xia. Midday.
Beyond the ruins, a white-painted building, another in construction, and on the left a chai house!! Dream of dreams. And it's a great one. Six metres square. Walls blackened by smoke. One square table in the centre. Speckled shaft of sunlight filtering through smoke-hole in roof. Large built-in clay cooking range. The skinny man in loose grey flannels welcomed us to the table. His wife poured us tea then started chopping vegetables. She had a happy work-worn face and wore blue overalls with a white apron. No meat here, only veg. Blue, hot sky outside. Little girl in pink top and trousers with pigtails leaning on the door-frame watching. The man is making noodles; mixing and kneading dough, pounding it flat, cutting it to strips and then the fascinating part: picking up several strips, one end in each hand, and stretching them by bouncing them and slapping them on the wooden work-top. They thwack down and bounce up as he pulls his arms wide. He throws them with a flourish into the boiling wok of water. Hey presto – fresh noodles!

There were four or five other adults hanging around. Some of the men were presumably truck drivers. Their vehicles were dark green with slatted wooden backs, closed cabs and bulbous noses like grown-up Morris Minors. Sometimes, back near Dunhuang and Liuyuan, we had seen more modern trucks with square or flat noses, high-up cabs and enclosed backs. By the middle of the day, there was a truck going past about once every half-hour. This gave me hope that at least someone else used this route so that further on when things became desperate we might be able to get water from them. Nick was less prepared to turn himself loose at the hands of fate.

Nick. Day 44. Xing-Xing-Xia. Early Afternoon.
We're studying the map, trying to envisage what lies ahead. D says, with typical understatement: 'Yup, there's still quite a lot of light entertainment left on this trip.' We've had a good brunch here. We need to stock up well as there's nothing until the edge of the Hami oasis. As far as we can deduce, that's about 160 kilometres then another forty to Hami itself. Probably the road after Hami will also be dirt. I don't mind agreeing with D that we don't really need any food, but one litre of water is a pitiful offering for such an undertaking. I'm going to drink half of it at fifty kilometres, the other half at 100 kilometres, then struggle the last sixty kilometres thirsty.

Nick was perfectly right when he said that we left Xing-Xing-Xia with mighty trepidation. Few cyclists anywhere in the world attempt a 160-kilometre journey with only one litre of water and no food. Let alone on a dirt road. Least of all across the Gobi Desert. We had a certain perverse expedition ethic that we would never carry any food. Having survived all the trials and tribulations so far, I almost believed that we had divine protection from all evils and misfortune. The vegetation thinned out almost immediately we left Xing-Xing-Xia. The track headed downslope. We left Gansu behind and tipped over the boundary down into Xinjiang. The track got no better. It was rutted gravel frequently interspersed with patches of sand. It started getting quite hot. We had to wear clothes as protection against the sun. The air was parchingly dry. According to the map, we'd lose more than 1,000 metres in height before the next village, 160 kilometres away. It would get quite a lot warmer. It was small consolation that the track went downhill because it was an imperceptible slope on an incredibly rough surface.

A short distance out of Xing-Xing-Xia, maybe four or five kilometres – say, about half an hour – the track deteriorated further. Nick seriously questioned the logic of blindly hacking on. We stopped to consider our predicament. It was debatable if there would be any water for possibly two days. Nick suggested retreating to Xing-Xing-Xia to get proper water-carriers. I argued, rather perversely, that we'd never done more than thirty-six kilometres before without some sort of habitation so there was no special reason why this should be an exception. He pointed out that there was an incredibly large amount of luck involved in applying my statistics to this desert. We could see here, more clearly than anywhere else on the trip, the contrast between our two methods of planning. Nick always assumed that there wouldn't be anything ahead except that which

could be deduced from all the available information, so if there was
something more, then it was a bonus. I stretched the available information
and assumed there would always be an unexpected extra bit of good
fortune and if there wasn't I was shocked.

Nick. Day 44. Reflections on having left Xing-Xing-Xia.
By the time we walked out of the chai house and into the glaring
midday heat, the seeds of doubt sown by the chai-man's
statement that the next water would be 160 kilometres away
had rooted themselves in my small and precious pot of courage.
Only rare traffic continued beyond Xing-Xing-Xia. We knew
that. Maybe there would be a truck or two a day. Maybe not.
The next oasis was saline. Undrinkable. The urge to re-track to
the chai house and buy something to carry more water was near
overwhelming. The extra weight would slow us down. But it
might save us. I felt slightly sick. All along I'd expected at some
moment to be called to peel off that last protective layer. Now
that moment had come.

Later, Nick said: 'Setting out from Xing-Xing-Xia was the biggest
moment of the trip. I had to confront a previously undreamt-of fear. Up to
this point, I don't think we'd encountered anything which we'd not met
somewhere else before in some guise or other. The heat, the cold, the
exhaustion, the agony, the crowds, were all elements with parallels, albeit
smaller, less daunting parallels, in previous adventures. To enter empty-
handed into the unexpected void beyond Xing-Xing-Xia was new.'
We stood up to move on again, united in trepidation. We settled into a
steady pace, each wrapped in his own dreams of what might have been if
the Silk Road had been tarmac. Though we would have missed out on all
this exciting adventure, I personally would have been extremely happy to
have sped smoothly to Urumqi and called it a day. We could have been
home in a week. Picnics by the Thames and all that. A far cry from our
present predicament.
One and a half hours out of Xing-Xing-Xia, just when I was beginning
seriously to worry how quickly we could drink our water, the first truck
came by. We flagged it down immediately. The driver and his mate were
surprised at first, then impressed by our audacity in trying to cycle across
here. They offered us water from a large green metal hip-flask. They urged
us to chuck our bikes in their trucks and take a lift, then stared in disbelief
as we cycled off again.
Two hours later, our water was half-drunk and we were measuring each
sip. We began to fret about where we might be lucky enough to find more.
There seemed to be nothing on the horizon except heat haze, hallucinations and featureless expanses of stony desert. To our delight we came
across a caravan. Not a camel-caravan nor a mirage, but a shiny aluminium
caravan with tall aerial. It belonged to a geological team drilling for water.

As far as we could ascertain they'd been there for a week, and would move on soon. It was a luxury caravan with bunk-beds and kitchen units inside. Hot water to quench our thirst. Tasty sesame bread to sink our teeth into. They told us the word for this was *na*, so our vocabulary was increasing. We now knew the words *shui*, *momo*, *mifan*, *churfan*, *na*, *yingguo* and sometimes *tsey-tsey*. They mean 'water', 'dumpling', 'rice', 'food', 'bread', 'Englishman' and 'thank you'. As we left, they forced twisted sticks of bread and two hard-boiled eggs into our hands. We couldn't rightly refuse – our expedition ethic was never to carry food, Nick observed, 'humorous really' – so we pedalled two kilometres out of sight and sat down for a picnic. A bizarre but private moment – two Englishmen sitting on a lonely black knoll in a sea of brown sand, eating their last food for a long time: each engrossed in his own diary. We had days when we talked quite a bit, and other days when we were each wrapped up in our own battles. It was very pleasant to break off for a few moments from the headlong rush to the Centre of the Earth. The sun was a bit too hot for comfort. Sitting still, little beads of perspiration broke out across our foreheads.

We continued on our way and the wind dried our faces. The gently sloping sand and gravel plain continued. Light interest was lent by randomly dispersed little black knolls and, at greater intervals, red-brown ridges. There was very sparse vegetation. Way off to the right were some faint black mountains topped by snows. In places the track was corrugated – rough undulations jolting the wheels and thumping into my bum-bones. My arms took a lot of the struggle and twisting of the bike. My toes were battered numb. More often the track was slippery sand. We cycled all the time in low ratio. The twisting and wrenching on the handlebars was so bad that I got blisters both on the palm of my left hand and at the base of my right finger – my first injuries of the trip. Never did the pressure relent. If we paused from pedalling for one moment, our bikes sank to a stop like a sailing dinghy coming off a plane. It was desperate. Having no alternatives, we cycled on, telling ourselves that this journey would only get shorter if we made it get shorter. The track was very bad: the worst we had ever experienced. It was worse than a Welsh farm-track, drier than a Welsh Sunday. We'd have made more progress riding on rollers.

The lead alternated, sometimes Nick, at other times me. I found it easier to be ahead, the leader. I could set the pace. Nick seemed happy enough behind but rarely did I break away to make a sufficient gap that he'd be off my wheel. When I was behind, I hated the pressure of seeing him break away ahead and always having to catch up. As the hours evaporated, the landscape became a desolate plain: huge expanses of stony desert; rare, rounded, red and buff sandstone bluffs; flat wide wadis a few centimetres deep and several tens of metres wide, lined by silk-smooth sand, home to scattered small twists of scrub. We didn't think of very much that afternoon. Too many of our emotions were caught up in the present. At times when life is particularly dangerous, you don't allow dreams or fear to sweep you away. The world becomes cold and serious.

All your attention and energies are directed to working you out to safety. We knew we had to cover as much ground as possible before dark, get some good refreshing sleep. Then get the hell out of the Gobi.

The sun started its downward arc and the temperature was slowly reduced from scorching. There were progressively more and more sand stretches. It was the worst we had ridden. The track became indistinct. It spread out across a wide swath of desert. Each driver had tried to find his own best route. We flitted and flipped between our best choices. Nick had a preference for riding the bottom of the deep ruts of trucks where possibly the loose debris had been cut away down to a firmer base. I tried some of the untouched areas beyond the wheel-marks. For about forty metres I'd be successful and quick on a hard sand crust, then I'd drop through and dig a furrow.

Towards evening, on one of my experimental forays, I was diverted on to the bed of the wadi where smooth dry mud thinly coated the sand-bed surface. To my delight it was fast and firm. After a kilometre of this, Nick veered over to join me for some radical wilderness cycling. It was like being free again. Tim and Murph would have enjoyed this (Tim Gartside and Pete Murphy – veterans of Trans-Sahara 1984). In places, the surface of the dry river bed was mud-cracked, otherwise there were a few small scrub bushes and scattered pebbles, but in the main it was as sweet as riding the boards on the indoor cycling tracks.

Late evening, when we were starting to worry about where we'd bed down, I thought I spotted a squat rectangular hut about three kilometres ahead sheltered under a small sandstone bluff. It lifted my spirits. Once or twice it vanished then I saw it again. Nick wouldn't believe me. I accused him of pessimism. My hoped-for habitation never materialized. Ten minutes later it disappeared completely leaving only a knobbly sandstone block. We made distance until dark then had no option but to bed down on the desert. For as far as the eye could see, there was nothing in any direction except the gently undulating gravel plain. An endless choice of places to sleep! We chose a slight rise and each of us selected a suitably comfortable-looking stretch of gravel. My recollection is that we each spent about ten minutes lying down in different places, orientating our heads in different directions, until it felt right. There was a lot of room to move around if we got restless in the night! We'd come over sixty kilometres from the drill team – thereby setting ourselves yet another new world record for distance without habitation of any sort. Furthermore we'd done over eighty kilometres from the last permanent habitation and ahead of us lay sixty kilometres to the first edge of the Hami oasis. Considering we were nearly at the Centre of the Earth, in the most populous country in the world, we were an awful long way from anybody.

Nick. Day 44. 11 p.m. Gobi Desert.
Nearly dark – too dark to see. It's quite still. Not a sound. Flat tangerine sunset. Sliver of moon. Our sleeping bags are laid on

the stony desert. Goretex jacket and trousers as a groundsheet. Salopets as a pillow. I've ground a little hip-dip for comfort. We have no food, but we do have most of a litre of water each. Three times today we stopped trucks and the drivers let us slug their water. This isn't the Silk Road we'd imagined. Possibly some of the hardest stuff we've ever done. At 10 k.p.h., assuming no probs at all, it's going to take till 3 p.m. tomorrow to reach the next village.

We woke to one of the best views on the Silk Road – 360 degrees of stony desert. Neither of us could appreciate it. The wind was strong from the east. It was cosy in our sleeping-bags. We were very slow in getting up. Maybe an hour lost overall. I did a short item for the tape recording. I said slowly: 'We woke up.' Then a long pause as I gathered some more energy and continued: 'We're still alive.' The pace of my speech would have made even a Trappist monk seem like a chatterbox. There was a period of deliberation while I tried to remember if there was anything I had intended to say, then I said carefully: 'It's a long way.' That was the end of three minutes' tape-recording. I didn't say what was a long way but clearly I thought at the time that it was important to record it for posterity.

I was quite depressed when we set off. I don't know what was going on in Nick's head but he was also very quiet and committed. The prospects were not good. I didn't think that we wouldn't make it, but I did wonder how long it would take. The sun rose and we boiled. The same deep sand and loose gravel as yesterday. It was very hard work. Like pedalling a plough. After several hours of hard strife, we were relieved to see a truck. It was grinding along over the sands. We headed over and jubilantly flagged it down for water. After initial wide-eyed wonder, they greeted us like cousins – smiling brightly, gripping our arms, wowing at our bikes. By sheer good luck they gave us some bread and a hard-boiled egg. We offered to pay. They emphatically refused. We thanked them profusely, shook hands, then we each disappeared on our own separate ways, everyone a little richer by experience. This breakfast suddenly turned our world on its head and we felt much better. We were both wearing long johns wound round head and neck like bedouin tribesmen. We had peaked Chinese cap, snow-goggles and face-mask over mouth and nose. Inside, now that things were better, Nick felt 'pleasantly isolated from the heat and dust and effort of it all – able to daydream fairly comfortably'.

The first habitation after fifty-five kilometres that day, 136 kilometres of desert from Xing-Xing-Xia, was three mud huts and a starkly green grove of tall thin trees. A teenager in a white robe stood dumbstruck for five minutes as we tried to say 'Shui. Churfan.' One kilometre further was an Army outpost called Lo'to-cheung-tzu. It had a perimeter wall with green trees and a vegetable plot on one side, sand-dunes on the other. The 'lads' were very friendly and poured us big mugs of light tea then opened two cans. They contained jellied chicken and jellied pork. Quite surprisingly, despite raging hunger, we didn't wolf them down before you could say Jack Robinson. Instead, we ate them very carefully. Picking out each nugget individually and thoroughly chewing it and sucking it to extract full flavour. We vowed it was the best food we had ever eaten.

Twenty kilometres further on, we hit tarmac. We whooped for joy. We sat down on the hard black race-track and patted it, allowing the relief to sink in. Then in excitement we sprinted onwards trying to reach Hami before nightfall. There were smiles on our faces, the wind in our hair, our bottoms firm in the saddle, and, in our ears, the delightful whistle of rock-hard tyres on smooth black tar.

> *Nick. Day 45. Hami oasis. Late afternoon.*
> It took several minutes for the shock of tarmac to settle in. D set off at a blistering pace. At first through mixed sections of desert and oasis. Soon the oasis became continuous. Tall green trees like poplars marked the exact boundary between empty desert and lush farmland. The fields were all small and square, neatly fitted to each other and striped with crops. People working their tiny plots of land beside their houses. Mud-walled oasis villages and wiggly walkways. Children playing in the dust. A donkey cart plodded sedately by with the driver stretched out flat in the cart, sound asleep. The oases had a timeless air of having been in existence for centuries.

It was much like being back in India except that certain of the men wore Muslim caps and some of the girls had drain-pipe slacks with knee-length tunic tops and coloured head-scarves worn turban-style. As we got closer to Hami, there were more and more two-storey houses and shops. In addition to donkey carts, several tractors used the road, the occasional bus or truck, but mostly it was full of cyclists. To Nick and I it was Day 45, but to the locals it was Saturday, a day of rest. Many teenagers were going for picnics on the edge of the oasis. Boys wearing natty jackets raced their colourful bikes festooned with decals. Girls in party frocks and pretty shoes chatting while they cycled. Some had picnic boxes on their carrying racks. Others had a friend sitting side-saddle. The bikes were big black roadsters which beautifully complemented their frilly white blouses and happy faces. Several girls had matching ribbons in their hair. One girl in a straw hat with flimsy floral dress, billowing hem above her knee.

Since leaving Dunhuang and crossing the edge of the Gobi, we had come into a much more modern China. Few people were wearing the blue Mao suits and caps which were almost ubiquitous in Golmud and the truck-halts of the Plateau. Most people, not just the young, had Western-style clothes. We passed a group of youths sitting under a tree, bicycles standing nearby, with their transistor radio on loud. Xinjiang is one of the

up-and-coming areas of China. There are oil fields far to the north-west
and extensive mineral deposits. Much settlement has taken place during
the Green Revolution over the past thirty years in the oases which dot the
peripheries of the huge desert basins of Xinjiang. It is the largest
administrative region of China, covering 1.6 million square kilometres –
ten times as big as Bangladesh. The population, however, is small: only
fourteen million people, which is barely more than 1 per cent of China's
total. The Han Chinese are not predominant; indeed, nearly two-thirds of
the population belong to the National Minorities such as Uygurs, Kazaks,
Tajiks, Ozbeks, Tatars, Daur, Russians and Mongolians. Mostly they are
Muslims.

Further on, there was an electric pump by the road gushing water from a
wide-mouthed pipe. We stopped to splash and guzzle; we were violently
thirsty even though we had downed many cups of tea at the Army lunch.
We filled our bottles, popped in a Puritab each, waited impatiently for ten
minutes in front of an audience which grew to sixty people, swilled down
that water and repeated again. Two teenage girls directed us to the chai
house where we once more got heavily into liquids – soup, tea, then the
cook's pretty daughter rushed off and came back in her glittery red and
gold best frock bearing a gift of a bottle of dandelion-and-burdock-
flavoured fizzy pop. By late afternoon our total liquid intake was fifteen
litres each.

Despite the fact that the Army had fed us, we piled into another huge
mountain of food. The craving really took hold of us, and in contrast to our
restrained fascination in the Army camp, we ate in a frenzy. Sweat dripped
off our brows. We didn't know what we ate, we just bolted it down while a
dense crowd packed into the chai house.

*Dick. Day 45. Early evening. 177 kilometres from Xing-Xing-
Xia.*
I am totally exhausted with the noise, heat, people and excitement. Here is the largest crowd we've seen since India. More
than fifty people crammed in around our table. The children are
all being sent outside by the adults but they keep coming back
in. Now they've put a bar across the door. Half the kids have run
around to the front windows and are climbing in, the other half
are at the back windows! It doesn't quite rival Bangladesh – but,
then, nothing will. Nowhere else have the Chinese come in such
numbers or been interested for so long. They are persistent and
keen but do not crowd us. One might say they're reserved like
the English. In general these people are so much more sophisti-
cated and educated, not to say more cultured, than the people
we have met south of here.

With a couple of hours of daylight left, the pressure was on to make the
most of the new-found tarmac and bash on to Hami, which, we'd heard,

was an important military base rumoured to be command centre for the Lop Nor nuclear tests, and therefore very sensitive about foreigners. Possibly we thought we'd dash through the city itself in the fading light of day and get out to the other side before any officials realized. We'd been told several stories of people being arrested there. Mark Skinner had been sharply apprehended when he climbed off the truck which had brought him from the Turfan Depression. He'd been bundled straight on to the train to Liuyuan. We hadn't heard of anyone who had been through Hami successfully – excepting those who travelled non-stop on the railroad. Years ago in the mid-1930s a young German, one of the rare early twentieth-century foreigners, had disappeared, probably murdered, in the Hami area. Centuries ago, Hami was the feudal capital of the Gobi, where the Great Khans, successors to Genghis Khan, had their palace – the oasis was well known for singing, dancing, merry-making and its fighting spirit.

Nick. Day 44. Hami. Late evening.
Shortly after leaving our food stop, a green Chinese jeep went past. It had two smartly uniformed men inside and on the side in huge white letters GONG-AN. As it disappeared ahead, we turned to each other: 'Doesn't that mean Public Security Bureau?' Several kilometres later, as the sky started to become red with evening, we passed it again. It was parked on the side of the road. The two men were sitting inside. The engine was running. We cycled straight past. Before we were out of sight, they started up again. We pedalled close to the verge and pretended that we weren't there. They overtook slowly and disappeared ahead. I said: 'It's a stake-out.' D said: 'What's that?' 'We've been copped,' I replied. The suburban sprawl of Hami started getting thicker. We toyed with taking a back-road and missing the town centre. But, if we truly were being trailed, it was foolish to try to slip away. We stopped behind some trees. D hid the US Aero Map of Urumqi down his salopets. I disguised the outline of the tape machine in my breast pocket. Just beyond a railway-crossing, the jeep was stopped. A severe young officer with the face of a pinched corporal stepped out and flagged us down. 'Stop. Please,' he said. He wore a peaked green cap and red starry epaulettes. Holding up his arm, he repeated in measured English: 'Stop Please. Public Security Bureau.' With feigned pleasure, we pulled to a halt and grinned at him as though we'd cycled all the way across the Gobi just to meet him. He said: 'You will follow me.' We grinned more. D said: 'Oh, that's a shame. We don't really have time because we hope to get to the next town for bed. We've already eaten our supper.' He shouted in a high-pitched indignant falsetto, *'This is the Public Security Bureau.'*

'Follow me.' He climbed deftly back into the jeep, dipping his head under the canopy, and the driver drove off. He didn't look back. We dutifully followed three kilometres through the dust of an increasingly large town to the central barracks. There was a wide boulevard with traffic police outside, an impressive entry gate and two sentries on guard with guns. In the gate-house our bikes were taken away. We were shown into a small bare room with bars on the window. Little Hitler took our passports and closed the door.

ELEVEN

The Hottest Place in China

Fifteen empty minutes elapsed. The dying hours of the day closed in on the compound. Through the bars we could see the sentries marching up and down. Our captor stood impatiently by the gates waiting for his senior to come and interrogate us. Suddenly Little Hitler stood to attention. A high-ranking old officer came in view – the Superintendent. Within moments, our serious predicament became an amusing farce. The sentries stopped for a cigarette. The Superintendent looked dishevelled as though called out from home when ready for bed. With one hand he was fumbling with the buttons on his jacket. His cap was crooked. To our delight, he rode a large heavy sit-up-and-beg roadster. He raised his arm to signal left, and turned from the dusty main road in through the gates.

The gate-man switched off our colour telly which had been broadcasting the news in Chinese. We were escorted to the office of the Superintendent of Hami PSB. It was musty yet cleanly equipped and the Superintendent sat behind a large desk, his pyjamas sticking out of the top of his uniform. His cap was now on straight and he tried to look serious. There were no chairs. He waved for us to sit on the bed in the corner. Our captor, whom we re-named Junior, wouldn't sit down. He stood to attention and gave the Superintendent a briefing. We assumed he was listing our misdemeanours and suggesting that we should be locked up and thrown out of town on the railroad the next day. We realized that our ploy must be to befriend the Superintendent, charm him with our innocence, and hope that he would show lenience.

Junior acted as interpreter, and the first thing he said was that Hami is a strictly closed town: 'It is a very serious offence to attempt to enter in secret.' This message was repeated every few minutes while his boss asked important questions about our passports and visas. They were being very stern and we knew that if we went with the flow they'd have no option but to bundle us up. We distracted them with big smiling faces telling them how far we'd cycled to get to Hami, what a nice pair of lads we were, how much the success of our journey would benefit IT, and what great dividends their personal support would reap – the fact that very little was understood, and probably even less was believed, didn't detract from the fact that to chat away in good humour with smiles says a lot about a person's innocence. I hunched up small like a praying mantis and told them how, in a very short time, we'd be on the way home, then I held my arms outstretched and rolled from side to side humming like an aeroplane. Nick nodded enthusiastically.

The Superintendent smiled. Junior remained impassive and repeated the offences. The Superintendent looked serious again but couldn't contain his grandfatherly interest in our adventures. He made us a tin mug of tea. Junior was fuming. The Superintendent tried to appease both sides, and was keen on our idea that we should get out of Hami as fast as our little legs would carry us. Junior seemed to be insisting that we should be fined, locked up, maybe even shot. The old man won the day. After an hour on tenterhooks we were led back to our bikes. It was 11 o'clock at night. Both men came to the big iron gate. Junior had mellowed and was keen to ensure that we knew the direct route out of town and that we'd stick to it. The Superintendent walked in pride as though he were our chief sponsor. We all shook hands sincerely at the gate and with big smiles they waved us off into the middle of the night.

The middle of Hami was lit by street-lights. It was a lot bigger than we'd expected – a symbol of the fresh expansion of China. It was busy and confusing. We lost our route at the first roundabout. There were multi-storey buildings by the roads, lots of vehicle fumes and much dust. We cycled into an area where there were many brightly lit roadside chai houses, some with billiard tables in the street. All crowded with people. We tried to ask the way but no one seemed able to help. We set off down the biggest road we could see. It split into several big forks. We started panicking. We had to get away before Junior and his mates came to catch us again.

Nick. Day 45. Hami. Evening.
Somewhere near the railway lines we got confused and a crowd of bicycles started boxing us in. Suddenly D was no longer there and I found myself heading along a backstreet wondering where on earth he'd got to. When it turned out that he'd simply scooted when the crowd started forming, and hadn't bothered to see if I was following, I was slightly peeved!

Hami turned out to be a very extensive industrial city. We found another large road and cycled through the mayhem for several minutes, then got out our compass to see if we were heading in the right direction. The road veered off to the south. We tried several roads for half an hour before we got across the railway and wriggled through a succession of unlit back-streets, many unsurfaced, to emerge at the edge of town in the moonlight beside a large tarmac road heading in our direction – north-west. We pedalled like mad for another half-hour to get away from the place, hardly daring to whisper: 'Success. We're free.' We needed to make sure we were well away from the industrial sprawl. In the event, our fear chased us right out of the oasis. We stopped after ten kilometres to search for a smooth patch of welcoming stony desert on which to lie down for some well-deserved sleep. The tarmac road was built up on an embankment, so we pushed the bikes 100 yards to one side away from the headlights of the trucks which came past intermittently. We could see the lights of factories and industrial sites shining in the distance in various directions. Up above, the sky was crystal clear. We were extremely relieved to have survived the Hami tight-rope.

> *Nick. Bedtime.*
> We laid our bags on the desert gravel. I lay for a while watching the stars and thinking of those hundreds of other similar nights in southern Europe, when the night sky had been the closing curtain on a day of pleasure.

When we woke in the morning just after dawn at 8 a.m., it turned out that, although we'd left the agriculture of the oasis, we hadn't left the spread of modern commerce. The place where we'd slept was part of a massive area levelled by bulldozers ready for the construction of new industry. There were power-lines and telegraph wires racing across above us. We could be clearly seen from the road – two colourful specks of tired humanity in a great grey area of new opportunity.

Nick and I had a little blow-up first thing in the morning. The stress of the sections around Xing-Xing-Xia and Hami were over, and it looked like we might be on tarmac all the way to Urumqi, so we were free to clear the air. He berated me for being slow to pack up my sleeping-bag. I got at him for always wanting me to race at the start of the day: not giving me enough time to get organized.

In prospect for the day was a succession of small oases linked to the principal Hami area. We expected they would be agricultural, though it turned out that several were large industrial zones. After that, we would enter a more barren area – we didn't know how barren – sleep somewhere, do a day of hard riding, sleep somewhere else, then hopefully reach the next extensive oasis which would be the Turfan Depression. Our route circled the northern perimeter of the Taklamakan Desert – the coldest desert in the world in winter at an average daily temperature of $-30°C$. Since it was now June, much more interesting to us was that it is also the hottest desert in the world in summer at an average daily temperature of $+40°C$. We wondered what sort of bitumen was used for the roads so they wouldn't melt. Later we found out that mostly the roads were dirt! Taklamakan in Turki means: 'Go in and you won't come out.'

The Taklamakan and the Gobi deserts interlink in the area of low hills between Dunhuang and Hami. Both are massive on a world scale, yet

quite different in their structural setting. The Gobi covers a topographi-
cally indistinct area of levelish steppe fronting several different mountain
chains: the Tibetan Plateau, the Altun Shan, and the northern Mongolian
mountains. It opens out to the coastal plains of eastern China. By contrast,
the Taklamakan lies in a tightly confined basin. It is oval in shape, rimmed
to the south by the walls of the Plateau, to the west by the Pamirs and to the
north by the Tien Shan. These mountains of the Tien Shan, the highest of
which is 7,400 metres, are permanently snow-capped. They're called the
Celestial Mountains. Ever since leaving Xing-Xing-Xia we had been able
to see them as dim shapes like clouds in the distance. On Day 46, as we
cycled out from Hami, they were a tall dark barrier blocking the road to the
north, channelling us westwards along their sloping pediment. The melt
from their snows feeds the oases which are dotted like jewels around the
periphery of the Taklamakan. At two points, Hami and Turfan, the Basin
is depressed below sea-level, respectively 154 and 240 metres. The Turfan
Depression is practically rainless, yet snow-melt irrigation has made it a
major centre in China for the cultivation of grapes and melons. Our road
would drop below sea-level shortly before Turfan. That would mark the
end of our first success.

The finish was almost a tangible distance ahead of us – including the rest
of Day 46, we had five days left before our fifty-day time limit ran out. It
seemed we might just make it and maintain our average above 100
kilometres per day. We set out hard and fast. The road was good tarmac,
mostly level. It rose and fell only a little as it crossed the small rises
between successive little oases. Numerous people were using the road. It
was about as busy as a chip shop at the North Pole.

It was the best-ever day for pre-breakfast riding. We did fifty-four
kilometres by 10.30 a.m. and reached a place called, in big letters on our
map, Liushuquan. Thinking that Liushuquan itself would be big, we
ignored several reasonably sized villages *en route*. Unfortunately, it
transpired that our target was no more than a dusty railway station with a
few nondescript chai houses outside in the shade of some dull grey trees.
The woman took a long time cooking up some food, so I went out twice to
the general store to get fistfuls of sweets, a bag of savoury dried beans
which splintered in your teeth, and a bottle of fizzy which we thought was
alcoholic because it made our legs go numb. We'd done the whole
morning's ride without a single drink. It was partly intentional because we
knew there were a lot of places along here where we could get water if
necessary. We didn't want to stop to ask because it takes a long time to go
through all the rigmarole. Way back before Lhasa we'd been stopping
every ten kilometres for drink, every twenty or thirty kilometres for food.
Since then, as we cycled day-in day-out across the high mountains of the
Plateau, we had become very fit. However, making accurate comparisons
of fitness is difficult because of the differences in altitude and terrain.
Things were good and we could dream. We made plans to capitalize on our
fitness as soon as we got back to Britain by entering several long-distance

time trials, especially the National 24 Hour. Neither of us had done that ride; it was one of our ambitions, along with a twenty-five-miler in under an hour, and my special desire, having run 100 miles in a day in the 1985 Western States Trail Race, to run ten miles in under the hour.

Racing along, we soon came to the next oasis of Yaerbashi – a similarly dusty area of lifeless trees and weak-looking crops. Yaerbashi was dominated by a huge coal-mining complex with vast open-cast seams and a towering grey processing plant. Diesel-engines and steam-engines were shunting wagons up and down a large branch of the railroad. Nearby was the uninspiring dormitory town of Ya-izu-chu'an with workers' three-storey tenement blocks, main streets lined with tired flowers, two cinemas and food kiosks on the pavements. It reminded me of a modernized version of miserable Hetauda. We were delighted to find ice-creams and lollypops on sale, so we had a ten-minute break then raced on excitedly towards Turfan. The world was rosy because we believed we had this expedition wrapped up. 'Tarmac all the way to Urumqi' is how we had interpreted the soldiers in the Army camp before Hami when they had pointed towards Xing-Xing-Xia and made wavy motions with their hands, then pointed towards Urumqi and swept their arm smoothly through the air. We hadn't realized they meant only to Hami and then a little further to the edge of the Hami complex. After that, dirt.

Nick. Day 46. Edge of Taklamakan. Afternoon.
A *big* shock at 3.40 p.m. The tarmac ended. I'm so used to these chronically random changes of fortune that it didn't bother me at the time. Two hours later it has begun to sink in. It's a touch boring – and coming to grips with an average speed of 10 k.p.h. again is a pain (it's taken two hours to do seventeen kilometres – truly a bad-quality dirt road). It happened twenty-two kilometres out of Ya-izu-chu'an. D was very despondent. He called it a calamity. The track has come slightly uphill all the way. It was very hard work. For a long time we rode in silence, each trying to assimilate this new turnaround. It means at least 200 kilometres of dirt until the Turfan Oasis. Maybe even to Urumqi. It's a great shame.

We had to ride with our bottoms out of the saddle so as not to get hammered by the bumps. All the pressure was on the balls of our feet, which burnt. The only way to take the pressure off was to do the toestraps up tight. That aggravated the discomfort on our toes, which were scrunched up in the fronts of our shoes. Small consolation was that, though it was worse than the Tibetan roads, it wasn't quite as bad as the earlier sections of Silk Road. The surface was hard-baked dirt with lumpy cobbles and loose shingle spread thinly over like marmalade on granary toast – how we wished we had some of that. We had to slip into dreams to escape the boredom. Any dreams we had of predictions for the future were now replaced on this depressing dirt by simple dreams of safety and comfort at home.

Dick. Day 46. Afternoon.
When riding, I spend a lot of time deciding what to write in my diary. I need a method of remembering it all or else it slips away so quickly in the excitement of food or water when we stop. This time I used 'tctcmdm'. I repeated it over and over again: tctcmdm, tctcmdm. It gives me rhythm like the drum of train wheels. Each letter reminds me of a specific thought; t for toeclips (how my toes hurt), c for comparison (between this track and other roads), t for traffic (in twenty kilometres we've seen two trucks, one donkey, one horse with rider, a flock of sheep and a man with three camels), c for calamity (reaching dirt), m for memory (how I remember it all), d for depression and m for Michèle because it's about time we finished and went home.

The road continued as a totally horrendous nightmare across bare black alluvial pediment stretching out from the Tien Shan and dropping away southwards, to our left, into the shifting sands of the Taklamakan. I found it a landscape reminiscent of the slopes of the huge volcanoes of the Galapagos, particularly Isabella where dark lava mountains sweep down to sparse scrub on lower slopes of grey ash, then sandy beaches and the wide blue open sea.

Nick. Day 46. Afternoon.
We pedalled up higher and at one point flagged down a blue lorry. The driver gave us two bottles of water each and a handful of apricots. It was the kind of instant and thoughtful gesture that we've seen so many times here – the Chinese people are naturally generous – with a smile, too.

After the start of the dirt there was nothing excepting a tiny oasis with five huts and barely twice as many trees. That's where we'd seen the other people. This was marked on our map as Liaodun; there was another place marked further on, but when we got there it didn't exist. The only other place was called Kiwanquan. We held out a lot of hope for it. It was forty kilometres from the start of the dirt. The road continued climbing, eventually reaching 2,000 metres again on a shoulder of an offshoot of a frontal range of the Tien Shan called the Paerh-k'u Shan.

Kiwanquan was a single stone hut. Outside seven young men were building a wall. It didn't seem to start anywhere nor did it go anywhere. They were simply building it. There are a lot of interesting walls in the world: Hadrian's Wall, the Great Wall of China, the wall around the Potala. The curiosity of Kiwanquan may one day join this élite group.

There were only two other things of interest in Kiwanquan. Firstly various small caves and the ruins of a quite extensive castle or château on the rocky slopes a short distance upslope. Secondly the possibility of food. The men were busy at their work yet friendly enough. Initially they didn't seem keen to make any food, then we showed them a few notes so that they knew we intended to pay. The man mixing cement was elected to take us to their hut. One room was their sleeping-room, the other we went into. Barring a clay stove, a pile of coal, a sack of flour, some kitchen utensils and its own four walls, it was empty. The young man pulled some water with a bucket on a rope from the well outside. He took some flour and made a huge quantity of noodles. They were boiled up in an enormous vat, then he tipped equal amounts into each of two enamel washing-up bowls. He shook something hot like raw chilli powder on to them, then looked at us with a smile. There seemed no way Nick and I could do justice to washing-up bowls full of bland noodles. We squatted down on the clay floor. For ten minutes we fished around in the boiling water hooking out chubby noodles until we'd eaten them all. He gestured that there was nothing for a long way further until a place called Qijiaojing, so like sparrows drinking from a cow trough we tipped up the big bowls and slurped all the liquid as well.

When we'd finished it was after nine o'clock at night so we had barely one and a half hours' daylight left. We could have slept there but it would have been no advantage for the morrow. We threw ourselves into the cycling without any attempt to enjoy it or hate it. We simply accepted it. The sooner we got to Turfan the better. Shortly before dark I punctured. We'd only done twelve kilometres from Kiwanquan – but it was twelve kilometres better than nothing. The first puncture since before Lhasa. It was due to a pinch when the tyre had been squashed flat between the wheel rim and one of the sea of rocks on the road. The underlying cause was probably because, in Xing-Xing-Xia, I'd tried to be clever and make allowances for dropping down into increasing heat and had let a little air out of my tyre to allow for air expansion. In the light of modern tyre technology, it now seems a silly thing to have done. The Specialized tyres we were using had done 3,000 faultless kilometres between punctures, 1,000 of them on dirt. Indeed, since there are two tyres on a bike, the average was twice that! While I fumbled around to mend the puncture in the failing light and increasing chill, Nick took a stroll up a nearby knoll to keep warm. He shouted gleefully that our track turned downhill in a very short distance. We'd be able to turn our backs on the 2,000-metre contour line and head down the next day to warmth. We finished the day by doing ten minutes' more riding to the start of the downhill.

At that altitude there was moderate scrub cover. The ground was undulating sandy hummocks interspersed with shallow shingle beds. We found a comfortable depression and for the third night in a row lay down under the twinkling stars. I wore thermals in bed but took my salopets off to use as a pillow. Nick went to bed fully dressed resting his weary head on the tough plastic of his shoes. In our state of exhaustion we fell asleep almost instantly. I vaguely remember turning a couple of times in the chill of the night, and pulling my wind-proof jacket over the top of my bag. When we woke at dawn, there was a vicious sand storm whipping over the land and piercing our sleeping-bags. It didn't feel like our sort of day. We pulled the hoods more tightly over our heads and tried to sleep a little longer. Sticking my head out a few minutes later, the flying sand stung badly. I wriggled about inside my bag sucking my contact lenses then putting them in. When I crawled out I saw that the small scrub bushes, barely two feet high, were springing up and down in the gale. Kneeling up, I was almost higher than the current of blasting sand which bounced across the ground a few feet thick. I had to kneel so that I could hold down all my gear and stop it blowing away. It was so cold we put on all our clothes then made haste to depart and hoped to find some warmer air and food and water, but not necessarily in that order.

The ride downhill was a lot better than the ride uphill, though it was nothing to write home about. After several hours we reached the place called Qijiaojing (pronounced She-Wha-Jing). Shortly before it, we'd crossed a tiny bowl at about 1,000 metres elevation where there was a salt lake. The track had changed to tarmac so this lifted our spirits. Qijiaojing, however, appeared to be nothing but a road junction with a signpost. Here the Urumqi road split. One branch went northwards crossing the Tien Shan then through the large towns of Qitai and Fukang bordering the Dzungarian Desert. The other fork turned south to leave the mountain terrain and continue along the borders of the Taklamakan to Turfan. Both led to Urumqi and both, as far as we could see, were tarmac. We had debated on several previous days which of these two routes we should take. The northern was slightly shorter, but the southern included the Turfan Depression and the well-known tourist rest-halt of Turfan with its wine and shady vines. A lorry came past and we rushed to flag it down. It slowed but drove on by. A second came and this one stopped for us. The driver and his mate were typically friendly, giving us water and telling us that the town of Qijiaojing did exist. It was about an hour along the northern road and there was food. We'd decided we didn't really want to go that route, but on our map it looked nearly 100 kilometres to the next place-name on the southern route. After much wasted time in discussion, a preference for guaranteed food prevailed and we planned that after eating we'd backtrack to here. Setting off again across the mini-plateau, we got two kilometres into a headwind and then, when we were nearly losing sight of the other road branching off to the left, we stopped for a rethink. This time, a preference for chancing our luck and not having to fight into the wind then backtrack to here prevailed. So we started pushing our bikes over the intervening wasteland to regain the southern route. In the fashion of the fickle weather of the high Qinghai Plateau around Tongteyho and Tang-gulashanqu, a rain squall rushed down on us. It lasted ten minutes and soaked us. It was followed by a severely cold wind. Before we reached the southern road we were shivering. Furthermore we were very hungry. Luck was on our side and we saw a truck coming down the very road we had followed from Hami. We prayed it would take the southern fork. It did. We started to sprint for the road before it passed. The driver and his mate had seen us and pulled up to wait. They had a lovely modern truck with spacious cab and a heater and let us climb up inside for half an hour's haven. We are eternally grateful to them, so if you ever see two young men, one beefy with a boilersuit driving truck number 04-0092, the other slim with a gleeful smile and a little moustache wearing a dark blue suit like a wily gangster, then give them our best wishes and a copy of this book. They gave us *all* their food – bread and Chinese sugar cakes, and most of the hot water from their vacuum flask – yet they absolutely refused *any* payment. It was typically generous truckers' camaraderie. The only thing we did for them was drip water all over their seats and slow their journey by half an hour. They were *en route* to Urumqi and would reach there the next day.

> *Nick. Day 47. Middle of day.*
> Really kind truckies gave us food, water and shelter. Twenty minutes later, an Army truck overtook, stopped up the road, and the officer in charge flagged us down. Nothing sinister; he introduced us to each of his team of black-jacketed cadets. They gazed at the bikes and had great pleasure in giving us six twists of fried bread and some foul-tasting water (radiator?). We were well stocked up on calories for the hundred 'K'. Everything looked rosy. But in the same way that good luck turns up just when it's needed, so does bad luck just when it's not. The road we're following isn't on either of our maps, and appears to cut the corner through the mountains, down into the Turfan Depression. The tarmac climbed to a wind-blasted col separated by fang-toothed grey mountains, then plunged arrow-straight down an even, fast gradient (both of slope *and* of temperature). Then we hit the day's big shock: the tarmac ended. We nosedived back on to the dirt. We are sweltering. Each side of us the bare stony desert stretches into the haze and infinity of the Taklamakan. It's hot and blowing a gale.

The wind became very strong. It swooped down off the Tien Shan on our right in an icy blast of heavy cold air off the frozen mountain tops above. Considering this was meant to be the hottest desert in the world, it was extraordinarily cold. All the way we rode individually, leaning our right shoulder down into the teeth of the gale, forcing our bikes to move through the gravel road surface. The wheels slipped sideways. It was safer to pedal hard and continuously, pounding the bike through patches and ridges of sand and shingle so that momentum kept the bike upright. I felt that I had, during the past few weeks, done my apprenticeship for riding dirt. I could hit it fast and sail over. Nick was already an expert – he'd cycled dirt in Morocco, Greece, Norway and, among many other places, the Rift Valley with Ados two years back. When I came to Bangladesh, I had to slow right down for gravel and double my heart rate; now I could slice straight down the centre. However, I dreaded the hammering all the jolts were giving to the axles, particularly the rear one which we already knew was slightly loose and therefore prone to fracture. The wind was so strong that in places it had swept the track free of loose cover, so we rode at times on baked flinty clay. Twisters of spinning air, their vortex sucking up sand and stones, sped across the desert. They'd stand still for a moment, like orienteers checking their maps, then race off again.

We stopped for a few minutes for a breather. After commiserating mightily with each other, we pulled off again. Three kilometres later, we realized I'd left our compass behind. I voted to leave the compass. Nick ordered me to go back and get it. He said we needed it to locate the Centre of the Earth, if we ever got there. Dutifully, I set off back. It was a small compass. In fact, to make it lighter, we'd taken the oil-filled centre out of the smallest version of compass that Black's had in stock, and thrown the bevel away before we left Britain. Generally, one stretch of gravel looks much the same as another, but I'd seen so much in the past few days that I located our particular stretch fairly quickly and found the compass. Nick was a long way away; we were much further apart than we'd been for more than forty days. I felt quite lonely in the wilderness.

Nick. Day 47. Somewhere in the Taklamakan. Afternoon.
I'm sheltering from the howling typhoon while D makes a martyr of himself going back for the compass he forgot. He left in good heart, shouting for me to time him for a new world six-kilometre out-and-back record. If it had been me I'd have been too sick to utter a word. I wonder how he's getting on? He's been away for forty minutes of double-plus purgatory.

Once I'd located the compass, I gritted my teeth and set off intending to curse him all the way for sending me back. Once more luck was on my side. A truck came grinding along into the wind. With a slight reservation about taking the first motorized transport since the luxurious black taxi we'd ridden in Lhasa, I threw my precious Raleigh in the back and climbed on board for a ride. When I got back to Nick he was doing all right. He was snoozing. He woke with a start when the truck stopped. Then, like my sisters Sarah and Emily when they've been to different films in an evening, we had a long excited natter about the different things we'd done while we'd been apart.

We blasted on some more. The wind blasted back at us stronger than ever. It was too noisy to shout at each other. We thrashed away in our own little worlds. By and by we became separated. The railroad loomed ahead – a thin black line stretched taut and fast across the desert. I didn't realize

I'd lost Nick until I got there. He must have been a long way back because, even though it was an absolutely flat plain, I couldn't see him and the track got lost in the sand storm. At this railway crossing, the only one in the desert between Hami and Turfan, we had hoped there would be a hut and a little old man smoking his pipe. There was nothing. The wind was so powerful that when I had a pee it didn't water the desert but atomized almost immediately and spun off into the void. I sat down in the shelter of the kilometre post and waited.

There wasn't much to look at. I daydreamed. A noise startled me and I craned my neck around to see a train bearing down on me. It zoomed by a few feet away, blocking the gale for a moment. I could see the passengers inside the windows. I felt as incredibly small as I did when going to marvel at the steam-engines when I was a toddler. In a moment they were gone and I felt even smaller in this vast sea of emptiness. Sven Hedin, the explorer, who knew deserts well, thought the Taklamakan was 'much more of a desert than any other in the world'.

I started to worry about Nick. Sir Clarmont Skrine, British Consul-General to Kashgar in the 1920s, wrote in his book, *Chinese Central Asia*: 'In a clear dawn, the view is inexpressibly awe-inspiring and sinister. The sands of the Taklamakan, like the giant waves of a petrified ocean, extend in countless myriads to a far horizon. Here and there a vicious desert storm towers like a King. Whole caravans have been swallowed up in the past. The desert silently clamours for travellers to engulf.'

I decided that, as I'd been sitting there nearly half an hour, I ought to go back to see if he was in trouble. When I stood up, I was nearly flattened by the wind. I needed three attempts to get on my bike; tight grip on the handlebars, racing hunch. Once started, I made no more than walking pace in absolute bottom gear. Nick appeared down the road, fighting towards me. I stopped. He'd punctured. Only his second of the whole expedition. He said it had been a perfect puncture mend. It had been blowing a gale, so every small item of the puncture kit had to be clamped between his knees or weighted with stones. He continued: 'Such a wind, I couldn't hear the hiss of the hole. So I had to curl around the inner tube and sense the jet with my lips!' At the time I felt sorry for him having to do it all alone, but I read later in his diary that he had had a 'relaxing' twenty minutes doing it – so I don't feel so bad. In fact, if it had been me, I'd have taken my time about it. A puncture is a fact of life and, however much people may want you to hurry, it is a Heaven-sent delay.

Nick. Day 47. Early Evening. Lost in the Taklamakan.
The wind was fiercer than ever and as the road bent west a bit we found ourselves being shoved with a massive force. So hard in fact that it was a fight to keep control of the bike, with the handlebars trying to wrench themselves free with every bump. We just had two wheel-ruts, one foot wide, with high walls of gravel to ride in. Catch your front wheel in this and you're

dragged off. Doing just this I got my foot stuck in the toeclip and crashed down – my first real injury.

I remember nothing of the next two hours until the dreamlike appearance of the easternmost edge of the Turfan Oasis complex. There was a line of small trees, like a black marker-pen underlining the solitude of the desert, then several fairly barren fields which to us were thick jungle. A little boy played with a cardboard box in a pile of sand. There was a mud hut. Then a short stretch of more desert, then a much bigger oasis. We had come 170 kilometres from the last permanent habitation. We hadn't had a proper meal for what seemed like years. We hadn't taken our clothes off for four days since Zhangjiaquan. We sat down for a little rest. About ten kilometres before the oasis there had been a temperature inversion. The northerly gale of the morning and afternoon amazingly blew over our heads. We dropped down into thick warm air which came moist and soothing into our lungs. All day we'd been losing height. The elevation of this side of the oasis was about 600 metres and the Taklamakan Basin was levelling out. In theory, and in practice, it was much warmer. Sitting stationary we perspired. We could have kidded ourselves that we'd never seen living things before. We felt like Jonah having crossed an ocean by some improbable means, and then having been safely beached on a distant shore. There was water in the pools, lots of birds singing, rows of trees, some flowers in the shade. Most important of all, there were people. Later, with utmost sincerity, I wrote in my diary: 'We are thankful to be through that desert.'

We made another short distance of dirt that day to reach the village of Qiktim (pronounced Chickatia) at 10 p.m. There was a café and several tight dry streets of mudbrick homes. Although there was another half-hour of daylight in which to make another few kilometres, there we gratefully stopped. It was dusty and warm with lots of children and hordes of flies – more than we'd encountered since the foothills of Nepal. Quite a few adults and boys came round, and also several girls. They were all quiet and absorbed. The boys watched us (we sat eating noodles and stir-fry), the men squatted down to discuss the bikes, the girls pretended they couldn't see us and watched the men and boys. Everyone was dressed in dusty Western clothes: shirt, slacks and shorts. All the men, almost as a mark of adulthood, had some sort of headgear, either blue Mao caps or white Muslim skull-caps. Only a couple of children were barefoot.

After eating, while Nick wrote up his notes for the day, I set off into the twilight led by a couple of local kids to try to find the shop. In the dying hours of the day a huge dry storm had blown up carrying choking dust through the trees. Visibility was down to about twenty paces. The gusty wind was blowing hot from the west as though it arose out of the heat of the Turfan Depression and was trying to blow the afternoon's cold gale back up to the mountains. The headlights of a bus glowed up at me like the Loch Ness monster in deep murky waters. My eyes filled up with dirt. I had to go back into the café and take out and clean my lenses, then wrap up tight in goggles, face-mask and cap before venturing out again. I was surprised to find that walking was quite slow and uncomfortable. The kids charged off into the gloom, with their T-shirts or caps clasped over their mouths, then came darting back to get me. The dust was deep and fine in the road. As I walked it presented no resistance but, at each step, flew away in a cloud. Loess as fine and light as baby's talcum powder. We hammered on the door of one place which they assured me was a shop but no one came. At the second place an old man with skin as dry as parchment had a paraffin lamp illuminating the shadows of several virtually empty shelves. He had a few boxes of tobacco, packets of cigarettes, a large sack of garlic, and a wooden tea-chest of peanuts. When I got back, Nick was washing.

> *Dick. Day 47. Qiktim. 11 p.m.*
> Nick's neurotic about cleanliness; he complains most days about being dirty and is doing a full wash here. He's nearly as fanatical about soap as he is about food. Although I have double portions, he typically downs nearly twice as much as me. He'll be upset tomorrow when I get him up at dawn for the charge to Turfan.

I was wrong on all counts. I also had a full body-wash that night standing up in an enamel bowl exactly the same as the one we had eaten out of in Kiwanquan. And full of equally dirty water. It was five days since we'd been anywhere with enough water to wash. I stuffed myself full of peanuts which I'd brought back from the old man's shop in my over-trousers with knots tied in the legs (I took my legs out before I did this). We did manage to rise at dawn and Nick was ready to leave before me. We set off munching a cold momo. There was no wind. After a few kilometres the road was surfaced. It looked like being another momentous day.

We reached Shanshan for breakfast. Nick agitated to be moving again in forty minutes. The thin man in charge, who had a chrome-plated ghetto-blaster, took fifty minutes to cook the food. We fairly raced out of Shanshan on a good road with a pleasant following breeze, turning top gear. It was slightly downhill so we quickly dropped to a few hundred feet above sea-level. For almost the first time since leaving Bangladesh, we could ride part of the way without goggles. The sky around the horizon was slightly overcast, glazed by dust in the air. Above our heads it was clear blue.

It was a beautiful day's cycling in pleasantly warm dry air through a series of plush oases like rolling Warwickshire fields, and then into a splendid gorge leading down to sea-level. Before that part, however, was a minor hiccup when for twenty kilometres after Shanshan, crossing an interlude of barren desert, the road was unsurfaced. At first we felt like crying. But we hit it with a vengeance and it was all over in an hour. The bikes shot away with delight when we got back on tarmac. A line of smooth dry hills, almost translucent in the dust and heat haze, and covered by sand, paralleled us on the southern side all the way, then we turned left into the gorge and cut through, steeply down towards the Turfan Depression. The gorge was gloriously Egyptian. Big sandstone cliffs with smooth red sand screes hanging almost vertically above a tight green swath of reeds which squeezed into the bottom. In one or two places a ruined farmhouse clung to the walls. Sadly the gorge was barely two kilometres long. We issued past some intriguing ruins to a wide expanse of empty sands. We were a mere few metres above sea-level. The sands stretched southwards into the stifling heat as far as the eye could see. At the juncture, below the cliffs, was the rather twee village of Erh-pao – an Oriental counterpart of St Bees. A short way further on, 587 kilometres from Xing-Xing-Xia, after 24,720 metres of ascent (81,200 feet) and 4,896 kilometres (3,043 miles) of cycling, over a quarter of it (1,417 kilometres) on dirt roads, in an elapsed time of forty-seven days plus a few hours from where we dipped our fingers in the sea in the first paragraph of Chapter 1, we returned to sea-level.

We had finished flying over the hump. End of Part One!

Nick. Day 48. Sea-level.
It wasn't a particularly inspiring place for photographs. The scenery disappeared into the shimmering cauldron of heat. We could vaguely discern the shape of a row of hills to the north. To the south, well below sea-level, we could make out a thin dark line of trees marking the edge of a submarine oasis. Everything else was monotonous sand. There weren't even any dunes. Local topography was the line of telegraph poles. Local interest the strip of tarmac and the lorries which, this close to Turfan, were a steady flow. We balanced the camera on a pile of sand, set the delay timer and executed a couple of smiling poses by the 587-kilometre post.

Onward, ever onward! – as my late mum used to say. Twenty-five more fast kilometres took us into the Turfan main junction, three more into the town centre. It looked as big as Dunhuang but fractionally less modern. The Turfan Hotel was easy to find. We booked in, it seemed quite expensive (fifty yuan for two, as opposed to the four yuan we'd paid in Qiktim). The staff were somewhat offhand. Inside it was rather grand with immaculately clean white colonial-type buildings and several leafy courtyards singing with birds. We waved a jolly hello to the other tourists having a cool beer in the delightful shade, and we said gaily that we'd join them in 'just a mo' – after we'd powdered our noses.

We had a double room with a bed each. We installed the bikes as our head-boards then luxuriated in water. We showered for quite a long time, scrubbing our nails and soaping our armpits. Then we washed our clothes. My underpants had holes worn in them where my bones had bounced on the saddle. When we felt suitably satisfied with domestic chores, we put on Goretex over-trousers and thermal tops (everything else was wet) and strolled out in the calm dry heat of Turfan – the hottest place in China. Reputably it goes up to over 47°C on some days in summer. On the afternoon we were there it never exceeded 40°C, which is a little over 100°F, the temperature we had endured with such copious sweating and stuffy heads by the Ganges thirty-nine days before.

We'd heard so much about the relaxed pace of Turfan and its exotic charms. We headed first for the market. It was entered through a beautiful mosque-type frontage with colourful swirling geometric patterns and graceful Arabic script. We'd decided we were going to enjoy ourselves. It was a day off. The ride to Urumqi on the morrow was about 180 kilometres on a busy tarmac road which we thought we could complete easily. Then we would have reached Urumqi in under fifty days, in fact in an elapsed time of forty-eight and a half days, therefore giving us one and a half days to, as we thought, 'nip out on a day's joy ride and bag the Centre of the Earth'. Once more we thought we had it all sewn up. The rest of Day 48 was holiday. We strolled past the ice-cream sellers and the people displaying piles of fruit. We glanced at stalls of clothes and, on the ground, assorted bits of bicycles. Then we found the kebab stalls and the bakers selling hot fresh bread, some of which were flat like pancakes, others were dense and round like the Maryport buns Mum used to buy. Here we stopped to indulge. There was much to celebrate. Probably no one before had ever cycled over the entire Tibetan Plateau. By getting back to sea-level, we'd completed the equivalent of cycling from London to Rome three times, one of those times being on dirt roads, often at an altitude slightly less than that of Mont Blanc. We'd done it in six and a half weeks and ascended the equivalent of three times up Everest. On Day 48 we ate our way through a mountain of food from the first kebab until the last apricot before bed. Eleven kebab-sellers occupied this little alley in the market. Each had a tray of glowing embers. They skewered little hunks of meat or liver, four to a wire, then laid them across the edges of the tray, suspended over the embers. The kebab man offered us little glasses of fine black tea to wash the food down. We sat in front and snacked while we watched the market go by.

It was difficult to believe we were in the depths of China. Nearly everyone was of basically Caucasian stock. Men had finely sculpted faces, much more angular than the Chinese. Tall elegant women wore calf-length dresses. Small white Muslim skull-caps abounded. Han Chinese and Mao suits were not to be seen. Most of the people were Turkish-speaking Uygurs, who used to be the majority of the population of Xinjiang in 1955 when it became named Xinjiang Uygur Autonomous Region. Since then renewed investment has brought a great influx of eastern Chinese who today equal the Uygurs in number. However, Turfan remains a gentle market town, while Hami is a busy metropolis.

We wandered around the market for a while testing different fruits and exploring the back alleys. There was an ice-cream machine like an open barrel with a twirling brass tumbler. Somehow it made bright-yellow ice-cream which was scooped out into a large bowl and then spatulated into individual glasses. After the market we bought a few items in some modern shops, such as new diaries, clean face-masks, and a pile more food, then went back to the hotel. We had been saving up the pleasures of a cold beer. When we went to get one, we met, much to our surprise, Robert Goo. He'd sold his mountain-bike in Lhasa and bussed around to the edges of eastern China before coming here. He'd been travelling with friends but in Xining, 1,500 kilometres east of here, he lost them in a crowd. He didn't seem unduly worried. He thought that if they weren't here, then he'd probably bump into them again in Kashgar. Kashgar was 2,000 kilometres west of Turfan. Several days later we met Robert in Urumqi; he was 'relaxing a while', and thought he might reach Kashgar in a 'week or two'. Several months later, Brian Williamson turned up in London. He worked as a bicycle-courier then went down with malaria. He was laid up at the Hospital for Tropical Diseases. They reckoned his first bout of malaria must have been cycling the Lalung Le from Kathmandu to Lhasa. He said: 'Yes, I do remember feeling somewhat weak and having a sore back – but there were so many problems on that ride.' He had cycled out of China from Kashgar over the Kunjirab Pass to Pakistan – the first cyclist out that way. In Lhasa, Brian had met Mark Skinner, who has not been heard of since. Robert said that he'd heard the Kathmandu–Kailash cycling expedition had folded 500 kilometres short of the target. Who's having the next go?

Our several meetings with Robert and his casual attitude speak worlds about the nonchalance of long-term travellers, also about the restricted number of modes by which they journey, hopping by train, plane or bus over huge distances between successive tourist sights. They live on a series of tiny islands populated by other travellers, and linked, not by geography or mountains or deserts, but by abominable journeys where stations, bus depots or truck depots are the gateways. Robert was doing the relics around Turfan. He told us about the Buddhist cave temples of Bezelik, the fallen city of Gaochang and the Atsana graves. They sounded quite interesting; indeed, we might have passed close when we came from Erh-pao. His descriptions satisfied my archaeological wanderlust. I always think to myself that antiquities in general and, for that matter, grand scenery will always be there. Only the present changes. He himself said: 'There are mummies at Atsana. They're OK but it's better to see the ones in the museum.'

Later at night there was some wonderful dancing and music by an Uygur team. Instruments were varied; some like ukuleles, others like tiny guitars, then a violin, and a funny type of knee-violin with a three-foot stem and a soundbox like a football. There was a xylophone and flutes. The girls wore long dresses in flaming pink with chiffon leggings and tight black bodices edged with gold. They took tiny steps, wore tiny caps and, down past their waists and flying out sideways, they each had five long black plaits. The men had bright-blue tunics embroidered in gold, with baggy black trousers tight at the knees, and long black boots. The women looked Arabic, the men Cossack excepting their intricately embellished skull-caps and Turkish faces. They swept and twirled around the girls. The tourists in the front row watched it all with straight faces, squinting through the viewfinders of their cameras. The Chinese locals behind clapped and laughed. During the dancing, Nick was approached by a Chinese girl who said: 'Australian?' 'English?' 'Tourist?' 'Going to Urumqi?' 'You have girl-friend?' 'Does she have white hair and long nose like you?'

We went to bed at midnight having overeaten ridiculously. My stomach was so full that I was in severe pain as I tried *not* to laugh at Nick's wisecracks. I woke at first light and got up. I remember thinking I was lucky to be standing after all the food we had put down. I lamented that we had those uncontrollable eating urges. Possibly our stomachs had shrunk and become inured to the desert diet of bread, water and noodles, so that on returning to modern luxury foods with lots of grease, fats and refined sugars we found them hard to digest. In preparation for the ride, we each tried to munch a dry bread roll. I hoped that the fifty kilometres of cycling to the first village of Ti'enshan would put me right.

Nick. Day 49. Turfan. Early morning.
This is the last day – in theory – of the journey to Urumqi. So it's an exciting one. Then the nub of the adventure – actually finding the C of the E. It's strange now to think back over sections of the route, like Lhasa to Golmud, or Patenga Point to Kathmandu. Each section has been a major journey in itself. Run them all together and you have a journey too big to imagine. Today's ride is a medium-long one, through the desert up to 1,000 metres or more, over the Tien Shan, with perhaps two villages for food in the 183 kilometres. A couple of weeks ago the prospect of this would have been a bit of a frightener, but now it's as straightforward as tootling down to Clapham Common from the City.

The main road left the Turfan oasis almost immediately and we cycled abruptly back on to stony desert. Although, for the first half-hour, we could see tiny oases nestling under the low mountains to the left, there was not a shred of vegetation where we cycled. There was a clear sky, with strong sun. To stay cool, we cycled with our salopets rolled down to our waists, no T-shirt. We set off in good spirits, hammering into the short distance to the first village. The road was good tarmac laid straight across the alluvial pediment of the Tien Shan on our right. It climbed all the way, cutting itself free from the Taklamakan which was just over the low hills on the left. The road climbed more steeply up an open shoulder of desert to 1,000 metres. There was a lot of traffic on the road, more than we'd seen since Kathmandu. An Army convoy came past, soldiers lounging in the back reading magazines. Each lorry towed a camouflaged cannon.

We did fifty kilometres, and the village of Ti'enshan was nowhere to be seen. We hadn't had any water. We bashed on. Further on, we crossed the railway which also uses this pass to get over the hills to Urumqi. Then we entered a valley. Shortly the valley became a large gorge. Despite the yearning for breakfast, we immensely enjoyed the ride up the gorge. The mountains were large and dark, mottled in purples, yellows, reds and browns. They were completely bare of vegetation, yet in the stream valley the trees were thick – more trees growing naturally than we'd seen since Nepal. There were a couple of villages clustered tightly out of harm's way. We saw some flocks of sheep and a lovely grassy glade, like Constable's England – but sadly no milkmaids.

The gorge wound on and on. All the time climbing, all the time twisty so we couldn't see around the next corner. All the time we got hungrier and hungrier. After eighty-two kilometres, when we were beginning to feel weak, we saw three shacks by the road. Thankfully, all were chai houses. We chose the one with a truck driver sitting outside under the leaves of a handsome gnarled tree. It was an idyllic place for breakfast; a fabulous final meal before Urumqi. There were tweety birds in the trees, and breeze in the leaves. The owners had tomatoes, which we hadn't seen since Lhasa, and the wife made super soup. Nick also had noodles, but I was badly off colour, possibly after yesterday's ice-cream or the bag of tough little apricots which Nick had declined to eat.

Half an hour later, we cycled out of the claustrophobic gorge on to a beautiful flat grassy plain opening 140 degrees in front of us. It was twenty or thirty kilometres wide, looking like a billiard table dotted with tiny villages, galloping horses and groves of trees. More green than we'd seen since the foothills of Nepal. The river meandered snoozily across towards us then dropped foaming into the gorge. High above the furthest rim snow peaks floated like tiny clouds. It was the archetypal fertile mountain basin – a natural oasis quite at odds with the austere grandeur of mountains and deserts. Furthermore, quite different from the meticulously irrigated oases like Hami and Turfan. It was sunny and warm. We could have been on a cycle holiday in southern France. There were flowers, bulrushes and carpets of buttercups. It was centred on the town of Dabancheng, disappointingly renamed on the market façade 'Daban City'. It looked like a large busy market, though, having eaten, we surged past on the drops, not having the courtesy to give it so much as a 'by your leave'. Traffic was extremely busy: a steady stream of trucks, jeeps and buses. So many buses, we wondered who could be using the railway.

Shortly after Dabancheng, maybe seventy kilometres out of Urumqi, the rich grasslands faded away. With it our luck changed. A headwind got up in the afternoon, at first gentle, then progressively stronger until it became like riding into a wall. We had to crouch low on the bikes, taking turns to fight the wind in front. The resistance couldn't have been more if we'd had elastic ropes tied on our bikes and pegged down in Dabancheng. The scenery changed to barren desert. The altitude was well over 1,000 metres. Our road took a straight line down the south–north furrow in the Tien Shan. Several deep-blue salt lakes occupied the floor of the valley. Everything else was soul-destroying pale grey. It was a valley on the same scale as those between Budongquan and Golmud but infinitely more alien. Far off and up to our right the snow peaks continued. We passed the first of the salt lakes and then an unpleasantly desolate industrial complex where there was not a single blade of grass in sight. It looked like it should have been empty of people, but far from it. There were queues of chai halts by the road, lots of mechanics and garages, plenty of children yelling at us and many large tenement blocks.

The wind was extraordinarily fierce. Fifty kilometres out of Urumqi, we stopped by the road for a rest. Nick sheltered behind a heap of gravel and fell asleep. I drank the last dregs of the cold tea in my bottle. Little did I know at the time that there would be no more water until Urumqi. I was getting incredibly weak. My stomach was cramping after the excesses of Turfan. We set off again, Nick initially winding up speed into the gale. After 500 metres, on my first turn to take over, I glanced behind for lorries, lost my balance slightly, caught Nick's back wheel and was down in the road. It was our first true accident. It was symbolic – now that we were very nearly at our target, we could afford to relax our out-and-out cut-throat concentration, and feel a little sorry for ourselves. If Urumqi didn't come to us today, it would come tomorrow. However, neither of us ever dreamt of submitting except under severe pressure: for example, a broken leg. For ten kilometres, Nick led. I couldn't accelerate myself out of his slipstream into the work position in front. I couldn't find any reserves of commitment or energy. We prayed for a chai house but none came. The wind was relentless from the north. Urumqi crept slowly closer. We both worked very hard, both mentally and physically, to subdue this last tiny section. Typically, cycling is all about slipping into a rhythm and letting your mind wander: fantasies of food, friends, exotic travels or an evening by the fire. *En route* to Urumqi, none of this was possible. We were, in body and mind, out there in the dry heat and phenomenally powerful wind on the bare tarmac for fifty kilometres. Not for a moment did the reality relent.

Urumqi eventually was reeled in, not with a whimper but fighting fit; up a hummocky col, the wind blocking us to the last, then out of the oppressive valley and turning a last corner to look down on the first small patch of green, several ramshackle chai houses and the city in the world most remote from the open sea: Urumqi. The Heart of Asia. We felt we were looking at the trophy. The city itself appeared large, dark and industrial: dropped down like a mud-pie into an embayment in the mountains. Beyond that, stretching northwards seemingly to the end of the world, was the silent wonder of the Dzungarian Desert. Out there, unbeknown to anyone else in the world, was the Centre of the Earth.

TWELVE

Urumqi and the Public Security Bureau

Urumqi has been described by some as 'the ugliest city on the face of the earth'. On the contrary, we found it to be startling in its diversity of architecture and lifestyles, and everywhere close to countryside and mountains. It is a dynamic, expanding, modern Chinese city with nearly one million inhabitants and the focus of commerce for 1,000 kilometres in every direction. The city occupies a gentle north-facing valley. At its foot are the new agricultural lands, fed by snowmelt irrigation. They border the southern rim of the Dzungarian Desert in a belt fifty kilometres deep which stretches several hundreds of kilometres east and west along the base of the Tien Shan mountains – the backbone of Central Asia. Urumqi International Airport is below the city on the edge of the desert. There are parks and high-rise buildings – almost skyscrapers – in the centre of the city and at the top end is the heavy industry with large, smoky factories signalling the new China.

We rolled down from the lip of the salt basins towards the outlying tentacles of the industrial end of the city at 7.10 p.m. on Day 49. Like a winner in the Tour de France, I threw my arms in the air and yelled 'Success!' Nick said with sincere relief: 'The finishing line is in sight.'

I rolled beside him, aches and pains and weakness forgotten in the glory of the moment. 'Under fifty days. Only the shortest day-trip into the desert tomorrow to stand on the spot.'

'Too right, mate. It looks like we've done it.'

Nick's last comment had a hint of his typical caution – nothing's ever in the bag until it's actually in the bag. Though we didn't know it then, he was well and truly right.

We wanted to celebrate and savour our apparent success. Furthermore, we'd not eaten or drunk, other than our one litre each of cold tea, for the last ninety-five mind-blowing kilometres battling into the fierce head-wind. I was still getting stomach cramps and during the whole day had only had one dry bread roll in Turfan and one bowl of soup for the entire 180-kilometre ride. Both of us were suffering a massive energy debt. We dived into the very first chai house. It was a single large room painted all over in pastel blue, more or less empty excepting a few tables and chairs and a truck driver chatting up two local girls. There was a small kitchen at one end with steaming cauldrons. At the other end, we staggered into a small room used as a shop. To our delight, we saw sweets, biscuits, fruits and . . . chocolate. Nick's eyes bulged as big as a punter winning the pools. Six bars disappeared down his throat before you could say PSB. We bought sweets, peanuts, a jar of apricots, and a lot more chocolate. Then we sat down and ordered noodle soup and tea. It did Nick good, but I could only manage liquids in small sips.

An hour later, we cruised on into the city centre ten kilometres further. The wind had disappeared and it was downhill all the way. The roads were very busy and we derived immense pleasure from being in a queue of vehicles and skirting a traffic jam. In London, they are the cyclist's constant companion, but we hadn't come across anything remotely similar since the four vehicles at the traffic-lights in Lhasa. Most of the vehicles were trucks, not so much the long-nosed green trucks we'd got used to beetling around the oases to the south, but modern heavy-duty ones: large flat-bed trucks, gigantic dumper-trucks, Chinese articulated trucks and coal wagons. The closer we got to the centre, the more coaches, buses and mini-buses we saw. Trams seemed to be doing good business: it was the late rush-hour and people packed on and off barely leaving enough room for the concertina doors to click shut before the conductress, leaning out of her window halfway down the bus, gave two firm blasts on her whistle. Numerous green Chinese jeeps – the ubiquitous Beijing 212 – nipped around. They are canvas-roofed and open-sided, so both passenger and driver seem to be perched on the top, leaning out sideways into every corner. There were not many cars; mostly they appeared to be official police, government or Army vehicles, otherwise taxis. As far as I can remember, nearly all were black. Quite a lot of people rode motor bikes, the majority of which would have been thirty years out of date in the West. The most magnificent bit of machinery was the Army motor bike and sidecar combination. Every example we saw was painted dull dark green. The bike itself was long and low with a huge wide saddle, and a separate one for the pillion rider. The driver sits bolt upright with straight spine, and the sidecar passenger, who was often an officer in green uniform with crisp peaked cap and straight serious face, sinks deep into the voluminous bullet-nosed gondola on the side.

Of course, there were many other cyclists. They seemed mostly to have their own traffic rules and regulations. Thus on the red light some would set off and wait by the traffic island in the middle of the road. On the green, sometimes, many would stop and their eyes would be searching for something ahead which we couldn't see. If the men and women on bikes were unruly, then the donkey carts and men with wheelbarrows or mobile ice-cream stalls were lawless. They moved extremely ponderously: maybe they were beyond the grasp of the law. One of our advantages was that we were as fast as the motor vehicles and could accelerate easily into a gap, then brake quickly if we got into problems. It was fun – and also a grand entry to this tremendous city.

All the main roads, and most of the minor, were tarmac. There were many tree-lined streets and wide avenues with ornamental flower-beds down the middle. Everywhere had pavements. There were monuments and statues. Tenement blocks were five or six storeys high. Many windows had flower-boxes outside – this was an eye-opener because nowhere else had we seen flowers privately cultivated for pleasure, so we wondered if they indicated a prosperous society with spare time and money for leisure. Office blocks, hotels and government buildings were in places grand, sometimes up to twelve or more storeys high. There were telephone wires, street lights, neon lights and carefully prepared window displays for shops – a far cry from the wizened old man in Qiktim merely two nights ago.

We came down into the centre and found the two rivers and public park of Hong Shan Mountain by which the traveller orientates himself or herself in town. Hong Shan Mountain is not so much a mountain as a molehill. It has a pleasant pagoda on top. However, the two rivers marked grandly on our maps turned out to be tiny streams three metres wide running in alluvial trenches with outsize fifty-metre bridges crossing them every few blocks. Nearby was a large covered market crammed with individual stalls. Throngs of people moved in and out; indeed, there were also many simply 'hanging around', possibly waiting for films to start or waiting to meet friends for the evening. There was a confusing range of facial types and dress styles. Urumqi is approximately half Uygur, who are the traditional farmers and traders of this area, plus maybe 10 per cent other National Minorities such as Tatar or Kazak, with the second half, or the new half, being Han Chinese immigrants who have come here as a result of government stimulation of the area in the past thirty years.

Following various snippets of advice from other tourists we'd met in Turfan, Dunhuang, Golmud and Lhasa, we headed for the best hotel in town. 'Dormitory rooms are quite cheap,' they'd told us, 'five yuan, about one pound, each – and you get a television room and hot showers at any time of day.' The Kun Lun Hotel was certainly a smart establishment. It had a huge façade towering over the fountains in front. The lobby was marbled and of international style so we discreetly left our bikes outside. There were several hundred rooms. We felt we deserved a treat so we ordered the best. When you pay as much, relatively speaking, as we did – twenty-five yuan each – then you're allowed to be dressed bizarrely and to rush filthy dirty through the lobby carrying bikes heading for the lift.

Our room had twin beds, private bathroom, telephone, television, cups and kettle for tea, a maid constantly on duty at the end of the corridor, and a wonderful view of 5,445-metre (18,270-foot) Bogda Feng, the snow-capped highest peak in this central section of the Tien Shan. This was one of the mountains we'd been able to see all day from the moment we exited from the tight gorge after breakfast in the idyllic glade of trees. All bar the top bit of icing on the cake, we had been cycling that high merely two weeks before. However, our current priority was high-class luxury and real food.

Despite our tiredness, we were eager to go exploring. We went out of the hotel and slowly walked a short distance down the street to a knot of food stalls and chai houses on a busy corner. Though night had fallen, it was quite active. The shops were well stocked with endless varieties of clothes, shoes, crockery, cutlery; the only things not in evidence were electrical goods like hi-fi, radios and televisions. Food shops had good selections of all sorts of tinned and jarred things and fresh meat, vegetables, fruits and bread. Our particular interest was biscuits, sweets and similar goodies such as chocolate, of which there were at least seven varieties on show. We bought one of everything, tasted them all at the counter, then bought numerous bars of the best chocolate and several handfuls of the best sweets. As our first presents to take back home we each bought a Flying Eagle Safety Razor which comes with a spare set of blades in a tiny brass tin with an eagle embossed on the lid. Interestingly the shop-signs, and many of the sweet-wrappers, toy-boxes and books, were in both Arabic and Chinese – not that it mattered to us because we couldn't read either. A few also had English, and therefore had unusual signboards; English reading left to right, Arabic going right to left, and Chinese up and down in the middle.

Nick tucked into noodle stew, but my appetite hadn't fully returned so I bought some Turkish flat breads and chewed on them. The walk back seemed to be a long way, although it was probably only two hundred yards. For fifty days, we hadn't walked any long distance, in fact we had hardly walked anywhere. Our legs bent like creaky old trees in the wind.

By the time we were back in our room, it was midnight local time, therefore 4 p.m. in Britain. Despite our tiredness, we tried to telephone Steve Bonnist and tell him to get the press machine underway to start the fund-raising for IT. The first stunning thing that happened was that, following one trip downstairs to chat up the pretty telephonist, our telephone was connected to Britain in under fifteen minutes (calls apparently have to go 3,000 kilometres to Beijing first, then be beamed out of China). Steve was very well, so were our various relatives whom Steve rang up every few days for a chat. We gave him our news about imminent success and asked him if he had received our packages from Dhaka, Kathmandu and Lhasa. Yes, he said cheerfully. Then came the awful moment of truth. We asked him what was the level of press interest and, very importantly, were the photos good? We could hardly believe his answers. He said 'none' and 'unusable'. We were dumbfounded. It meant very little fund-raising would be possible: no magazines, no book and no lectures. That more or less finished the phone call and doused any thoughts we had of phoning anyone else or planning anything for the next day. We collapsed morosely into bed.

Neither of us slept well. Nick fretted about the photos. Was the film damaged? Had the camera been out-of-order from the start? Was our photography useless? In the dead of night, I had a heated thirty minutes in the loo submitting to the final frenzied throes of gut rot. In the morning, we each, as it were, attended to the other's problem. Nick saw to his stomach and stocked up on Continental breakfast in the hotel, I telephoned my dad and then my brother Chris. In Malvern Wells it was 2 a.m., but Chris and his wife Fred didn't sound too upset at having to get out of bed to attend to my needs. Chris had been directly receiving and processing all our films then getting the better slides duplicated and sent to Steve. Apparently the dupes weren't good quality, but Chris, who's not given to flattery, said that as far as he could see the originals were 'same as your usual standard'. I rushed down to tell Nick. He was over the moon.

We could now get on with the last remaining item of business: where exactly was the Centre of the Earth? How far was it from Urumqi? And how would we get there?

We had done a couple of rough calculations in Britain before departing. We thought it lay about fifty kilometres due north of Urumqi just beyond the limits of the irrigated agricultural zones on the edge of the desert. We thought therefore it would be moderately remote yet not inaccessible. For the next few hours of Day 50, we planned to retire to our room, calculate the exact position then maybe set out and get nearly there by nightfall in order to finish off the job early the next morning. That would be Day 51, but as explained earlier, because we started on Day 1 at noon, not Day 0 at 00.00 a.m., to finish on Day 51 at noon would mean an elapsed time of under fifty days. The four-hour difference in time zones between Bangladesh Time and Beijing Time gave us an extra four hours' safety margin for our fifty-day target. Therefore we were still nicely on schedule.

Way back in Dhaka before we started, we'd stayed up very late one night poring over an assortment of US Air Defense Maps of the Asian coastline identifying the bays, inlets and river estuaries liable to be those closest to the Centre of the Earth. Using basic geometrical theory, it can easily be shown that three points are necessary to define irrevocably an equidistant centre. We had done sufficient preliminary calculations to know that those three points would be: on the central northern section of the Russian coastline, at Bo Hai Wan at the top of the Yellow Sea in China, and somewhere on the Ganges Delta. All the co-ordinates of the various points liable to be the nearest open sea on the different coastlines had been checked and double-checked, then written down and carried to Urumqi – the maps had been left behind for reasons of weight. In Britain, I'd perused several books on yacht navigation and discovered the formula giving the straight-line distance between any two points on the surface of the globe:

$$\cos D = \sin L_1 \sin L_2 + \cos L_1 \cos L_2 \left(|\lambda_1 - \lambda_2| \right)$$

where D is the straight-line distance, L_1 and L_2 are respectively the latitudes of points 1 and 2, and λ_1 and λ_2 are respectively the longitudes of points 1 and 2. D is in nautical miles, L and λ are in decimal degrees. A correction relating to northern and southern hemispheres and east and west of the Greenwich meridian must usually be made but was not needed for the case of the Centre of the Earth on the Asian continent, all of which is north of the equator and east of Greenwich.

In our ultra-lightweight luggage, we had carried a solar-powered calculator all the way from Patenga Point to Urumqi. It was a truly cosmopolitan item: made in Japan, bought in Bahrain, flown to Dhaka, cycled to the depths of China. Now it came into use. Our true reason for not firming up the exact co-ordinates of the Centre of the Earth before leaving Britain was that the coastline around Asia appeared in detail to be so minutely variable that many different choices of the point of closest sea, or open sea, to the Centre of the Earth seemed to be possible (in fact because the Bangladesh coastline is so intricate we did carry a small fragment of that map to Urumqi). Nick, the geographer – he's got a University of London degree – had agonized for many days over what constituted a coastline. Was it mean sea-level, the limit of tidal influence, the edge of mud-flats and/or lagoons and marshes? Was it anywhere the water was salty, or where supertankers could sail? How big would an off-shore island have to be before it was part of the mainland – for instance those in the Mouth of the Amazon or, more specifically, the Mouths of the Ganges? A good suggestion came from Hol, who said it should be that point at which, for the person standing at sea-level on the mainland, not in an estuary, there would be an unimpeded view of open sea.

By varying our choice of definition we thought we could vary the final location and then simplify our own problems of crossing the desert by choosing the most suitable location. It was a little bit like cheating, however; no one else had made the decision of which definition to choose, so the ball was in our court – we could maximize our chances. By deferring the decision, we thought we would preserve our options until the last moment, indeed until we saw the lie of the land. For instance we might have discovered that one of the possible Centres of the Earth, although close to Urumqi, was in the middle of an Army camp. We wanted to find a Centre of the Earth which was as close as possible to Urumqi so we could get there quickly and easily. We thought it would be possible to define one only forty or fifty kilometres away.

Nick pointed to the calculator. 'Come on. Let's get started.'

'A bit scary. Isn't it?'

'There's no going back now.'

'It's like the ultimate step. We've got to commit ourselves to a specific spot.' As soon as we had defined a set of co-ordinates, then we had no choice but, come what may, to go to that Centre of the Earth.

We set about the computations just before noon. I did the bulk of the work because I'd been a maths freak at school: fascinated not only by the mystery of numbers but also by Mr Rothwell's humour – drier than the lick of a Bedouin's tongue. He has since left Keswick School but Cranes still stagger on through maths lessons. Altogether twenty-one continuous years of various brothers and sisters from my elder sister Bar to my youngest sister Emily. The computations on Day 50 were long and involved – hopefully not as long and involved as that! We used a process of iteration. Firstly we chose the first three sets of co-ordinates for which we wished to compute the equidistant centre. Then we made a guess for the likely co-ordinates of the centre. The above formula was applied in turn to the distance between each point of nearest sea and the guessed centre. All three distances were compared. They were never exactly equal so they gave a clue to a slightly better estimate for the equidistant centre. The computations were then repeated. When, after several successive runs, a suitably close equality was achieved between the distance to each of the three points of sea, then the centre, as defined by those three particular points, was plotted on the map.

We had laid out our map on the floor and distributed our various notes and calculating aids – for example, biscuits – around the rest of the room. It took many hours of tapping away to compute several possible Centres of the Earth. Only one of us at a time could use the calculator, the other had to dream. By mid-afternoon, Nick was fast asleep on the carpet.

I murmured gently: 'Nick. I think you have to wake up. Things are not hunky-dory.'

Nick replied drowsily: 'Whooorrt?'

'I've tried various different places, but nothing's getting closer.' I'd made all the different sorts of combination I could justify but they all gave Centres which were a long way off in the middle or north of the Dsungarei.

'What?' said Nick. Then a moment later: 'Sorry, what did you say?'

'There doesn't seem to be any C of the E that's close to Urumqi.'

'But what about that one we had back in London?'

'It never really existed. It was only a guess.'

In an instant, Nick was fully awake. As far as I could ascertain, the widely varying positions which could be chosen as open sea (for example, near to Patenga Point for an unrestricted view of open sea, or nearly 100 kilometres away up the Ganges past Dhaka at the extent of tidal influence) made very little difference to the overall position of the Centre of the Earth. Clearly my guess back in London had not been an educated one.

'Damn,' said Nick. 'It's going to be much tougher than we thought.'

'I'm afraid so.'

Then speaking much more slowly, almost inaudibly, he said: 'Our fifty days go out of the window.'

I had to agree. It would be a minimum two- or three-day journey to whichever centre we chose. Quite possibly we'd have to prepare heavy expedition equipment such as walking-boots, water-carriers and food. It was a depressing thought. We had come so far, always it seemed that the fifty-day target was slipping away, at the last moment we had clawed it back, then on the final step it had vanished. 'We've blown it.'

It was a severe blow which turned our day from one of success to one of serious setback. It had been the adrenalin of the imminent finish which had kept us powering on through accumulated exhaustion. Suddenly we felt tired and defeated.

We aborted any further consideration of which Centre of the Earth to go to. Indeed, we made a pact not to talk about it for the whole of the rest of the day. Instead we decided where to go to get some food. We thought that would make us feel better. Someone had told us about a place called 'Boris' or 'Wokkas' in the middle of town where we could get a slap-up meal. We searched but we couldn't find it. That didn't raise our spirits, nor did the restaurant we did enter, which supposedly had fish, but it turned out to be canned and had turned to jelly. They suggested we had some beer so we ordered a jug, but the lady came back saying the beer urn was empty. She said hopefully: 'It'll be re-filled tomorrow.'

Back at the hotel it was nearly midnight. Our minds were so bewitched by the Centre of the Earth, for half an hour we stared in silence at the map of the Dsungarei, ONC F-7, wondering if some solution would leap out in the dead of night. Our immediate problems were so great that they didn't bear thinking about. We were exhausted. Then we crashed out for a beautifully peaceful sleep.

The next morning we woke up much fresher and more mentally alert than we had been for many days. Because the pressure of the fifty-day time limit was now removed, we had a relaxed breakfast in the hotel restaurant. It's a place with high ceilings, ornate pillars, glittery chandeliers and white table-cloths. The service is attentive and the food, to us, was sumptuous. It was a grand start to the day and we thought we could see our problems in a new light.

Nick. Day 51. Kun Lun Hotel.

Today we started by rechecking the important calculations, then D drew envelopes around the different groupings of the Cs of the E. To cut a long story short (it was interrupted by a delicious multi-dish hotel luncheon), there were two principal envelopes, each measuring about twenty kilometres across. The variation within each envelope depended on which point we chose in the Ganges Delta. The difference between the two envelopes reflected the choice of definition on the Soviet coast. (There was no choice on the Chinese coast, because Bo Hai Wan is a large bay with smooth curving outline.)

For a long time we studied our fragment of the Bangladesh map. Eventually we decided that 'end of estuary', 'mean sea-level', etc., were all unidentifiable and the only workable definition was Hol's 'unrestricted view'. This made Feni Point our choice. It's the tip of the promontory between Feni River and Little Feni River, north of Patenga Point and twenty-five kilometres due south of the town of Feni through which we'd cycled a long time ago.

We tried to apply Hol's definition to the Russian coast-line. There were two possible solutions: Obskaya Guba or Baydaratskaya Guba. The first a long narrow curving inlet, the second an open bay. We thought we could legitimately adjust our definition to fit either. Which was more valid? Unfortunately our large-scale map of the Russian coast, for reasons of both lightness and because we thought it wouldn't be needed, had been left behind in Dhaka. I did a bit of lateral thinking and suggested we took the number one bus down the Fanxiu Lu to the Hongshan Department Store. There, in the stationery department, we found a big globe. In front of the bemused shop assistants, we stared at the Russian Arctic coastline and talked intently for fully fifteen minutes before declining to buy the piece (though, at £6, was a real bargain). Guessing from the globe, Obskaya Guba was about 400 kilometres long and 100 kilometres wide. [On return to Britain we checked again and discovered the inaccuracy of that globe because Obskaya Guba is 800 kilometres long and barely 100 kilometres wide.] Was it the point we wanted? It was an impossible dilemma to resolve with 100 per cent objectivity, because we already knew that one of the Cs of the E was difficult of access.

I slipped away from D to conduct a secret poll of four Americans and a Swede sitting in Kun Lun's restaurant. They voted two for Obskaya Guba being closest 'sea', one for the International Offshore Limit, and two abstentions who claimed they 'didn't understand Brits'. We racked our brains for any other access to a solution. Then I remembered that the *Guinness Book of Records* had the only written statement we'd seen. Neither of us could recall the precise wording. By midnight, D had managed, after much effort and chatting up of pretty receptionists, to get a call through to Steve Bonnist. By 2 a.m., Steve called back and read, word by word, the text for the 'REMOTEST' entry: '. . . 1,500 miles from the open sea.' There we had it: Hol had hit the spot the first time and the definition had to be 'an unrestricted view of the open sea'. Obskaya Guba was out: Baydaratskaya in.

Baydaratskaya Guba/Feni Point/Bo Hai Wan put the Centre of the Earth at L 46°16.8'N, λ 86°40.2'E, 2,648 kilometres from the nearest open sea. It was located on the north of the Dzungarian Basin, north-north-west of Urumqi, across a distance of about 300 kilometres of trackless sand-dunes. It was approximately fifty kilometres south-west of the nearest notable habitation: a village called Hoxtolgay. There was a track marked on our map crossing the northern side of the Dsungarei reasonably close to the Centre of the Earth. Hoxtolgay was 500 road kilometres away from Urumqi around the southern and western edges of the desert. If we were lucky, it would be two or three days' cycling there and then another day to the Centre. We realized that it could quite likely be tarmac all the way because it was the only road to one of China's biggest oil-fields at Karamay under the western flanks of the Dsungarei Pendi touching the Soviet border. Without a doubt the whole area would be politically sensitive. Almost certainly all access to foreigners was prohibited. We would need Aliens' Travel Permits to go anywhere north of Urumqi, though once we got near Karamay they would be useless. We vaguely hoped that the security forces only watched the normal entry points at airports, bus halts and truck depots. Two tiny cyclists sprinting hard, we hoped, would not be seen until it was all over.

If the Obskaya Guba/Feni Point/Bo Hai Wan choice had been justifiable, then the Centre of the Earth would have fallen 2,497 kilometres from the nearest open sea at L $45°34'$N, λ $88°30'$E. That was 200 kilometres north-north-west of Urumqi – right slap-bang in the middle of the Dzungarian Desert. About as far away as you can get from anyone else. Aesthetically very pleasing, but incredibly difficult to get to. According to our detailed map, it would be at least a 100-kilometre journey over an endless sea of barren sand-dunes from the closest-possible human beings, who would be nomadic shepherds or goatherds in the semi-arid desert to the north-west below the Altun Shan on the Mongolian border. Once the intrepid explorer arrived, if he arrived, there would be nothing by which to locate his target except a dry salt lake and a faint depression lying a short distance to the west. For an hour we did consider whether we should modify the truth and pretend that this was it. There was no reason why we would have to tell anyone of the various other computations. Then, instead of doing another boring old 400-kilometre bike-ride, we could have set out on a fantastically exciting journey to the Centre of the Earth.

By the time we'd made our decision it was early evening. We had checked and re-checked our computations and hadn't noticed the critical time of four o'clock in the afternoon slip by when our original fifty-day time target expired. Our minds were locked into the new scenario – finish or be damned. The old race against time had been banished. We went down to the hotel restaurant for dinner. It was much to our liking. The receptionist told us it was Friday. We'd been out of the hotel only once in the day – to see that globe and replenish chocolate supplies.

We finished Day 51 by checking, cleaning and polishing our bikes ready for the morning, then stripping down our equipment and leaving non-essentials behind: balaclavas, gloves, broken camera, used films and tapes and . . . our sleeping-bags. On Day 52, the fear of the ride ahead sent us on a carbo-loading banquet at breakfast (my stomach problems were long forgotten). We both ordered both English and Chinese breakfast: two fried eggs, white toast and jam, Chinese substitute for coffee, a couple of little cakes, plus deliciously bland rice soup complemented by pork salami, cold snippets of roast beef, pickled onions and a plate of pickled cabbage which was like a cross between Korean kimchi and European sauerkraut. Two little sweet cakes to finish. We also brought in, lest we felt we'd not had enough, our own four loaves of Turkish flat breads and six bananas!

This was something completely different from the banquets Peter Fleming was thinking of when he wrote in *News from Tartary* that 'The Province's traditions of hospitality are all its own'. He meant 'The death rate is appalling'. In 1916 and 1928, grand banquets in Urumqi had become blood-baths for the political power struggle. Urumqi, being the capital of Central Asia, had always received the focus of government and military activity. The place is meant to be rife with spies, informers and insurgents. The police are notorious for making life difficult. Mildred Cable and Francesca French observed that 'No man trusts his neighbour', and added 'it is full of people who are only there because they cannot get permission to leave'. We thanked our lucky stars that we'd slipped through the net and glibly set out thinking we'd never return.

> *Nick. Day 52. Noon. Changji.*
> We rode out of Urumqi mid-morning. A lorry workshop lent us a can of oil. Thereafter it's not been one of the happiest days of my life. It was a horrendously busy road thick with trucks and open man-holes. The traffic was continuous in both directions; tooting, pooping and overtaking frighteningly. It was hot. The air was dirty. We had a headwind. We came to a motorway! It said: 'No Tractors, No Hand-carts, No Bulldozers, No Pedestrians, No Bicycles'! We rode along it.
>
> Now we are stopped having soup and noodles in a chai house in Changji. For every centimetre of the thirty-five kilometres to here from Urumqi, I couldn't stop thinking how I'd stupidly believed D back in the UK when he'd told me that the C of the E was roughly ten or twenty kilometres out of Urumqi. Now I'm wishing I'd put the effort into slogging through all the calculations myself. We could have pinpointed it two months ago. By leaving it until arriving at Urumqi we have given ourselves yet another massive mental hurdle to overcome. I just won't be able to lift myself from this gloom until we make Karamay and Hoxtolgay. I'm just not interested any more in slogging on – although I'll do it, because I know it's the only way we'll succeed. I'm about as thoroughly dejected as I can get.

The stop had been not so much to recharge our energy stores but to dump our out-dated mental program which for fifty days had prepared us to stop as soon as we got to Urumqi. In Changji, we loaded a new package informing our systems that we were once more doing some hard cycling in China. We set off again, heading westwards, skirting the border of the Dsungarei Desert on the big main road. The countryside was interesting because it was well cultivated as far as the eye could see. There were areas with many trees, and others with endless patchwork fields, like parts of northern Germany and France. The fields were the biggest we had seen in the entire journey, probably because in Bangladesh, India, Nepal, Tibet and the oases of the Gobi and Taklamakan cultivation has been continuous for centuries: tiny family plots being handed down from father to son. Here on the borders of the Dsungarei Pendi the cultivation was modern, with mass production in mind, barely one generation old. Consequently there was a lot of traffic and many chai houses. This is how we'd expected the Silk Road to be.

Seventy-five kilometres from Urumqi, we stopped at Hutubi and sat in a shop chomping biscuits, drinking fizzy pop, and eating jars of fruit with our chopped-down chopsticks. Then we set out on the last sixty or so kilometres to a place called Manas where we hoped to, and in a very strange way did, find a bed for the night. For the first hour it was an excruciatingly hard struggle into a strong headwind. We stopped for a moment's relaxation to watch small-village life: sheep, dogs, chickens, donkeys, horses, pigs, people shouting, a school-yard of kids, birds in the trees and the putt-putt of a mini-tractor. Pedalling westwards once more, we got swiped by a ten-minute sudden desert storm of blotchy rain, swirls of dust and a howling wind. Then thankfully we came out from under the black cloud into the outskirts of Manas. We passed a beautiful brand-new Gong-An motor cycle and sidecar combination. Three kilometres later, with light humour, we noted its crisp white and blue livery once more beside us. It had a smart blue light on a pole, and the driver was dressed in khaki. Our light humour turned to mild dismay when we realized that the two neatly dressed officers riding pillion and sidecar were studying us intently. We bent low over our handlebars, twiddling the pedals strongly, peering into the distance ahead, looking for all the world as though we couldn't see them. They had serious straight faces, and since they were also doing 25 k.p.h. at a distance from us of one metre on a straight road on a bright day, they could clearly see us.

They accelerated ahead, pulled in and flagged us down. One of the officers was young and chubby, the other was worn and small. Then ensued the same convoy through town as had happened in Hami. We ended up in the central barracks of Manas Public Security Bureau. It was not up to the modern standards of Hami, it was more like a very low-ranking colonial Indian outpost. At the entrance there were a couple of ornate gate-posts like the leaning tower of Pisa. It had a pleasant but overgrown courtyard surrounded by single-storey buildings with sloping tiled roofs, fronted by verandas. We were shown into an empty room lit by a single unshaded light-bulb on a string. There were two or three chairs, a bed and a wooden desk with a plate of sweets.

It was difficult to tell if the men who had arrested us were the most powerful police officers in Manas or if they were juniors. They paid no attention to our pleasant chit-chat about our innocence, where we'd come from and what good friends we had in Hami (this sort of information was possibly not at all relevant here because Hami was 700 kilometres away over the other side of the mountains. Golmud and other places could have been on Mars). They were fascinated by tipping the contents out of our pannier bags. Because we'd trimmed down the weight in Urumqi there was virtually nothing there. However, our camera-gear, two book covers and letters of official support provided some interest, so did our list of Chinese phrases. The funniest being: 'Where do we get an Alien's Travel Permit?' Luckily, Nick had been wearing the tape recorder inside the breast pocket of his salopets all day, I'd stuffed the ONC F-7 map down my underpants in a moment of confusion as we got off the bikes and entered the room. They never seemed to notice that slung under our bottom brackets was a second bottle-cage with our plastic pots of radio tapes, tools, inner tube and pills.

For an hour they fiddled about with the bikes while we ate sweets and drank a lot of tea. We thought they'd let us go almost immediately, but nothing happened. Eventually a bent village elder in faded blue Mao suit was ushered in. We smiled. He was the schoolteacher and he had two large dog-eared dictionaries one under each arm. They looked so old we feared they might be Shakespearian English – we'd need a translator from his English to our English. He set to work. Firstly his specs came out of a brown envelope. He burrowed down into his books, then, meticulously, word by word, he translated, checking back into Chinese and double-checking. Each word required studying several pages of dictionary from a distance no greater than that between a well-inflated inner tube and the tyre retaining it. Eventually he looked over the top of his specs and said: 'Manas is closed.'

That was not all, for over the next half-hour he continued: 'Shihezi is closed. Kelamayi [old name for Karamay] you must not go. Manas is closed. Urumqi is good. Turfan is good. No others.'

It seemed he had summed it up. The officers then got him to read and check our passport credentials. This process took well over an hour; indeed, merely discovering the meaning of 'United Kingdom of Great Britain and Northern Ireland' took nearly half an hour. *'Dieu'* and *'Mon Droit'* didn't get a look in. A more senior officer appeared; he was as large as the young man and as middle-aged as the small man. He wanted our names and birth dates written down. Since our teacher insisted on keeping the pen this was a difficult, but not insurmountable, task. The teacher, Nick and I went into a huddle and in no more than twenty minutes had produced a piece of paper with several approximate names and dates and suggested translations to Chinese. By 10.30 p.m., the proceedings had become quite humorous. The upshot was that the Manas PSB decided that they weren't sufficiently *au fait* with the current regulations to be able to handle our case. We thought this meant they, like the Hami PSB, would let us go quietly on our way. The senior officer asked if we'd eaten. We answered with an emphatic *'We're starving'*. And then had a most hilarious night-time ride.

Nick. Day 52. Manas. Midnight.
On the motor cycle combination. The engine makes an eccentric thudding. The whole machine shakes. Dick's sitting on the hugely sprung pillion seat, bouncing up and down. I'm sunk down low, with my knees up to my chin, in the fairground-style sidecar shouting to the Chief of Manas Gong-An next door at the throttle: 'Faster. Faster, Marlon.' Dick's crying with laughter and slapping his cheeks to try and keep calm. We're racing along and sweeping around blind corners with the headlight bending out of sight into dark little yards. The second-in-command of Manas PSB is hanging on to the spare wheel on the back of the sidecar behind my head. There's a cloud of dust behind us. This is terrific fun.

We ate under the scrutiny of the officers, paid for the food, then had a repeat of the motor bike fun. They took us to a place they called a 'hotel'. We were escorted to the urinals by a Gong-An officer with a torch and escorted back to our room. Just before they left, we asked what time we could leave in the morning. Nick wrote in his diary that the reply from the sour superior came in sign-language index-finger inscription on the palm of the hand. It said: 'Ten o'clock.' Then the officer pointed to the security man who would stand guard all night. Just before he closed the door, he wrote, in the same silent fashion, one horribly ominous word which sealed our fate: 'Urumqi.'

'"Back so soon?" my host enquired' – thus began a poem from my childhood days about a man who took his chance too recklessly and returned early to his maker. I felt the same was true of us. We were back like failures in Urumqi barely twenty-four hours after setting out to finish our journey. We'd been copped. The Manas PSB had bundled us into a Gong-An minibus for a hair-raising 135-kilometre ride along the main road. The engine power had far exceeded the suspension and our bikes had rattled around on our knees while the van sucked in all the dust and fumes contained in the entire Dsungarei Pendi. From behind the bars we had seen, slipping back away from us, places like Changji and the landmarks we'd strenuously cycled past the day before.

On return to the big city, we had been handed over to the Headquarters of Xinjiang Public Security Bureau. Unlike the staff at Manas, they didn't need dictionaries or thinking time. The man to whom we were allocated spoke very good English and, quick as a flash, had confiscated our bikes and our passports. He put us in a taxi to the Kun Lun and told us that 'Today is Sunday. You must return tomorrow to learn your future.' Never to be beaten, we asked him why we couldn't be cleared today, and how were we going to catch up this lost time. He was not in the least amused. 'You must not ask me questions.'

Thus on Day 53 of Journey to the Centre of the Earth, we booked into our old room, number 510, at the Kun Lun. It was like coming home.

There was nothing to do all day except write diaries, do our washing and watch telly. Then we would have to go back to the PSB the next day for the Chief Justice's verdict: there was a faint chance it would be a jolly smile and we'd set off once more for a successful adventure, but more probably it would be a slap on the wrist and extinct expedition. It was depressing to think that after all our efforts we might be scuppered on the very last step. It was so potentially frightening that we could not register our fear. There was nothing we could do to change the course of the next day's events. We could not worry about any future alternatives for JCE because everything rested on the Chief's verdict. As a result of the inevitability, that afternoon and evening were a gap of freedom for us between pressing endeavour. A hiatus in effort. We could relax – for a while.

Nick. Day 53. Kun Lun Hotel.
The day passed with nothing untoward occurring. The only interesting incident was a long post-lunch chat with four unusual travellers who'd just flown into Urumqi from Kashgar having crossed the Kunjirab Pass from Pakistan. Three of them were Brits, Sean Jones, Brian Beresford and Richard Gayer, their main business theme being Reho Travel, which is well known for bargains to the Far East and Australia. The fourth, Dan, was Canadian. They were on a strange looping three-month journey to get down past Golmud and Lhasa and back along the south of Tibet to film local festivals at Mount Kailash and Laka Manosavar, which is only a few hundred kilometres from Pakistan where they'd started. They thought, and this was information we'd also heard rumours of from other sources, that the Nepal–China border had been closed at the beginning of June to independent travellers. If this was true, then with incredible good luck we had slipped through a tiny window of opportunity in the flux of official regulations relating to the opening up of Chinese Central Asia. They gave us two films for our camera and also a chance to talk about Oxford Street, the Strand and the City of London.

All of Day 53 faded away in a state of limbo. All of Day 54 faded away likewise. We did what little we could but, contrary to expectations, little came of it. It looked like we might be under the umbrella of the law for a long while to come. The words of Mildred Cable and Francesca French rang true. We worried that, back in Britain, Steve and Co. might have been on the verge of sending out a press release about us finding the C of the E. Nick spent several fraught hours trying to phone, then finally got through to Rob Walker at Penang Farm near Chiddingfold, where he'd lived with Jeannette and Elaine for several years. 'Say, Rob. It's Nick. I'm in China. I'm going to talk quick. – Please telephone Steve Bonnist at 8 a.m. tomorrow and tell him under no circumstances to reveal the information regarding our destination. We've been arrested! The bikes are confiscated! Thanks.' Nick returned, saying: 'That must have been a surprising kind of call to get on a Sunday afternoon in Surrey.'

> *Dick. Day 54. Late Evening. 10 p.m. Kun Lun Hotel.*
> Surprise, surprise. Still here. Once more I'm perusing ONC F-7 to see if we change our target and trek to the depression by the dry salt lake in the middle of nowhere rather than cycle to Hoxtolgay. However, all my, and Nick's, private deliberations are irrelevant because the Gong-An seem to be ganging up against us – no one was prepared to make a decision today, the bikes and passports remain confiscated, the only open cities are Kashgar, Turfan, Urumqi and Shihezi, and all the roads everywhere are out of bounds, i.e. not only are bicycles out of the question but also no one's allowed to truck or bus anywhere without a permit. When we point out how far we've cycled they say flatly: 'Yes, you've been breaking the rules.' We said to our custodian: 'But there are other foreign cyclists in some cities.' He said: 'I know. You should see the collection of bicycles in my office!'

One good thing did come of Day 54. The Gong-An suggested we try asking for support from either CITS (China International Travel Service – they organize official foreigners' tours) or the Foreign Affairs Section of the Xinjiang Government. We had no joy with the former but a visit to the Office of the Director of the latter was lined up for the morning of Day 55. This useful step was only possible through the great help of friendly Giang, a seductive telephonist at the Kun Lun who spoke good English and wore a pale brown knee-length dress of soft, tightly woven wool. She looked only half-Chinese, and for that matter so did her contour-hugging dress. Giang persuaded her friend the taxi-man to drive us around town between different headquarters. She breezed into all the offices spurring the men into action and spinning through the business. We briefed her in the car before each stop then followed bemused by her figure and knee-high socks as she poured out our woes in Chinese.

On Day 55, we went to the Office of the Director of the Foreign Affairs Department of the Xinjiang Uygur Autonomous Region. The traffic was bad and we got there in a panic with only seconds to spare. One of the senior officials, Abdukerim, listened with sympathy to our story and tried his hardest to help. Within the hour he'd persuaded the Deputy Director to come to meet us. Mr Zhang Xiao-de was almost fluent in English and both friendly and open-minded. Surprisingly he already seemed to know all about us. He even knew things which we hadn't told to Abdukerim – we wondered if in the elapsed hour he'd been briefed by the PSB: if that was true, then the efficiency of the Chinese infrastructure was astounding. He explained that foreigners weren't allowed to travel in Xinjiang anywhere outside the four open cities, excepting on official government business – usually for oil or mineral exploration or production. We embellished our story grandly and told him everything about the hardships we'd endured so far, the IT help in the Third World, the fun of our earlier exploits, and our final target – the Centre of the Earth. We brought out a local map we'd bought in the Hong Shan Store on which we had marked a neat X on the target. 'All very well and good,' he said, 'but you are lucky to get this far. You have broken the rules in Xinjiang. Something will be done.'

We went back to the Gong-An to learn our fate there and see if we could get bikes and passports returned. The answer seemed to be: 'No chance. You must check with so-and-so at CITS first.' We dutifully headed off there. Another tiring and expensive journey across town – our money was being depleted rapidly by the languishing time in Urumqi. The necessary contact wasn't there so we booked to see him the next day.

Once more we were thrown into limbo for the day. We went exploring for food. Around the area of the Government Offices and CITS are the older parts of town where the buildings are lower and packed much more tightly than the modern posher area of the Kun Lun with its wide tree-lined avenues. In the older part of town where the Ugyur people are in the majority, the streets are much narrower, more crowded and more intriguing. There are mosques, kebab stalls and markets. Most of the street-vendors of fruit, ice-creams or cheap jewellery are women. With their head-scarves and bulky skirts, they could have been drawn from 1940s Britain. Typically, they were beefy women with rude red faces and jolly smiles. Quite a contrast to the modern end of the city where the Han Chinese are predominant, where older women go bare-headed and wear trousers, where selling goods in the streets seems harder although the younger girls, often employed in offices, wear smart modern skirts and dresses. The whole of the city is swept clean of litter and dirt. Dogs are nowhere to be seen. Only the volatile weather spoils the pleasant illusion because it can change from sun to cloud and rainshowers, or from calm and cool to a dust storm in an hour. In winter it's extremely cold and in summer extremely hot.

Nick. Day 55. Downtown. Afternoon.
I set my heart on finding some reading as a solution to the present claustrophobia. Wandering around the old town, we spotted magazine-hire stalls. They have a steeply angled board with several rows of dog-eared magazines under a loose plastic tarpaulin: teenagers and men squat on tiny stools in the street reading these popular works of fiction. It reinforced my word starvation. Since we couldn't read Chinese, we asked for the English Language bookstore. After much walking and many wrong turns, we found it. There was a limited supply of abbreviated works in paperback: *Gulliver's Travels*, *A Tale of Two Cities* and a few others intended to help Chinese people

learn English. All the long words had been scrubbed. Filling another rack of shelves were hardback copies of Marx, Lenin and Engels: *Revolution and Counter-Revolution*, *Das Kapital*, *What Is to Be Done?* etc.

Back in our own room we took an overview; either we continued trying to finish JCE legally and maybe find in the end that it was no go – we might even get ordered out of the country – or we slipped off illegally and went to the Centre of the Earth in secret. Both Centres of the Earth were once again serious possibilities; we even started calculating the necessary quantities of food and water and the best clothes to wear for a 200-kilometre desert trek. However, common sense prevailed – if we tried to move illegally and were then caught, we wouldn't just be ordered out of the country; we'd be beaten about the head and thrown out – never to return.

On Day 56, we slowly started making progress. At 8 a.m., dawn in Urumqi, when people are barely out of bed, and work certainly hasn't started, we got a call from Abdukerim. He said Mr Zhang had been asking some questions. He had, if we wanted, obtained permission for us to go with an escort to Karamay where we could try asking the Regional Security if it was possible to get a special Alien's Travel Permit to go to Hoxtolgay. We imagined a two-day bike ride with a Gong-An motor cycle combination beside us all the way. It could have been worse. He said he didn't know what our chances would be in Karamay – he'd never heard of any foreigners except oil specialists getting to Karamay, and had heard of no one going north of there. If we did get the permit, then once we got to the end of the road in Hoxtolgay he didn't imagine we'd be allowed further, but he said: 'Surely that will be good enough for you.' Both Nick and I knew in our heart of hearts that to get to within fifty kilometres, even within one kilometre, of the Centre of the Earth yet not to reach it, would be as meaningless as having stayed for a fifty-day holiday in Bangladesh. However, beggars can't be choosers. Relative to any other options it was an incredibly good offer – we were clutching at straws so we said loudly 'Yes, please' and hoped that we might find a way to turn it to our advantage.

Our first errand in town was to go to CITS. We were surprised to be met by the well-spoken Gong-An who'd taken our bikes. He led us to the man we had to meet, who was in fact his boss. Amusingly, he was one of the iron-faced men assailed by Whirlwind Giang two days ago. To our delight, he metaphorically gave us back the bikes – in reality they were across town at the PSB HQ. In the process he relieved us of 200 yuan (about forty pounds) in fines. He gave us an official receipt of moneys which apparently said something along the lines of 'fined for cycling illegally 1,000 kilometres across the Gobi Desert'. The fine was sufficiently stiff by Gong-An standards to be saying: 'We'll let you go this time, but next time – you're in the clink.' Briefly, for a period of almost thirty-five seconds, we had our passports back in our hands. Then the second we'd signed our confessions he took them back again. Before he waved us away, he handed us a document which he said the Foreign Affairs Department had asked for. It seemed he knew all about our planned visit to seek more permission – it was an Alien's Travel Permit for Karamay made out in our names. The police escort would be ready in three days. We smiled gratefully and left the office.

I said: 'Shame we can't leave sooner.'

'Yeah, it's a pity, but considering the problems a few days ago it's a big step in the right direction.'

'True,' I mused, 'though I don't relish the thought of a two-day flat-out ride beside the Gong-An.'

'Maybe they'll let us take a bus to Manas. Re-start there. Our continuous bike ride would remain intact.'

'Good idea.'

We went optimistically to see the Foreign Affairs Department. Unfortunately, it seemed that one more problem had arisen. Mr Zhang met us. He shook our hands but was very serious, as though good friends had broken his trust. He said: 'This morning I studied your so-called Middle of Asia and I find it is not in the middle of Asia. Why is this? What is your real motive for going there?'

Fear flashed in front of us. What had happened? Had our chances been ruined? Did they think we were spies?

He strode over to the map, then drew a ruler from his pocket and started measuring distances. Our worries vanished – he was using Mercator's Projection and, as we all know, that distorts the image. Thinking we would have a bit of fun, we introduced him to the navigational techniques. Almost immediately he turned alien again, got hot under the collar and ordered us to stop. One of his aides was sent rushing out of the room. He paced up and down. Once more we sweated in limbo, not knowing if we were to be smiled on or shot. A few minutes later the aide returned leading another young man. Mr Zhang told me to start my discussion again. The young man, whom we suspect was a numerical specialist, scribbled like mad, catching the Great Circle theory and iterative geometry like scooping the secret formula for silk manufacture. When the fun was over, we were left for a few minutes by ourselves. A message came for us to go and visit someone. We were taken to Mr Zhang's room, then he led us for an introduction to Lee Deng Ying, the Director. He greeted us cheerfully, and wished us the best. We never met him or Mr Zhang again; they had done their bit.

Things had taken a distinct turn for the better. We went to the Gong-An HQ to collect our bikes before they changed their minds. They scolded us and said: 'Don't let us catch you again.' Quickly we rode back to the Kun Lun, not caring to stop once or look at a single policeman. It wasn't easy for us to disappear into the crowds because in, addition to our bright red and blue salopets and blondish European hair, we now had, as Nick so correctly observed, 'as high a profile as any foreigner in Urumqi'. We were marked men. While riding, all the images of long-distance bike rides in the deserts of Asia came flooding back like an awful nightmare. In our room, we mulled over the new prospects: three spare days, a 300- or 400-kilometre bike ride under escort, more PSB red tape in Karamay, nearly but not quite reaching the target. Time was sliding away. We needed to get sorted out quickly. The telephone rang. It was Abdukerim. Were we ready to depart at first light the next day? We said Yes!

THIRTEEN

At the Centre of the Earth

At 8 a.m. on Day 57, we set off once more on the quest for the Centre of the Earth. This time not on bikes but in the hotel lift. Waiting in the lobby was our escort, Chang Le. He said he was from the CITS but on his safari jacket was an ominous little label: Gong-An. He was to be our constant guardian. We unslung the wheels from the bikes and slipped them and the frames into the boot of a taxi. Then drove to the airport.

Abdukerim, the previous night, had finished his telephone call by telling us that next day's departure was by air. He'd booked three seats to Karamay. We were taken aback. The implications were enormous. Firstly, it meant that the Foreign Affairs Department was trying its hardest to help as it thought best. Secondly, our continuous bike ride from the open sea would be broken. That destroyed the purity. We had used local taxis internally in Kathmandu and Lhasa, I'd ridden the truck in the Taklamakan, but always we'd re-started cycling where we'd left off. Unless we backtracked to Urumqi and set out again with our permits to Karamay, there'd be a gap in the cycling.

Owing to the pressure of uncertainty, we were keen to try to finish the expedition in any way possible. If that meant flying, driving, helicopter-ing, in fact if it meant horses, donkeys, camels or walking to the Centre of the Earth – we'd do it. For us, the target had outgrown the method of reaching it. This view had been at the back of our minds since before we left London.

> *Expedition overview. London. 18 March.*
> Importantly, Journey to the Centre of the Earth is unusual for a modern expedition because reaching the final objective far outweighs the route to it. The journey is the build-up. If we fail cycling, then it is valid for us to use any other mode of transport. We are harking back to the great days of expeditions when Columbus discovered America, Lord Hunt got a man on top of Everest, and the Americans set foot on the Moon; it doesn't matter how you get there: to arrive is success.

Because the Centre of the Earth was the one and only objective, it meant firstly that Nick and I were obsessed about getting there, secondly that the expedition by its very nature had numerous contingency plans built into it should the cycling fail. There were a number of different routes to the treasure. If something had gone wrong with crossing the border from Nepal to China, then we would seriously have considered cycling several extra thousand kilometres across the north of India and coming via the Karakoram Highway out of Pakistan. If that failed, we could have flown to Hong Kong, then Lhasa or Beijing – maybe to try cycling from Bo Hai Wan. If the worst had come to the worst, we could have flown direct to Urumqi. Once at Urumqi, we had always assumed the problems would be finished. However, the reality was that Urumqi was a hard nut to crack. We were now heading a little further, but still there was no finish in sight.

Nick. Day 57. Flying over the Dsungarei Pendi.
Although this flight from Urumqi to Karamay is a nice injection of excitement into a week of idleness, for me it's a slightly morose journey because I have little faith that it will lead us to our target. The officials can't possibly let us go much beyond Karamay. Five days have drained away in Urumqi and with them the urgency of the expedition. Looking down on the desert, I'm trying to imagine what it will be like trudging across it in a few days' time on a secret mission to the C of the E.

Through the despondency it is a fascinating journey. We are flying at 5,000 feet. Firstly over the irrigated borders of the desert. A patchwork of enormous farming collectives. All the irrigation channels are in a straight and rectangular pattern. Every few kilometres, a wide dry river-bed breaks the fields with an expanse of sand, heading northwards into the Dsungarei. Villages are twenty to thirty rectangular boxes in square grids linked by straight roads. Cheeky footpaths crawl across the land. Our north-west route takes us directly over Changji. I can make out the tiny houses below and the bends in the road. I'm sure I can identify the chai house where we stopped. It's bewildering to be flying high over the big west road where six days before we cycled so fanatically, had our adventures, and came bowling back in a Gong-An bus.

Everyone else on board the plane looked like a businessman. Fruit drinks and a bag of sweets were handed around to all. We each got a little gift. I got a comb and mirror – was that a hint? Out of the tiny windows we could see the wing above our heads, the wheels permanently in position as though ready for an emergency landing. We flew out northwards from the irrigated belt over the encroaching sand-dunes. Vehicle tracks could be seen leaving tiny scratch marks over the first few kilometres of desert from the edge of agriculture. Then even they faded out. The dunes were

continuous rolling waves. The scale was impossible to guess. They may
have been twenty metres high. There were isolated tiny shrubs and
patches of mudflats in between.

Nick. Day 57. Karamay.
We're dropping steeply towards the desert and Karamay and
have passed a couple of oil derricks with clusters of mobile
accommodations linked by spidery cobwebs of churned vehicle
tracks. Through the cockpit windows, Karamay looks a big
city: spread out and modern with virtually no green to be seen;
fringed on the west by an abrupt range of dry barren hills – the
western edge of the Dsungarei and the Russian border. Karamay seems to be an area of oilmen's offices in the midst of a
much greater area of oil storage, oil-processing works and
drilling-camps. Agriculture doesn't get a look in.

The wheels squealed as we touched down. They opened the door, and as
we stepped out into the bright sun a wall of heat hit us. It was so dry that
our mouths gummed up on the first breath. Chang Le, Nick and I walked
across the concrete to the small airport terminal. Mr Zhang and
Abdukerim back in Urumqi had done us proud – two officials from the
Karamay Division of the Government of Xinjiang were waiting for us.
They knew our names and misdemeanours; luckily they also knew about
our overpowering desire to get to the mysterious Centre of the Earth.
Chang Le, looking every bit the office junior with chubby cheeks and
ill-fitting bell-bottom trousers, handed over our passports to the senior
official, Mr Qiu Zi-fan, who led us to a van.

Nick. Day 57. Karamay.
We were driven to a very slick (by Chinese standards) hotel.
Two luxury single rooms waited, numbers 114 and 115. The
receptionist spoke perfect English. I went to my room, washed
face and hands, made a pot of tea, then carried my lidded yellow
mug to the foyer, to find D applying pressure on Mr Qiu at a
p.s.i. of around a thousand. Maps were out on laps. Qiu was
nodding, unable to slip a word into D's monologue: 'We are
going to this point . . . Hoxtolgay . . . look, here is where we've
come from . . . Bangladesh, India, Nepal, Tibet . . . five
thousand kilometres . . . now we have nearly finished . . . just a
short distance to go. . . .' It was a familiar story. Chang Le
hovered, confused. Qiu's response was to say that it was a 'very
long way' to Hoxtolgay, 'two hundred kilometres, and one
hundred more to this spot' – he put his finger on the X which
marked the C of the E. I just couldn't believe it. Far from just
saying 'No, it's out of the question', Qiu was reduced to picking
at practical minutiae. D then piled into minor considerations, to

distract Qiu from the big issue. 'How much would it cost to hire
a car for the journey to Hoxtolgay?' Qiu disappeared to return
fifteen minutes later with '320 Yuan'. D told him that when we
got close to the C of the E we'd like to take the bikes from the car
and make a symbolic bike ride for the last few kilometres. By
this stage, Qiu didn't seem to mind. I was nearly falling off my
seat with nervous excitement. What we were talking about was
no longer how close we could get to the C of the E, but how we
would do it. Qiu said he'd go to obtain the permissions.
Dutifully Chang Le followed him out.

At lunch, there were others eating, including two French, but though we
said, 'Hello, bonjour, ça va?' we chose to sit alone because there were
various things on our minds. The Centre of the Earth was getting closer,
but it seemed the closest we got might be in a car. That would further spoil
the purity of the bike ride from the sea. Our first priority was to reach the
Centre by any means; later we could worry about symbolic cycles. We
debated the importance of not being able to get the last few kilometres and
decided unanimously that it wouldn't count if we didn't get there. What if
we had to have Chang Le and the driver beside us all the way – and at the
Centre? They would then also be equal first. We decided it didn't matter.
The only important point, we repeated to ourselves, was to get to the
actual Centre of the Earth.

In the afternoon we slept a while, then took a short wander around the
centre of town. It was a richer city than Urumqi, with better-quality
chocolate. Back at the hotel, Chang Le, lighting up yet another cigarette,
said the taxi was booked (costing, we were staggered to hear, nearly £200).
With a smile, he showed us our Alien's Travel Permits for the very unusual
destination of Hoxtolgay. That meant we were allowed officially to go to
within fifty kilometres of the Centre of the Earth. We felt relieved. We
metaphorically edged closer to the Centre of the Earth, though we were
not quite there.

At 8 a.m. on Day 58, we set off once more on the quest for the Centre of
the Earth: not on bicycles, but in a shiny new Mitsubishi van. Ahead were
200 kilometres of road to Hoxtolgay. Our bicycles rattled in the back.
Sitting beside us, Chang Le lolled dozing: tired from the party last night.
Beyond Hoxtolgay we weren't quite sure what would happen. Behind us,
before yesterday's air flight from Urumqi, before the arrest in Manas, had
been 5,000 kilometres of cycling across the Himalayas, the Tibetan
Plateau and the Gobi Desert. That had been a lightweight, cheap and
rough adventure. JCE had now become an officially sanctioned high-cost
luxury expedition. However, the end was nearly in sight. It was Day 58 –
way outside our initial schedule. Whatever might have been our thoughts
at the end of Day 49 coming into Urumqi, they had changed and changed
again since then. In the real world it was 27 June 1986. Purely by
coincidence this was the same day on which, exactly three years ago,

Running the Himalayas had finished after a similarly monumental adventure.

The first minor incident, even before we left Karamay, was that the silly driver said he was nearly out of petrol. Half an hour was wasted waiting for the petrol station to open. Then we started again. The driver wasn't in a hurry, he cruised sedately along a hard-surfaced road avoiding potholes and preserving the van from wear and tear. The first fifty kilometres from Karamay were through a maze of industrial hardware; power-lines, telegraph-wires, drilling-rigs and nodding donkeys – slang name for the black seesaw pumps which crowd the Texas landscape. Suddenly, there was a forlorn block of four-storey flats plonked down in the semi-desert, then there was only arid wilderness. Certain areas had clumps of trees and acres of green like East African savannah, other areas were yardangs blasted by wind and sand into fantastic tall shapes like castles and battleships. One of the sinister patches, where the wind howls around the rock towers and sings to intrepid travellers, is rather unimaginatively called Ghost City.

At 1 p.m., after 140 kilometres of low bare hills with intermittent semi-desert and a couple of dull oases, we reached Hoxtolgay. Its few houses and grove of trees lay beside a dry river-course in a widely open valley. The main road swooped down into the village then rushed through the dust, straight out the other side without the slightest quiver and over the hills. A few dirt tracks led off on both sides. A better-quality dirt road headed off north-west towards Soviet-held territory. Our target lay due south-east about sixty kilometres. A place called Hsia-tzu-chieh was marked on our US Air Defense map about thirty straight-line kilometres in that direction. A fine line was drawn across the north of the Dsungarei. If we could get to Hsia-tzu-chieh and find that track, then we would have halved the distance and would have a hope of reaching the Centre of the Earth. That track could be quite indistinct because it had no habitation marked on it for 160 kilometres to a place named Ting-Shan. Chang Le was good enough to direct the driver to try to find the route to Hsia-tzu-chieh. There were various men hanging around a building on the corner. Rather unemotionally they pointed to what looked like a tank trap on the edge of the village. No one seemed very excited about the fact that they lived at the bus stop closest to the Centre of the Earth.

Beyond the concrete blocks, the track was continuous but at first very rutted. The van bobbed around sickeningly on its soft road-springs. The driver was very tense and quiet. His livelihood depended on this vehicle remaining in pristine condition. Five kilometres from town we drove away from the side-hills around Hoxtolgay which had caused the track to be trapped close to the river bed and therefore rough. The flat plain stretched ahead with only minor irregularities. Climatologically the area is arid, but irrigation has enabled numerous small areas to be cultivated. The fields weren't lush like many we'd seen in oases south of here but they looked dry, almost pathetic, gasping for water, starved of nutrients. There were few trees, except as wind-breaks by the road which had become a reasonably well-finished dirt road built up slightly higher than the surrounds. The driver drove cautiously as though he thought the next patch might be quicksand which would swallow him up. It was mostly a dead-straight road, passing little hamlets of one- or two-room mud farmsteads every few kilometres. Nick and I silently urged the timid driver onward.

Fifteen kilometres from Hoxtolgay, near a little hamlet called Tem, there was an irrigation trench cut across the road. He pulled to a halt six feet before it and stared. He had a long discussion with Chang Le and then Chang Le said: 'He says it's too deep to cross.' As he said this, a truck whizzed past and bounced over the ditch to disappear along the road in a cloud of dust. Our driver pointed out he wasn't a truck but a person who had to earn a living. He reversed his precious van away from the ditch and started turning round.

Chang Le said with a note of relief: 'That's it. We will go back to Karamay now.'

Instant dismay! We weren't ready to wave goodbye to the Centre of the Earth. We leapt into action: 'Chang Le, we only need to go a little further. Chang Le, we can fill the ditch with dirt. Chang Le, you said we could drive as far as possible. Chang Le, we can walk. Chang Le, let's have a picnic. Chang Le, let's stop for a rest. We only need to go a little further.' We needed any way of stopping the van here so that we had a moment to plan how we might urge the driver to go on, or alternatively to persuade Chang Le to continue alone. The driver had clearly finished his journey, yet Chang Le could see that we were determined to go further. He was caught between two stools. On which side should his allegiance lie? Should he humour his countryman or look after the guests – his charges? He looked quite worried, thought hard, and came up with a solution. He said: 'We will stop the van here. The driver can have some refreshment in this farmhouse. You can go a little further riding your bikes symbolically. I will watch from here. Go as far as maybe that corner or those distant trees.'

We needed no further gift. Our bikes were out and assembled in seconds. We grabbed our packed lunch and stuffed it down our salopets, filled our bottles with water. We waved goodbye and leapt on our bikes. Chang Le looked miserable and spoke loudly as though he didn't believe what he was saying: 'No further than those distant trees. Don't be too long. Half an hour.' As we scooted, I yelled back: 'OK. Those trees or maybe a little further. Back in an hour.' Chang Le had already turned his back and consigned himself to fate.

Nick. Day 58. Afternoon.
It was 2 p.m. when we left the van. We set off in a crazy adrenalin surge, pounding the bikes over spinning gravel, blood coursing in our veins. By the time an hour had elapsed we were

fifteen kilometres to the south-east. Hsia-tzu-chieh was meant to be ten kilometres, but it was twice that distance along a dead-straight track before the little oasis village appeared on the left. Nothing seemed to tie in with our two maps. D rushed into the village to ask. A truck came by and I stopped it, urgently asking: 'Which way to Ting-Shan?' They looked confused. I said, 'Ting-Shan?' and pointed questioningly in the four compass directions. The three men in the cab went into an involved discussion. Every minute which ticked by was a minute less to find the C of the E, and I was gripped by a sick realization that it was 'now or never'. We simply couldn't afford to go wrong. We only had a few hours before Chang Le would be after us.

I'd also found some men who knew of Ting-Shan. I got some water, had to refuse their offers of tea, then rushed back to Nick. We bashed on, fearful that at any moment the Gong-An would catch us. We sprinted without a moment's pause, barely daring to turn to look if the van was following. One vehicle came past us, a heavy water-tanker: we shut our eyes and prayed they couldn't see us. In places, we were badly slowed by deep sand and had to push. Some of it was so bad it had no equal anywhere in the known world excepting the infamous Silk Road. There were several route choices in the next five kilometres but we guessed them all correctly by relying mainly on the compass. At one place three boys sitting on a wall pointed the route and invited us to join their fizz-drinking session. Then, just after 4 p.m., we made a bad choice and cycled off a reasonably bad dirt track on to a reasonably bad footpath then down into a semi-dry wadi which had waist-high bushes. We lifted our bikes over an irrigation ditch and climbed out the other side. Beyond was a little village of a dozen mud huts.

There was no order to the village. The huts were orientated in different directions around an open area. Most huts had small walls enclosing private yards used for animals or produce or for piles of metal or wood. Two men came by with spades strapped to their heavy roadster bicycles. Four young adults disappeared as we approached, then a friendly old woman came out to chat away with us. She got us some water but couldn't help us with the route. In our desire to find someone who could help we tried most of the huts. One was a school room. Class was being held outside. The first child who saw us stared for a minute before yelling loudly, then all twenty or so clustered around the teacher. We walked over slowly so they wouldn't be too perturbed. Their clothes were ragged and almost all had bare feet. He was friendly and tried hard to help us, finally suggesting we went up over a nearby low gravel bank heading north-east where he said we would see several trucks and some houses.

We pushed the bikes as quickly as possible across the wadi, then leapt aboard and rode. We cursed ourselves for losing time on the wrong route choice. Luckily we quickly found the trucks and a proper road again.

There were several young men mending trucks so we asked them. They thought we were good fun and asked us down a flight of steps, into their bunker. It was an underground room, almost a large cavern, lined with bunks. Eight to ten men played cards on a table in the only pool of light, which came from a tiny window in the roof. Someone played guitar. Tea boiled in the corner. We couldn't stop. The time was about 5.30 p.m. We were now one and a half hours late returning. The chase might already have begun. We needed route directions quickly. Someone came to show us where to go between the houses and through the trees to find the road. We thanked him and shot off.

Nick. Day 58. 5.40 p.m.
Beyond the truckers' warrens, there was a main road. We turned east – overjoyed to be heading in the right direction. Wonderfully, it was tarmac and for several minutes we really believed that we were at last on the main highway across the Dsungarei to Ting-Shan. The tarmac was some sort of main street, lined with trees and buildings. This was probably the place marked on our maps as Collective Farm 184. The road should lead on from here. Halfway down, a man was reading a notice-board covered with posters. He looked intelligent (too intelligent – people who are a bit too clever are the worst sort to ask for route directions). He knew some English words and, with much labour, said, 'north, east, west, south', pointing in all the wrong directions. One of his alternatives was that Ting-Shan lay along the tarmac road, which since it was pointing due east was exactly the info we wanted to hear. But just 300 metres further on the tarmac ended and the road turned 90° right – back on to dirt and back into a southerly direction.

The only alternative was a tiny pair of ruts heading out beyond the village. Two men pulling weeds from a field of crops couldn't help us. We chose to follow the main route and hoped it would curve back east. For nearly five kilometres it headed dishearteningly south; our hopes rose when it kinked east for a few hundred metres but then it twisted south again. We stopped to study the maps but nothing tied up. Were we lost? We climbed on the bikes and cycled madly hoping to find someone to ask. We were probably getting hungry and thirsty but we didn't notice it because the panic was on. There was no time for the dreams we typically travelled with. Breathing down our necks were the PSB. We calculated that if Chang Le chased us with a local copper who knew the area he'd need only one and a half hours' driving to reach us but would lose an hour or more mobilizing a local man. If he somehow persuaded the timid taxi-man to go, then they'd be two and a half hours catching us. Either way he wouldn't raise the alarm until two or three hours after we'd left. That meant he could be on us in less than an hour. We pedalled furiously.

Nick. Day 58.6.20 p.m.

I was in near-panic, having been swamped by a terrible sensation of impending disaster. Now that we could not get back to Mr Chang till 8 or 9 p.m. at the earliest, midnight more probably, it was clear that we'd already caused so much trouble that we'd never be allowed a second chance to get to either C of the Es. In all probability, we'd be fined again – massively – and kicked out of China. The ghastly fact now was that we were so lost that it looked uncertain that we'd find the Centre of the Earth before dark. The idea of not reaching the C of the E, and being bunged out of China was appalling. Failure made me feel sick. The cruelty of missing it all at the last moment was too much to think about.

The track petered out in a dry farmyard. The middle-aged farmer smiled benevolently. Luckily he'd heard of Ting-Shan and had no hesitation telling us it was back up the road we'd come down, then turn right at the large village (which presumably was the place marked on our map as Collective Farm 184). We thanked him, asked for some water, thanked him again and shot off. Six p.m. Backtracking was grim. The road seemed to be slightly uphill, the gravel seemed deeper than before, there was a headwind. We pounded at the pedals and regained lost ground. Our tyres bumped on to the short tarmac main street of Collective 184.

'It'll be that dirt track at the corner.'

'Lost nearly an hour on the wrong turn.'

The ruts wriggled around the back of the village and became a halfway-reasonable Land Rover track. The very last house was a single-room mud hut with a low thatched roof. Outside a teenage girl, maybe just back from school, in dark skirt and white blouse, saw us and stood wide-eyed in awe. Beside her and shorter than her was her stooping grandmother. She had a toothless grin and a baggy blue Mao suit. She, like most people in the villages around Hoxtolgay, was Han Chinese. She must have some tales: her youth might have been spent in some rich, fertile and wet area of eastern China – maybe the sea. What a surprise she would have got if we could have told her that she and her granddaughter were the people in the world who lived closest to the world's most remote point. I paused to ask them the direction for Ting-Shan. Ahead, Nick, compass out, was waving madly. 'East! It goes east!' he shouted.

The rutted track headed level over the scrubland, among bushes two or three feet high. Then it started to climb gently away from the central bowl of the valley on to the rise of the escarpment. The vegetation thinned out.

'If the van comes, it'll be difficult to hide.'

'Don't talk. Pedal!'

An estimated fifteen kilometres to go. Nearly 7 p.m. Mr Chang would be on the war-path. We rode like demons, hammering the pedals relentlessly. Our heart-rates were rising exponentially as time elapsed. On the rise, after thirty minutes' hard ride across rough stony desert, we had to stop for a breather. There was a tall metal post like a cairn for route-finding. We were close enough to start identifying hummocks and general dips in the topography on our map. The track cut directly east, rolling over several large-scale undulations in the basically smooth and featureless scrubland. We struck out again. Making the bikes move was increasingly difficult; underneath the sand and gravel was a rough and knobbly hard-base. We sweated over two rises. Our goal closed in. From behind, a truck approached. We panicked a moment. Then breathed a sigh of relief – it wasn't the van. Since time was short, we decided to cheat. Both of us enthusiastically flagged it down. The two young men didn't really know what to make of us but willingly gave a lift. Into the back we unceremoniously threw the two trusty 753s which had cycled all – almost all – the way from the open sea.

We hung on to the slatted sides, jolting over the bumps, bouncing around. We were revelling in the luxury of a fast ride for the last four kilometres. The wind was on our faces, dust in our eyes, we shouted above the engine noise.

'How much further do you think?'

'That's the northern scarp marked on the map.'

'Coming up in two hundred yards is the stream-bed.'

'No, it's not. It's the next one.'

'Are you sure? I don't think so.'

'We must get the compass lined on to that scarp and the rise back there.'

'I vote we go a bit further to check.'

'Me, too. Then we can see from the hummock how far to backtrack.'

A little later: 'Here?'

'Here.'

After all those thousands of kilometres, we were in agreement. We banged on the roof of the cab to stop. They put us down, shook our hands and gave us a bottle of pop. We thanked them profusely. They drove off heading for dusk and the village of Ting-Shan 100 kilometres away, shaking their heads at the lunacy of two boys wanting to be dropped off in the middle of the desert a few hours before dark. We sat down to some accurate navigation.

We looked back along the track towards Collective 184. We were on the rise to the eastern side of a low, wide bowl which sloped slightly south. There were several distinct features such as a fifty-metre scarp to the north. Beside us a large bare red hillock like Ayers Rock 100 metres across. Two kilometres south above the gentle south-east exit of the dry stream we could see some small rocky pinnacles. In this bowl was the target. From our calculations it was one kilometre from the red hillock, 300 metres south of the track, and five metres west of the stream-bed. For the first time in the history of the world, a mere mortal was knowingly looking at the Centre of the Earth.

We plunged down to it, riding the last half-kilometre across the dirt, then striding exactly 300 paces south of the track. It was singularly uninspiring. There was a lot of sand, a few wiry scrubs, several animal tracks and some dry camel dung. The time was 8.10 p.m. Nick dug a little hole and we ceremoniously buried a letter of well-wishing from IT, plus an Associate's application-form so that a future opportunist can send a donation to Intermediate Technology, Myson House, Railways Terrace, Rugby, CV21 3HT. We looked around at the emptiness, took a few photos for the record and, with typical understatement, Nick observed: 'It's not the sort of place which is tailor-made as a long-term tourist attraction.'

Postscript

When we'd finished prancing around like chimpanzees taking photos of ourselves, it was 10 p.m. Chang Le was going to be mad. We took one backward glance at the Centre of the Earth, then raced. Before dark we reached Collective 184 where we bought a jar of fruit and glugged much needed liquid. We hoped to hitch a lift on a truck but there was none. At 11.30 p.m. we got to the hamlet where the little boys had offered to share their pop. The local shop was still open and by the light of a paraffin lamp the man sold us a flashlight. We sweated on into the dark. Many dogs chased us into Hsia-tzu-chieh. Then light rain, very rare in these parts, started. It was reminiscent of Day 1, the only other day when we had cycled on into darkness – then the rain had indeed been hard. It got quite cold. By the stars, we headed up the straight dirt road we'd sprinted down twelve hours before. In places it was easier to ride the hard stone desert. In among the tough scrub we spotted a long-legged desert mouse darting away to safety. At 4 a.m. we reached Tem. No van, no Chang Le. We had no choice but to wake the farmer to ask if there was a message. Chang Le was in Hoxtolgay with the police. The farmer, despite the atrocious hour, was incredibly kind – a final example of the generosity and hospitality we had received for all of our journey. He cooked boiled eggs and noodle soup. He refused any money – we Westerners have some lessons to learn. Revitalized, we powered on. The east was beginning to glow as we fought the last few kilometres into the hills of Hoxtolgay. There was the van. Beside it two large four-wheel-drive pickups. Chang Le was swollen-eyed and silent. The Head of Security had come 200 kilometres from Hoxtolgay to organize the search starting in one hour. Nothing was said. We put our bikes in the van and were driven back. At Karamay, nothing was said. We put our bikes on the plane and were flown to Urumqi. Without a word we were sent to the Chinese National Hua Qiao. We wrote a fifteen-page report accepting all blame for everything which had happened in the missing eighteen hours. We felt we had broken the trust of Mr Zhang, Mr Lee, Chang Le, Mr Qiu – indeed, of all the many hundreds of others who had provided shelter, sustenance and support throughout our journey to the Centre of the Earth. However, they had compassion for us. They accepted our apologies, came to congratulate us, organized our return tickets, and we parted the best of friends: an officially successful expedition of the Xinjiang Uygur Autonomous Region of China.

APPENDIX ONE

Equipment

CONTENTS
Clothes
Equipment for survival or everyday use
Equipment for recording the expedition
Medical
Communal paperwork
Bicycles
Bike equipment
Bike tools
Bike spares

All the equipment was very carefully chosen: it had to be tough, light, versatile – and necessary. The bikes fully equipped weighed 22 lb. The total weight of all the rest of the gear which each of us had, including the clothes and shoes we stood up in, sleeping-bags, water-bottle and pannier bags, was 18 lb (of which about half was recording gear: camera, tape machine, films, tapes and diaries).

Clothes

Been Bag Salopets. Knee-length, high-chest, stretchy skinfit. Polyester fleece inner weave, tight outer weave. Short top front zip to get in and out at nights. Weight-saving short fly zip. Mock leopard-skin insert. Drip-dry, but most often dried while cycling. Inside breast pockets modified to make small compartments for ready cash, chopsticks, spoon, compass, tape machine, contact lens case. Bum pocket with zip – great for quick easy access; for example, for gloves. Worn all day every day, excepting in Kathmandu, Lhasa and Urumqi where we washed the salopets properly and walked around in Goretex over-trousers and thermal top all day.

Madison cycle-touring semi-stiffened shoes. Plastic soles, leather/nylon uppers. We wore them all the time and found them very hardwearing. Toes slightly too tight for our feet (both of us have wide feet).

British Home Stores socks and underpants. Socks were thin cotton/

polyester fine weave. Easy to wash, quick to dry – or worn wet. One pair each only. Socks in perfect condition at finish. Underpants had holes worn into the seat.

Thermals. Thin 'moisture wick' Thermalite polypropylene leggings: worn most days above 3,000 metres, and also as a head-dress in Bangladesh and India and the Central Asian deserts. We bought thick 'Musto' sailor's thermal tops with high zipped neck, very long arms and low waist. Worn under the salopets, they were a tight snug fit used almost continually from Lhasa to Golmud. Worn outside the salopets, they were a comfortable loose top.

Intermediate Technology T-shirt, cut-down in length so it was just long enough to tuck into the top of our salopets. Worn all the time.

Been Bag acrylic leg-warmers, used as leg-warmers on the Tibetan Plateau, as sunburn protectors for arms in Bangladesh and the plains of India, and as loose, warm footsocks in bed at night when the temperature fell sub-zero.

Madison Caldo Goretex silver-grey cycling jacket from Beta Bikes. It has thick elasticated waistband and cuffs which form a good air-seal. We wore it most of the time on the Plateau, partly against wind chill but also for warmth. The flimsy hood attached by small zip was cut off and replaced in Kathmandu by a more substantial heavy-gauge hood sewn permanently to the neck of the jacket.

Beta Bikes Madison Caldo weatherwear over-trousers in Goretex.

Black's thermal mitts, fleece-lined in red weatherproof shell. They were used a lot because taking gloves on and off (also balaclavas) is effective for fine temperature regulations without the hassle of stopping to remove jackets or trousers. Also used on very cold nights for toasty warm feet.

Balaclavas. We carried two each. One was a fibrepile Helly Hansen, warm and snug and also useful turned inside out as top cap with visor, or as neck-warmer in lieu of scarf. It was worn in one way or another continuously from Patenga Point to Dunhuang. The second balaclava was a thin thermal Sanctuary Mountain Sports balaclava which was useful as a neck-warmer and face-mask but could really have been left behind.

Mao cap bought in Golmud to replace use of fibrepile balaclava. The peak kept sun and wind and desert sand storms out of our eyes.

Chinese white roadworker's face-mask. Bought in local stores, used from Lhasa onwards. It's intended to keep out Tibetan and Gobi dust, which it does effectively, but we found one of the big benefits was protecting us against sunburnt lips and nose, and moistening the cold dry high-altitude air we breathed.

Snow-goggles: CEBE from Black's with good optics, leather nose-guard and side-shades to cut out peripheral light – this was extended with sticky plaster in Dunhuang to help hold the dust at bay. Snow-

goggles worn almost all the time, everyday when cycling: Bangladesh, India, Nepal, China.
Contact lenses: hard plastic. We each had one spare pair, both of which
were carried in the same tiny plastic clip-case pared down to minimal
size. We did not lose any lenses on the trip but Dick did snap one of
his in half while it was wrapped up in his salopets which he was using
as a pillow at night. Dick's method of storing his lenses at night was to
roll them into a small strip cut off the edge of a handkerchief. Nick's
were stored overnight in half a proper plastic screw-top lens-
container (the other half of the container was forfeited in Hetauda as a
replacement pedal-cap on Dick's bike). Each morning we licked/
sucked our contact lenses for half a minute to cleanse them – saliva is a
mild antiseptic, the inner surfaces of the mouth are soft and sensitive
and do not scratch the lenses as can happen when rubbing with
fingers.
Pair of spectacles for emergency. Never used.
Black's Icelandic 3 G.D. sleeping-bag. Goose down, nylon outer, cotton
inner. Weight 3 lb. Full-length zip useful for cooling in Nepal and the
Gobi. Sleeping-bag also used on very cold days as extra top layer
wrapped around our torsos under our Caldo jackets.

Equipment for Survival or Everyday Use

Chopped-down chopsticks (one pair each).
Plastic teaspoon (5 ml hospital), holes drilled in handle (one each).
Compass (one only). Smallest Silva lightweight supplied by Black's. We
flicked off the retaining band and carried only the oil-filled centre.
Thus we could find north and from there estimate other angles.
Carried in Dick's breast pocket.
Needle (one only), carried in the back of Nick's diary. Four feet of cotton
wrapped around the sawn-off spoke-key.
Smallest Swiss Army penknife (one only). Two tiny blades.
Plastic digital watch (one only). Strap removed, carried on string attached
to Nick's lapel, positioned in Nick's breast pocket. It wasn't much use
because it wasn't luminous and the alarm was not audible. Nor did it
keep time. In practice a watch was not much use because we could tell
the time roughly by the sun, we rose at dawn and went to bed at dusk.
If accurate times were needed then it was because we were in a town
or hotel and in these places someone else always has the time.

Equipment for Recording the Expedition

School exercise-book used as diary. We each got through six books, hence
each wrote about 80,000 words during the fifty-eight days.
Lightweight biro (one each); thin, half-length or simply the ink tube
minus the outer shell.
Nagra SN tape machine lent by BBC Radio 4. It was carried in a breast

pocket, partly in order to minimize vibrations and protect it from jolts, and partly so that it was ready for instant use. The microphone was hidden under our IT chest banner. At the end of each tape we swopped the tape-recording gear for the camera gear, so we each did half the work.

Spare tapes for Nagra SN. Thirty used in total on journey. BBC mailed fresh tapes to Kathmandu and Lhasa. Nineteen tapes were carried from Lhasa northwards – wrapped in plastic bag then all fitted into Dick's plastic bottom-bracket pot.

Mini-earphone for Nagra to check it was recording.

Spare microphone for Nagra (initially it had a long wire and jack plug for the machine, but we cut this off and carried only the head so that if we had to use it we would have had to wind the bare wires together with sticky tape).

Pentax MX camera. This was manual with mechanical shutter so it was trouble-free and we always had full control over the pictures being taken. It was the same body as had travelled the length of the Himalayas in 1983, and indeed to the summit of Kilimanjaro. Eventually the light-meter shook loose, but only after a thousand kilometres of dirt road – most other cameras we have tried in the past fall to bits much quicker. Pentax ME body bought from Kenji Aoyagi in Golmud.

Pentax lenses, 28 mm, 50 mm, 120 mm: 50 mm used for half the shots; 28 mm used for most of the rest, because people are nearly always close and scenery is nearly always massive; 120 mm rarely used excepting for cycling shots with compressed scenery.

Films, Kodachrome 64, and Kodak 400 ASA b&w. Two colours and one b&w were always kept handy in their little black cartons ready for quick change. The cartons were padded to stop rattling with a small square of Karrimat. The rest were taken out of their cartons and carried packed in an opaque black plastic film-bag beside the medicines. We took nine colours from Lhasa and three b&w. In total on the journey we used twenty-two films. New films can be bought in most places these days. Used films were sent back to Britain with friendly people we met in Dhaka, Kathmandu and Lhasa.

Batteries. Four spare for tape machine (it uses two at a time, but they lasted so long the spares were never needed). Two spare camera batteries, one of which was vitally important because the camera battery did go flat.

Medical

Malarial prophylaxis; full course: one Paludrin per day, two Chloroquin per week, from one week before arriving in Bangladesh to four weeks after leaving Nepal. The resistance of different strains of malaria changes rapidly and must be checked before any travelling.

Diamox (twelve pills) for improved acclimatization/prevention of altitude sickness; bought in Kathmandu, used between Bharbise and Tingri. Thereafter we were sufficiently acclimatized to thin air.

Flagyl for amoebic dysentery and Giardia. One course is one tablet given three times per day for five days. Four courses carried from Dhaka, two courses carried from Lhasa, never used.

Septrin Forte, broad-spectrum antibiotic for internal infection. One tablet twice per day. In our case lung infections were particular possibilities. Septrin Forte can also be used crushed and sprinkled on to septic surface wounds. Four courses carried from Dhaka, two courses carried from Lhasa, never used.

Streptotriad for bacillary dysentery. One course is two tablets taken three per day for five days. We carried one course from Dhaka, and then none from Lhasa. The tablets are large and numerous. Bacillary dysentery is difficult to distinguish from a complicated condition of amoebic dysentery and traveller's tummy. As with the other stomach infections above, bacillary dysentery is inconvenient but not chronic, so if we contracted it, then we were prepared to sit it out for a few days until we reached a town large enough to have a chemist's and a stock of the necessary pills.

Dr Mike Townend of Cockermouth advised us on medical requirements for the areas in which we were travelling (any decisions on how much to carry were our own). He also procured all the drugs. We carried the Flagyl, Septrin Forte and Streptrotriad divided in tiny plastic bags, one course per bag, all in the same small plastic pot.

Puritabs: 236 taken out of foil and carried in small plastic pill-tube fixed by cotton wool. Much easier to handle than foil. Carried in Dick's breast pocket to stop rattles pulverizing tablets. Puritabs are chlorine-rich and in emergency could be crushed for disinfecting wounds.

Tiny glass bottle of Betadine antiseptic (as advised by Nick's sister Fiona Johnson). Note that crushed Puritabs or Septrin Forte could be substitutes.

Small roll of sticky plaster. Useful for mending bodies, clothes, snow-goggles, pens, etc. A must. Can be replaced in virtually any town with shops.

Small tube of antiseptic cream. A useful psychological dab for little hurts. Good for festering toes. Can be replaced in virtually any town with shops.

Communal Paperwork

Hildebrandt's map of China. Useful but inaccurate, cut to size.

Bartholomew's map of the Indian subcontinent. Mostly cut away. Later it had to be patched with bits of local newspaper to hold it together.

US Air Defense Mapping Agency Sheet ONC F-7 of the Centre of the Earth. Plus a cut-down corner of the Bay of Bengal on Sheet TPC J-10A which was needed in order to finalize calculations in Urumqi.

Casio fx-915 solar-powered calculator in order to calculate the co-ordinates of the Centre of the Earth.

Passports.

Spare passport photos (eight each).

Driving licence, bank cards.

Vaccination certificates.

Money. We took with us from Britain £3,180 (£42 left when we returned!). This was twice what we estimated we would need. It was split equally between pounds and dollars. Half of it was in the relative safety of traveller's cheques (which incidentally are often now easier to change in out-of-the-way places than cash), the other half in cash notes which can be swapped to other travellers (for example, for film) and easily changed in most places. At each border or in big towns, like Lhasa and Golmud, we changed into local currency twice what we thought we'd need for the sections ahead. It would be carried in masses of small notes ready to use and a few large-denomination notes for emergencies such as large hotel expenses or telephone fees.

Address list of forty friends and relatives or associates who had helped. All written very small on a sheet of airmail paper.

Letters of introduction on headed notepaper, though they seemed more or less useless.

Book covers from our previous adventures in order to impress officialdom.

It would have been useful to have carried a stock of photos of us two with bikes so that we could have given them as 'Thank Yous' to all the people we met *en route*.

Bicycles

The bikes were tailor-made, built to the highest specification by Raleigh. Gerald O'Donovan master-minded the project at his Specialist Bicycle Development Unit at Ilkeston, which has also produced the winning Tour de France team bikes.

Frames. The geometry was based on that used for the toughest professional races, e.g. the Paris–Roubaix, with a lengthened wheelbase, softer angles (74° seat tube, 73° head tube) and increased rake. Together these give a smoother, less 'twitchy' ride. The tubing was TI Reynolds 753 which is much in favour for professional racing because, although it is expensive, it offers the best strength-to-weight ratio; 753 is heat-treated manganese molybdenum steel which on our bikes was double-butted, top tube 24 gauge, down tube 23 gauge, i.e. the tube wall was about 0.5 mm thick in the middle and about 0.8 mm thick at the ends. The tensile strength is an impressive 80 tsi. The lugs, fork crown and bottom bracket were micro-fusion crushed steel (i.e. very fine-grained, precision cast) and all joints were silver-soldered. Each frame contains £20 worth of silver solder! The frames were hand-sprayed and stove-enamelled with five coats of paint in the

Raleigh Team colours: pearl, red, blue and yellow. They had long Campagnolo rear dropouts, and bosses for bottle cage and a single (the rear) gear lever.

Wheels. Bob Arnold of F. W. Evans built strong wheels capable of withstanding pounding on dirt roads for several thousand kilometres. They had Mavic M3 CD rims with 36 × 36 stainless-steel single-buttoned spokes on Campagnolo small-flange hubs. We hit numerous rocks and several large pots at high speed, one of them near Amdo catapulting Nick into Outer Space, but the wheels remained true. The tyres were Specialized; one Touring K4 and one Expedition 700 × 35C. Although rated at 75 psi, we rode them at 90 psi on both tarmac and dirt. Because the wheels and tyres had to be high-strength, hard-wearing, they contributed greatly to the overall weight; pushing it up from the 17½ lb which our bikes would have weighed if fitted with sprint wheels and tubes to the 22 lb all-up weight including Blackburn alloy rear carrier and bottle cages.

Equipment. Cinelli bars and stem. Shimano Dura Ace levers for Campagnolo side-pull brakes. Brooks Professional saddle on Dura Ace seatpost. Shimano 600 EX chainset (49/39 teeth for Nick, 52/40 for Dick) with Shimano Uniglide chain to Sun Tour Perfect freewheel (14 to 28). Control was from a cut-down Simplex gear shift to a Shimano 600 EX derailleur. In order to save weight, there was no front derailleur or lever, we used heel kick-down for lower gears and finger lift-up for higher.

Over a quarter of the distance was very rough dirt road, and the bikes had to suffer monsoon rain and humidity, snow and ice, dust and sand and temperatures ranging from −10°C to 46°C. The only breakdown we had was a broken cable caused by Tibetan children playing with the gear lever – easily mended – and only two punctures each. The bikes were impeccably designed and built, comfortable, utterly reliable and as at home in the Himalayas as they were crossing the Gobi Desert.

Bike Equipment

Karrimor Kalahari cycle panniers. Two each. Excellent. At the end of the ride they showed no signs of wear. Always they were easy to use, quick to clip on and off the bikes. We did modify them slightly by snipping off the gaudy orange buckles and black nylon loops which are put there for those cyclists who are liable to get extra bits of equipment to carry *en route*. We also removed three of the four reflective strips, leaving only the offside rear reflector. In place of one we sewed an IT badge. The elastic clip-on for the pannier frame tended to allow the bag to bounce on rough ground so we removed it and replaced it by hooking the lower nylon strap around a boss on the pannier rack, low down near the wheel-hub, then extended this loop up and over the top of the bag long enough so that the two straps from different sides could be clipped together on top to make a secure, integral, and quick-release, system.

Blackburn pannier racks fitted by Bob Arnold the day before we left London.

Down-tube bottle cage with large-size one-litre plastic water-bottle.

Bottom-bracket containers. We fixed a bottle cage to hang below the bottom bracket (between the pedals as they turned). In it we carried not a drinks bottle but a plastic pill-pot six inches high, four inches diameter. It was used for carrying heavy/dense loads, e.g. spare Nagra tapes, penknife, bike tools. It was also used in places where we stopped and needed to offer our own cups for butter, salt tea or yak's yoghurt.

Bike Tools

Madison 'Air-Loc' frame-fitting pump. Loss or malfunction of the pump was a constant source of worry because without it to re-inflate tyres after puncture or to adjust pressure, we were stuck. Truck pumps and Chinese bicycle pumps do not fit. In the event, we never lost the pump, nor did the tyres lose air.

Campagnolo cone spanner 13/14 mm, drilled for lightness.

Adjustable wrench four-inch long.

Allen keys, 6 mm and 4 mm. These adjust handlebar and seat height and mend derailleur. The Allen keys for pannier rack and bottle cage were left behind.

One plastic tyre-lever. The rounded end of the adjustable was used in lieu of the other lever.

Plastic spoke-key sawn in half.

Chain link breaker with handle removed. In the event of a total failure of a derailleur we would have bypassed it by shortening the chain to make single speed.

Puncture patches, Nutrak, four big, sixteen small. We had only four punctures in the entire trip. If by chance we used all our patches then we could have substituted them with Chinese patches or strips of car tyre rubber.

One-inch-square piece of emery paper.

Small tube rubber solution.

All bike tools carried by Nick, mostly in his bottom-bracket bottle, the cone spanner in his pannier, pump on his frame.

Bike Spares

Stainless-steel spokes plus nipples. We carried sixteen spare spokes from Patenga Point and then only six spare spokes from Lhasa. The wheels never gave the slightest trouble, but if a single spoke had gone, then, however much we carefully adjusted spoke tensions, the rest of the wheel would probably have weakened quickly. There would be no other source of replacement spokes. Once a wheel gave up then we would have had to bend the frame to accept a 'local' wheel or ditch the bike and buy a Chinese one.

Inner tube, Specialized imported from Japan. We carried one spare in case of failed valve or blowout. If we had more blowouts than our puncture patches could mend then one alternative would have been to stuff the tyre with grass or rags.

Spare tyres. Specialized Expedition tyre 700 × 35C. We each carried one. It was folded in three and stuffed in our panniers. We had thought that the tyres would wear out on our 5,000-kilometre journey but in fact the spare was never used.

Spare washer for Madison pump.

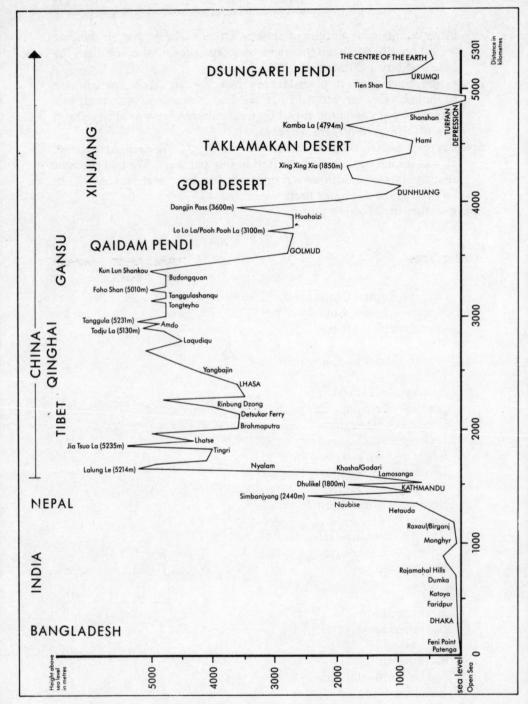

Altitude profile cross-section of ride

APPENDIX TWO
Daily Log of Distances and Ascent

DAY	PLACES	TOTAL KM	DIRT KM	ASCENT M
1	Patenga Point – Chittagong – Misarai	61	4	0
2	Misarai – Feni – Comilla – Daudkhandi	152	0	10
3	Daudkhandi – Dhaka	60	0	0
4	Dhaka	0		
5	Dhaka – Aricha – Goalundo Ghat – Faridpur	144	2	0
6	Faridpur – Kamarklighat – Jhenida – Jessore – Benapol – Bangaon	190	0	300*
7	Bangaon – Ranaghat – Krishnagar – Debangram – Katoya	102	0	0
8	Katoya – Siuri – Dhumka	109	0	1000
9	Dhumka – Bhagalpur – Monghyr	174	0	400
10	Monghyr – Monghyr Ghat – Bauroni	57	2	0
11	Bauroni – Muzzaffarpur – Motihari – Raxaul	240	0	0
12	Raxaul – Birganj – Hetauda – Bhainse	62	0	400
13	Bhainse – Simbanjyang Pass – Kathmandu	129	0	3500
		1480	8	5610
14	Kathmandu	0		
15	Kathmandu	0		
16	Kathmandu	0		
17	Kathmandu	0		
18	Kathmandu – Dhulikel – Lamosangu – Bharbise	88	5	700

* a notional 300 metres of ascent is added on Day 6 to compensate for all the minor ups and downs across the Ganges Delta from Day 1 to Day 7 inclusive.

DAY	PLACES	TOTAL KM	DIRT KM	ASCENT M
19	Bharbise – Kodari – Khasha – Fourmancot	52	50	2400
20	Fourmancot – Nyalam – Lalung Le – Rogues' Camp	85	85	2050
21	Rogues' Camp – Tingri – Baiba (Shektar Dzong)	129	129	0
22	Baiba – Jia Tsuo La – Lhatse	79	79	1120
23	Lhatse – Tsuo La – Rock Gully	124	124	600
24	Rock Gully – Xigatse – Detsukar Ferry	112	110	400
25	Detsukar Ferry – Rinbung Dzong – Twin Caves	84	84	500
26	Twin Caves – Turquoise Lake – Kamba La – Quzu Dzong	102	87	600
27	Quzu Dzong – Lhasa	56	0	200
		2391	*761*	*14180*
28	Lhasa	0		
29	Lhasa	6	0	0
30	Lhasa – Yangbajin	84	2	600
31	Yangbajin – Damxung – Yak Dung Store	168	0	600
32	YDS – Laqudiqu – Amdo	212	0	600
33	Amdo – Todju La – Tanggula – Tented Snow Camp	96	0	1500
34	TSC – Wenquan – Yanshiping – Tongteyho	137	0	0
35	Tongteyho – Tanggulashanqu – Foho Shan Camp	162	0	1300
36	FSC – Wudoulian – Budongquan	115	0	700
37	Budongquan – Naij Tal – Golmud	179	0	500
		3550	*763*	*19980*
38	Golmud	0		
39	Golmud – Qarhan – Lake Titicaca – Five Star Camp	157	10	200
40	FSC – Xitieshan – Lo Lo La – Pooh Pooh La – Huahaizi	183	158	600
41	Huahaizi – Dangjin La – Aksay – Dunhuang	187	40	600
		4077	*971*	*21380*
42	Dunhuang – Zhangjiaquan	52	24	0
43	Zhangjiaquan – Liuyuan – Railroad – Malingching	145	74	1000
44	Malingching – Xing-Xing-Xia – Gobi Desert	120	120	600
45	Gobi Desert – Lo'-to-tzucheung – Hami – Hami Bivvy	122	67	200

DAY	PLACES	TOTAL KM	DIRT KM	ASCENT M
46	Bivvy – Yaerbashi – Kiwanquan – Sandstorm	150	56	1300
47	Sandstorm – Qijiaojing – Qiktim	128	80	600
48	Qiktim – Shanshan – Erh-pao – Turfan	130	25	300
49	Turfan – Dabancheng – Urumqi	186	0	1300
		5110	1417	26680
50	Urumqi	0		
51	Urumqi	0		
52	Urumqi – Changji – Hutubi – Manas	135	0	0
53	Urumqi detention	0		
54	Urumqi detention	0		
55	Urumqi detention	0		
56	Urumqi detention	0		
57	Karamay flight	0		
58	Hoxtolgay/Tem – Hsia-tzu-chieh – Centre of the Earth	56	56	0
		5301	1473	26680

Note: Certain totals include places where we cycled kilometres additional to the direct route, usually because we were searching for somewhere to sleep, rarely, e.g. Siuri, because we got lost, once (in Liuyuan) because we assumed the wrong route, and once in the Dsungarei Pendi near Hsia-tzu-chieh because neither we nor anyone else knew where we had to go to find the Centre of the Earth. The breakdown of extra kilometres is: Daudkhandi 4, Siuri 6, Bauroni 10, Lhasa 6, Amdo 3, Liuyuan 11, Day 47 Taklamakan 3, Turfan 6, Day 58 Dsungarei 19.

The average per day up to Urumqi is 106 kilometres and 510 metres of ascent.

Following our arrival at the Centre of the Earth, we had to cycle sixty-four kilometres of dirt track back to Hoxtolgay through the night to be re-arrested. Therefore, total cycling equals 5,365 kilometres. *En route* to the Centre of the Earth, the flight to Karamay and the van ride to Tem added 355 kilometres to the journey making it approximately a road journey of 5,600 kilometres from the sea to the Centre of the Earth. The journey is roughly equivalent to cycling London to Rome return, then going back again on dirt roads!

During the expedition as a whole there were fifteen stationary days, though until arrival in Urumqi, we had only cycled no forward distance on eight days. The greatest distance in one day was 240 kilometres in the heat of the Indian Plains. This only just beat the more significant 212 kilometres at 13/14,000 feet altitude on Day 32. However, in sheer physical terms, the hardest ride was 183 kilometres, virtually all on dirt, at 10,000 feet altitude on Day 40 on the Qaidam Pendi. The greatest amount of mountain climbing in one day was 3,500 metres of ascent (12,000 feet) on Day 13 over the first wave of the Himalayas. The lowest temperature we experienced was −10°C in the road camp just past the Tanggula on Day 33, yet the chilliest night was the wet cold of −1°C on Day 25 in the Rong Chu Valley. The hottest two days were 42°C (115°F) in high humidity on Day 9 before Monghyr and a similar temperature in the intensely arid air of Turfan on Day 49. We spent seven nights in the open and for all fifty-eight days wore the same pair of underpants.

We were probably the first cyclists to cycle over the Tibetan Plateau (Lalung Le to Dangjin Pass) covering 2,260 kilometres in twenty-one days at an average altitude of 12/13,000 feet, and including about 8,500 metres (28,000 feet – the height of Everest) of ascent.

Biggest uphill is 15,000 feet (4,600 metres) of continuous ascent in 153 kilometres from the Sun Kosi at 1,966 feet (600 metres) in Nepal to the Lalung Le at 5,214 metres (17,000 feet) in Chinese Tibet.
Biggest downhill is 8,000 feet of continuous loss of altitude in 180 kilometres from the Dangjin Pass on the Altun Shan to Zhangjiaquan in the Gobi Desert.
Longest downhill is 183 kilometres from the Kun Lun Shan at 4,767 metres to Golmud and gently on to the lowest part of the salt marshes twenty-five kilometres north of Golmud (elevation just below 3,600 metres).
Steepest downhill is the twenty-four kilometres from the Kamba La at 4,794 metres to Kamba Partsi beside the Brahmaputra at 3,500 metres therefore losing altitude at the rate of 146 metres per kilometre.

Hol's prediction, posted 14 May to Steve Bonnist, for finishing date had been 24 June. Interestingly this was based on a calculation of his own: miles as the crow flies times wiggliness factor divided by estimated miles per day equals elapsed time. For instance from Kathmandu to Lhasa he estimated:

$$\frac{350 \times 1.6}{60} = 9\frac{1}{2} \text{ days}$$

In fact, we departed Kathmandu on the morning of Day 18 and arrived Lhasa on the evening of Day 27. If we hadn't been arrested in Urumqi, Hol would have been spot-on.

Bibliography

Books quoted from or otherwise mentioned in the text:

Crane, Nicholas and Richard, *Bicycles up Kilimanjaro* (Oxford Illustrated Press, 1985).

Crane, Richard and Adrian, *Running the Himalayas* (New English Library, 1984).

David-Neel, Alexandra, *My Journey to Lhasa* (Heinemann, 1927; reissued Virago, 1969).

Fleming, Peter, *News from Tartary* (Jonathan Cape, 1936; reissued Futura, 1980).

Harrer, Heinrich, *Seven Years in Tibet* (Rupert Hart-Davis, 1953).

Hopkirk, Peter, *Foreign Devils on the Silk Road* (Oxford University Press, 1980).

—*Trespassers on the Roof of the World* (Oxford University Press, 1982).

McWhirter, Norris, *The Guinness Book of Records* (Guinness Superlatives, 1986).

Moorhouse, Geoffrey, *The Fearful Void* (Granada, 1974).

Newby, Eric, *The Atlas of Exploration* (Artist's House, 1975).

Books used for reference in Britain and Dhaka:

Anderson, E. W., *The Principles of Navigation* (Hollis & Carter, 1966).

Globetrotter's Club, *The Globe* (BCM Roving, 1986).

Royal Geographical Society, *Expedition Planners' Handbook and Directory 1986–7* ed. Winsor, N & S.

Seth, V., *From Heaven Lake* (Chatto & Windus, 1983).

Shufeldt, Capt. H., and Newcomer, K., *The Calculator Afloat* (Granada, 1980).

Werner, D., *Where There Is No Doctor* (Macmillan Press, 1977; revised edn, 1981).

INDEX

Abdukerim, 198, 200, 202, 203, 205
Afghanistan, 8, 9, 154
Aksay, 139, 140
Altun Shan, 137–41, 167, 192
Amdo, 106–7, 111, 114, 128
Arctic Ocean, 1
Arnold, Bob, 18
Atlas of Exploration, The (Newby), 145
Atsana, 179

Baiba, *see* Shektar Dzong
Banepa, 54
Bangladesh: climate, 12, 30, 35, 45, 112; character, 15, 141, 194; elections, 17–21, 22–3, 29, 39; Indian border, 22, 28
Barouni, 35
Barratt, Col. Mike, 51
Baydaratskaya Guba, 191
Beijing, 9, 61, 93, 95, 98, 143, 184, 186, 187, 204
Bell, Steve, 11, 52
Ben Nevis, 36
Bengal, 18, 29, 87
Bengal, Bay of, 1, 9, 105, 143
Beresford, Brian, 197
Berlin, Mrs, 21
Bezelik, 179
Bhainse, 42–4, 78
Bharbise, 57–9

bicycles, 222–5
Bicycles up Kilimanjaro, 5, 6, 7, 36, 51, 53, 56, 130
Bihar, 32
Birganj, 39
Bo Hai Wan, 1, 9, 109, 187, 190, 191, 192, 204
Bogda Feng, 185
Bolivia, 6, 34
Bonington, Chris, 48
Bonnist, Steve, 9–10, 23, 47, 48, 49, 52, 96, 148, 186–7, 191, 197–8
Booth, Theresa, 49
Brahmaputra, River, 51, 74, 75–82, 89, 90, 98, 105
British Aid Guest House Association, 22
British Broadcasting Corporation, 5, 19, 47, 115
Buchaille, 5
Buddhism, 49, 65, 66, 78, 95–6, 115, 142, 143, 179
Budongquan, 117–18, 120–3, 124, 128, 138, 148, 182
Burma, 50, 105

Cable, Mildred: *Gobi Desert*, 8, 193, 197
Calcutta, 23, 25, 50
Carpini, 154
CATMOUS, 57

Celestial Mountains, *see* Tien Shan
Centre of the Earth: calculated, 7–9, 187–92; located, 213
Chang, Victor, 50–1
Chang Ch'ien, 145, 154
Chang Le, 203, 205, 206–13, 215-16
Changji, 193, 204
Chapman, Roger, 47
Chengdu, 93, 94
Chimborazo, 65
China: annexes Tibet, 3, 60, 65, 66, 87, 104; tourists, 11, 51, 70, 86–98; Nepal border, 47–8, 50, 55, 56, 58, 143, 197, 204; Pakistan border, 131. *See also* Gong An
China International Travel Service, 198–202, 203
China Sea, 123
China UK Travel Bureau, 11
Chinese Central Asia (Skrine), 174
Chittagong, 1, 13, 14, 15, 25, 28, 57
Cho Oyu, 73
Chungking, 50
CITS, *see* China International Travel Service
Collective Farm 184, 210, 211, 212, 215
Colombia, 139
Columbus, 203
Comilla, 17, 151
Crane, Ados, 5, 6, 7, 53, 54, 65, 132, 173
Crane, Charles, 5, 36
Crane, Chris, 5, 36, 187
Crane, Hol, 5, 7, 36, 49, 188, 190, 191
Cycling in Europe, 130

Dabancheng, 181–2
Dalai Lama, 66
Dam Qu, 109

Damxung, 101–2, 105, 106, 109
Dangjin La, 138, 142, 147
Darjeeling, 6, 68
Daudkhandi, 18–20
Daur, 161
David-Neel, Alexandra: *My Journey to Lhasa*, 92
Deadman, Alan, 74–5
Delhi, 45
Detsukar Ferry, 79, 80, 87, 98, 132
Dhaka, 12–13, 20–1, 22–4
Dhulikel, 54, 58
Dhumka, 32
Dihang, *see* Brahmaputra
Dinajpur, 22, 23
Dsungarei Pendi, 8, 145, 189, 190, 192, 193, 194, 196, 204, 205, 207, 210
Dudh Kosi, 72
Dunhuang, 140–2, 143–6
Dzongi Dzong, 50
Dzungarian Basin, 191
Dzungarian Desert, 171, 182, 183, 192

Ecuador, 6, 65, 75
Elliotsganj, 18
equipment, 217–25
Erh-pao, 177, 179
Evans, F. W., 18
Everest, Mt, 1, 46, 53, 54, 55, 72–3, 74, 83

Faridpur, 26–7
Feni, 15, 190
Feni Point, 190, 191, 192
Feni River, 190
Fielder, Richard, 13, 22
Fleming, Peter: *News from Tartary*, 193
Foho Shan, 115
French, Francesca: *Gobi Desert*, 8, 193, 197
Friendship Bridge, 60
Fukang, 171

Galapagos Islands, 6, 169
Gandhi, Indira, 53
Ganges, River, 14, 18, 23, 26, 31,
 33, 34, 39, 46, 51, 67, 75, 92,
 94, 105, 178, 187, 189, 190
Gansu, 153, 155
Gaochang, 179
Gartside, Tim, 158
Gayer, Richard, 197
Genghis Khan, 2, 154, 162
Giang, 198, 200
Goalundo Ghat, 25, 94
Gobi Desert, 1, 2, 8, 14, 21, 23,
 48, 55, 76, 86, 129–42, 143–63,
 166, 167, 194, 200, 206
Gobi Desert, The (Cable and
 French), 8, 193, 197
Golmud, 126–8, 129–33
Gong An, 129, 162–3, 164–6,
 183–202, 203, 204, 209, 210
Goo, Robert, 93–4, 179
Gosainthain, 68
Greece, 5
Greenstreet, Mike, 21
Gruisen, Lisa van, 50, 52, 55, 67
Guayaquil, 151
Guinness Book of Records, The,
 7–8, 65, 191
Gyangtse, 77, 78, 79, 80, 86, 98

Hami, 160–3, 164–7
Hanson, Bryan, 49
Haq, Nazrul, 19
Harrer, Heinrich, 66, 91
Hawley, Liz, 50
Hedin, Sven, 154, 174
Hetauda, 40–2, 45, 168
Higgins, Elliot B., 49–50
Himalayas, 2, 9, 37, 39, 44–52,
 53–64, 65–8, 72–3, 75, 77, 92,
 105, 125, 206; Running the
 Himalayas, 6, 36, 46, 50, 53,
 54, 55, 56, 130, 132, 207
Hindus, 17
Hong Kong, 9, 11, 48, 50, 204

Hong Shan Mountain, 185
Hopkirk, Peter, 79
Hoxtolgay, 191, 193, 198, 200,
 205, 206, 207, 208, 211, 215
Hsia-tzu-chieh, 207, 215
Hsuang-tsang, 154
Huahaizi, 136, 137, 138, 152
Hunt, Lord, 53, 203
Hutubi, 194

India: Bangladesh border, 22,
 28; Nepal border, 39, 44
Indian Ocean, 1, 105, 109
Indus, River, 51, 75
Inglis, Peter, 5
Intermediate Technology, 6, 7,
 9–10, 23, 145, 164, 186, 199,
 213
Islam, 17, 29, 142, 160, 161, 175,
 178
IT, see Intermediate Technology

Jamuna, see Brahmaputra
Jessore, 23, 27
Jhenigat, 27-8
Jia Tsuo La, 74
John o'Groats, 5
Jones, Sean, 197
Jostedals Bre, 5

Kailash, Mt, 51, 75, 94, 179,
 197
Kamba La, 86, 88–9, 94
Kamba Partsi, 90
Kampas, 69–71, 83, 95
Kangchenjunga, 68
Karakoram Highway, 9, 50, 61,
 204
Karakoram Range, 109, 118
Karamay, 192, 193, 195, 200,
 203, 204, 205–7, 208, 215
Karkavitta, 23
Kashgar, 9, 49, 75, 131, 174, 179,
 197, 198
Kashmir, 68
Kathmandu, 45–52

Kathmandu Basin, 42, 45, 52, 146
Katoya, 31–2, 34, 40
Kazaks, 142, 149, 161, 185
Kelamayi, *see* Karamay
Kenji Aoyagi, 130
Kenya, 5
Khasha, 60–2, 63, 125
Kilimanjaro, Mt, 5, 6, 7, 36, 51, 53, 56, 130
Kiwanquan, 169–70, 176
Kodari, 50, 51, 55, 59, 60
Krishnagar, 30
Kun Lun Pass, 123, 134
Kun Lun Shan, 118, 120, 123, 124, 127, 128, 136, 138
Kunjirab Pass, 9, 50, 131, 179, 197

La La Shan, 136
Laka Manosavar, 197
Lalung Le, 55, 66, 67, 68, 69, 75, 125, 138, 151, 179
Lamosangu, 53, 55, 57, 59
Land's End, 5
Lanzhou, 143
Laqudiqu, 105–6, 109
Lee Deng Ying, 201
Lemond, Greg, 139
Lhasa, 66, 70, 86–98
Lhatse, 76–7
Lhotse, 73
Liaodun, 169
Little Feni River, 190
Liushuquan, 167
Liuyuan, 145, 146, 147, 149–50, 152, 154, 162
Lodhwar, 149
Lop Nor, 162
Lo'to-cheung-tzu, 159
Lowe, Molly, 11

Magao Caves, 143
Makalu, 73
Malingching, 151, 152–3
Manas, 194–6, 201, 206

maps, 221
Maquan He, *see* Brahmaputra
Marion, 74
Matapan, Cape, 5
Meta, 74
Monghyr, 33–4
Monghyr Ghat, 34
Mongolia, 161, 167, 192
Mongols, 142, 149, 154
Moorhouse, Geoffrey, 133
Moron Us He, 109
Motihari, 35
Muir, Frank, 115
Murphy, Pete, 158
Muslims, *see* Islam
Muzaffarpur, 35
'My Music', 115

Nagqu, *see* Laqudiqu
Naij Tal, 124, 125–6
Nanga Parbat, 68
Naubise, 44
Nepal: China border, 47–8, 50, 55, 56, 58, 143, 197, 204; India border, 39, 44
Newby, Eric: *Atlas of Exploration*, 145
News from Tartary (Fleming), 193
Niichel, Janet, 55
Noël, Marc, 94
Norden, Denis, 115
North Korea, 60
Norway, 5
'Now Get Out of That', 5
Nu Jiang, 105
Nyalam, 50, 62, 67, 68

Obskaya Guba, 191, 192
O'Donovan, Gerald, 10, 30
Olsen, Laurie, 11
Ozbeks, 161

Pacific Ocean, 29
Paerh-k'u Shan, 169

Pakistan: China border, 131. *See also* Karakoram Highway
Pamir Range, 118, 167
Parsons, Mike, 11
Patenga Point, 3, 13, 14, 66, 78, 180, 188, 189, 190
Pearson, Sarah, 10
Pedalling Club, 57
Pelliot, 154
Peru, 6, 99, 125
Pilkington, John, 145
Polo, Marco, 2, 149, 154
Pooh Pooh La, 137
Pooh Pooh Shan, 136
Public Security Bureau, *see* Gong An
Pusan, 29

Qaidam Pendi, 118, 120, 132, 134, 135, 136, 142, 146, 152
Qarhan, 133
Qijiaojing, 170, 171
Qiktim, 175–6, 177, 185
Qinghai, 109, 118, 120, 142, 171
Qitai, 171
Qiu Zi-fan, 205, 215
Qomolangma Feng, *see* Everest, Mt
Quito, 151
Quzu Dzong, 90, 93

Raj Path, 42
Rajamahal Hills, 31, 32–3
Rangoon, 105
Rawalpindi, 6
Raxaul, 31, 35, 39
Rift Valley, 5, 173
Rinbung Dzong, 81, 82, 85
Rocky Mountains, 5
Rodd, John, 57
Rong Chu, 80, 81, 82, 83, 86, 87
Rongbuk Monastery, 74
Rubruck, 154
Running the Himalayas, 6, 36, 46, 50, 53, 54, 55, 56, 130, 132, 207

Sahara Desert, 74, 158
Salween, 105
Scafell Pike, 105
Scott, Capt. Robert, 109, 110
Shameen Ahmed, 13
Shanshan, 176
Shedatong, 124, 125
Shektar Dzong, 74, 83
Shihezi, 195, 198
Shisha Pangma, *see* Gosainthain
Siberia, 1, 9
Sikkim, 66
Silk Road, 2, 86, 138, 142, 143–63, 168, 194, 209
Simbanjyang, 44
Siuri, 32
Skinner, Mark, 131, 162, 179
Skrine, Sir Clarmont: *Chinese Central Asia*, 174
Snowdon, Mt, 36
South Korea, 29, 60
South Pole, 109
Stein, Sir Aurel, 154
Sun Kosi, 53, 54, 55, 60, 67
Swan, Robert, 109

Tajiks, 161
Taklamakan Desert, 8, 49, 145, 152, 166–80, 194, 203
Tanggula, 107–10, 124, 142
Tanggula Shan, 109, 118
Tanggulashanqu, 114, 115, 117, 171
Taoism, 142
Tatars, 161, 185
Tem, 208, 215
Thatcher, Margaret, 19, 53
Tibet: China annexes, 3, 60, 65, 66, 87, 104; Nepal border, 47–8, 50; Pakistan border, 131; tourists, 11, 51, 70, 86–98
Tien Shan, 145, 149, 167, 169, 171, 172, 180, 182, 183, 185
Ti'enshan, 180, 181
Times Atlas, The, 8

Ting-Shan, 207, 209, 210, 211, 212
Tingri, 74
Titicaca, Lake, 135
Todju La, 108
Tongteyho, 112–13, 128, 171
Turfan, 49, 131, 168, 170, 171, 174, 176, 178, 181, 182, 183, 185, 198
Turfan Depression, 145, 162, 166, 167, 175, 177
Turks, 142
Turquoise Lake, *see* Yamdrok Yamtso

Union of Soviet Socialist Republics, 8, 9, 66, 154, 161, 190, 191
Urumqi, 183–202. *See also* Centre of the Earth
Uygurs, 142, 161, 178, 179, 185, 199

Verne, Jules, 9, 94

Walker, Rob, 197–8
Wallace, Eamonn, 73, 74, 75
Wenquan, 107–8, 111
Whyte, Doug, 5
Williamson, Brian, 94, 96, 179
Winchcombe, Sue, 12
Woodcock, Jack, 21
Wu Ti, 145
Wudoulian, 117

Xian, 133
Xigatse, 77, 78, 79, 89, 94, 98, 109, 141
Xing-Xing-Xia, 153–6, 159, 161, 166, 167, 168, 170, 177
Xining, 179
Xinjiang, 154, 155, 160–1, 178, 196, 198, 205, 216
Xitieshan, 134, 136
Xizang Zizhique, *see* Tibet

Ya-izu-ch'uan, 168
Yaerbashi, 168
Yamdrok Yamtso, 77, 80, 81, 82, 86, 87
Yangbajin, 97, 98, 99, 101
Yangtse River, 109
Yanshiping, 111–12, 117
Yarlung Tsangpo Jiang, *see* Brahmaputra
Yellow Sea, 1, 109, 123, 187
Younghusband, Sir Francis, 66, 77, 79

Zanskar, 6, 66, 109, 134
Zhang Xiao-de, 198, 200, 201, 205, 215
Zhangjiaquan, 147–9, 152, 175

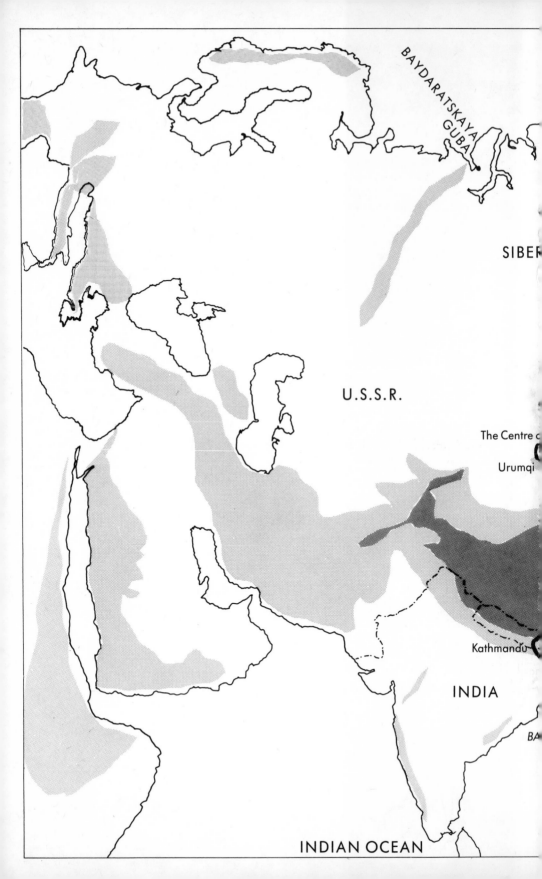

BAYDARATSKAYA GUBA

SIBER

U.S.S.R.

The Centre

Urumqi

Kathmandu

INDIA

BA

INDIAN OCEAN